GLENCOE
SCIENCE VOYAGES

Exploring the Physical, Earth, and Life Sciences

LABORATORY MANUAL
Teacher Edition

D1472856

Glencoe McGraw-Hill

New York, New York   Columbus, Ohio   Woodland Hills, California   Peoria, Illinois

Glencoe Science Voyages

Student Edition
Teacher Wraparound Edition
Assessment
    Chapter Review
    Standardized Test Practice
    Performance Assessment
    Assessment—Chapter and Unit Tests
    ExamView Test Bank Software
    Performance Assessment in the Science Classroom
    Alternate Assessment in the Science Classroom
Study Guide for Content Mastery, SE and TE
Chapter Overview Study Guide, SE and TE
Reinforcement
Enrichment
Critical Thinking/Problem Solving
Multicultural Connections
Activity Worksheets

Laboratory Manual, SE and TE
Science Inquiry Activities, SE and TE
Home Involvement
Teaching Transparencies
Section Focus Transparencies
Science Integration Transparencies
Spanish Resources
Lesson Plans
Lab and Safety Skills in the Science Classroom
Cooperative Learning in the Science Classroom
Exploring Environmental Issues
MindJogger Videoquizzes and Teacher Guide
English/Spanish Audiocassettes
Interactive Lesson Planner CD-ROM
Interactive CD-ROM
Internet Site
Using the Internet in the Science Classroom

Glencoe/McGraw-Hill

A Division of The McGraw-Hill Companies

Send all inquiries to:
Glencoe/McGraw-Hill
8787 Orion Place
Columbus, OH 43240

ISBN 0-07-824374-2
Printed in the United States of America.
1 2 3 4 5 6 7 8 9 10 009 05 04 03 02 01 00

Activities in *Glencoe Science Voyages: Laboratory Manual* do not require elaborate supplies or extensive pre-lab preparations. They are designed to explore science through a stimulating yet simple and relaxed approach to each topic. Helpful comments, suggestions, and answers to all questions are overprinted on reduced pages at the back of the *Teacher Edition.*

Activities in this laboratory manual are student-oriented. The scientific conclusions desired are not valid for any student unless he or she is directly involved in obtaining them. The activities should be performed by students only with your supervision. Directions are straightforward, so students can follow them easily. Students should be able to work through a problem to a satisfactory answer. The design of the manual is such that students should be interested enough to do their own investigating and not accept conclusions made by someone else. Students should discover their own mistakes through a review of the introductory statement, **Strategy,** and **Procedure.** If students still cannot reach a satisfactory conclusion, assistance in interpreting data may be needed.

Each activity can be torn from the book and handed in when the activity has been completed. Although the activities are not designed as a grading device, they can serve as a measure of progress for you and your students.

Most activities can be completed in a single class period. Some do not require the entire period; others require portions of two or more consecutive periods. Some require a preliminary setup followed by several inspections.

Glencoe Science Voyages: Laboratory Manual is organized into the following sections:

An introductory statement explains the science concepts involved in the activity. Specific information for the investigation of the problem is reemphasized. This statement appears under the investigation title.

Strategy provides performance objectives for student performance. If the student does not understand the goal of the activity, a rereading of the **Strategy** statements is advised.

Materials is the list of all materials and chemicals needed for the activity. The **Materials** section should be previewed so that any supplies to be contributed by students may be obtained in advance. Be sure to assemble these materials a few days before doing the activity. Everything should be ready before the beginning of a class period. Appropriate safety symbols and cautions are indicated in the **Materials** section.

Procedure is the step-by-step set of instructions for the activity. You may want to discuss the procedure with students before they begin the activity. Pre-activity discussions will help prevent misuse of equipment and injuries that can result from careless use of glassware, burners, and/or corrosive chemicals. Especially important safety caution statements are placed appropriately in the **Procedure** section. Each student should do his or her own computations except in those activities where group work or class averages are required.

Data and Observations includes sample graphs, charts, and tables to help improve student organizational skills. Emphasis should be placed on the need to record all observations during and at the completion of the activity. In many cases, recorded data provide the necessary link in cause and effect relationships.

Questions and Conclusions contains discussion questions and blanks for student answers at the end of each activity. These questions are designed to review main ideas, to direct attention to key parts of the procedure, and to relate the material to science concepts and applications. Answering these questions promotes and reinforces student learning.

Strategy Check allows students to evaluate their performance of the activity. If a student can place a checkmark in the blank provided, he or she has gained a skill, interpreted a concept, or learned a process.

PHILOSOPHY OF TEACHING SCIENCE BY THE INQUIRY METHOD

The inquiry method of teaching science serves three functions. First, the emphasis on the conclusions of an activity is changed to an emphasis on the processes involved in reaching the conclusions. Second, the activity procedure ceases to be just a series of steps that tells students what to do and what to expect. Third, the student is an actual participant in the laboratory experience. The distinction between lab and classroom is erased.

In order to function well in an inquiry environment, students must develop some basic skills. One skill needed for successful work in an inquiry environment includes making careful measurements. This skill entails among others a knowledge of units, the ability to use equipment correctly, and the ability to read units correctly. Five general categories of inquiry skills include:[1]

A. Acquisitive Skills
1. Listening—being attentive, alert, questioning
2. Observing—being accurate, alert, systematic
3. Searching—locating sources, using several sources, being self-reliant, acquiring library skills
4. Inquiring—asking, interviewing, corresponding
5. Investigating—reading background information, formulating problems
6. Gathering data—tabulating, organizing, classifying, recording
7. Research—locating a problem, learning background, setting up experiments, analyzing data, drawing conclusions

B. Organizational Skills
1. Recording—tabulating, charting, working systematically, working regularly, recording completely
2. Comparing—noticing how things are alike, looking for similarities, noticing identical features
3. Contrasting—noticing how things differ, looking for dissimilarities, noticing unlike features
4. Classifying—grouping things, identifying categories, deciding between alternatives
5. Organizing—putting items in order, establishing a system, filing, labeling, arranging
6. Outlining—employing major headings and subheadings, using sequential, logical organization
7. Reviewing—picking out important items, memorizing, associating
8. Evaluating—recognizing good and poor features, knowing how to improve grades
9. Analyzing—seeing implications and relationships, picking out causes and effects, locating new problems

C. Creative Skills
1. Planning ahead—seeing possible results and probable modes of attack, setting up hypotheses
2. Designing—a new problem, a new approach, a new device or system
3. Inventing—creating a method, device, or technique
4. Synthesizing—putting familiar things together in a new arrangement, hybridizing, drawing together

D. Manipulative Skills
1. Using an instrument—knowing an instrument's parts, how it works, how to adjust it, its proper use for a task, its limitations

1. Robert Sund and Leslie Trowbridge, *Teaching Science by Inquiry in the Secondary School,* 2nd ed. Charles E. Merrill Publishing Co., Columbus, OH, 1973, pp. 188–190.

2. Caring for an instrument—knowing how to store it, using proper settings, keeping it clean, handling it properly, knowing rate capacity, transporting the instrument safely
3. Demonstration—setting up an apparatus, making it work, describing parts and function, illustrating scientific principles
4. Experimentation—recognizing a problem, planning a procedure, collecting data, recording data, analyzing data, drawing conclusions
5. Repair—repairing and maintaining equipment, instruments, and so on
6. Construction—building items of simple equipment for demonstration and experimentation
7. Calibration—learning the basic information about calibration, calibrating a thermometer, balance, timer, or other instruments

E. Communicative Skills
1. Asking questions—learning to formulate good questions, to be selective in asking, to resort to one's own devices for finding answers whenever possible
2. Discussion—learning to contribute one's own ideas, listening to the ideas of others, keeping on the topic, sharing available time equitably, arriving at conclusions
3. Explanation—describing to someone else clearly, clarifying major points, exhibiting patience, being willing to repeat

In general, students look forward to an activity-oriented class. They view a laboratory as "true science." Encourage this attitude. Help create an atmosphere of excitement, curiosity, interest, and enthusiasm for the activities. You make the inquiry approach work. You devise the lesson plans and arrange laboratory time. It is in the laboratory that the skills are practiced and acquired.

With more responsibility for learning in the laboratory given to students, safety becomes a primary concern. Students must be trained in the use and care of apparatus and materials. This training should precede any laboratory work and be reviewed periodically.

LABORATORY EQUIPMENT

Storage of Equipment and Materials

A portable laboratory demonstration cart is useful if your science classroom lacks a demonstration table and utilities. This cart is available from several scientific equipment suppliers. It usually contains work space, a gas torch, a sink, water reservoirs, and storage cabinets. It can be wheeled to any spot within the classroom or from one classroom to another for science instruction. It can also be moved into an auditorium or multipurpose room for large group instruction.

Equipment may be stored in cabinets or in labeled cartons. Cardboard shoe boxes and plastic dishpans make good storage cabinets that stack neatly. You can probably obtain a good supply of shoe boxes from local shoe stores. You may store bottles, test tubes, wire, and so forth in separate labeled containers. However, if an adequate supply of equipment is available, you may want to organize it in kits. Each shoe box should contain a kit of materials for one activity. The kit provides ease of distribution and retrieval of equipment during class.

Samples should be labeled and stored in containers that can be displayed throughout the year. Plastic boxes (compartmentalized for nuts, bolts, or fishing tackle) work well for small samples. For larger samples, you often can find inexpensive plastic compartmentalized trays designed for dresser or kitchen drawers. Many pharmacies receive supplies in plastic boxes and vials, which they might save for you. When samples are displayed in clear plastic vials, boxes, and trays, the material can be examined easily without being scattered. Shoe boxes, egg cartons, or other small cardboard containers, while not as good for display, can be utilized by making dividers of cardboard and covering the top with plastic wrap.

If your supply of equipment and materials is limited, readily available materials can often be substituted.

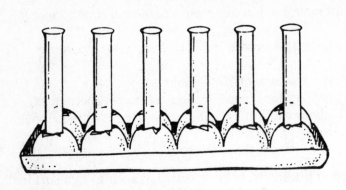

Figure A

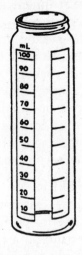

Figure B

Test-tube racks can be made from egg cartons by cutting a hole in the bottom of each egg compartment and then turning the egg carton upside down (FIGURE A).

Graduated cylinders are needed for measuring liquids. If these cannot be obtained, graduated baby formula bottles (metric units) and measuring cups may be substituted. Also olive jars can be calibrated for use as graduated cylinders. Calibrations can be marked on the olive jar by using two strips of adhesive tape with a small space between them with lines marked on the tape in milliliter units (FIGURE B). Also a glass marking pencil can be used to make lines directly on the glass. Spacing of lines can be determined by adding a milliliter of water at a time to the olive jar from a graduated cylinder.

Clear plastic cups can be used to hold solutions for activities. Glass jars can be used to store solutions. However, be certain that jars and all other glassware are stored carefully to avoid breakage. Label all containers so there can be no mistake about their contents. Use only heat-resistant glassware for heating solutions.

Hot plates are recommended as laboratory heat sources. **We do not recommend use of alcohol burners.** Alcohol burners are potentially dangerous.

Organisms in the Laboratory

The policy of the local school district should be checked before bringing organisms into the laboratory. If you plan to maintain organisms in the laboratory throughout the school year, arrangements for weekend and holiday care must be made. Temperatures in schools often are reduced during weekends and holiday vacations, and may be too cold for some organisms to survive.

Aquariums and terrariums are good ways to maintain organisms for class study. A variety of plants and animals grow well in them. Any glass container (four liters or larger) with a glass plate cover can be used as an aquarium or terrarium. Wash and rinse the container thoroughly before you use it.

To make an aquarium, place four centimeters of washed aquarium gravel on the bottom of the container. Add aged tap water (water that has been standing open to the air for three days) to a depth of five centimeters above the gravel. Anchor aquatic plants, such as eel grass, in the gravel. Fill the aquarium by pouring aged tap water in a saucer to avoid disturbing the gravel on the bottom. Let the aquarium stand for one day; then add guppies, goldfish, snails, duckweed, and other organisms. (Remember, guppies are cannibalistic, so keep young and adults separated.) Suspend a thermometer in the water so you can monitor the temperature. Maintain a temperature of 20° to 25°C. A lamp or sunny window can supply light and warmth. Cover the aquarium. Wedge a wooden splint between the cover and the top of the container to allow for air passage. Add small amounts of high protein baby cereal or special fish food daily. Snails will eat any food the fish do not consume. Keep the plants pruned so they do not fill the tank. Keep tap water aging to replace any water lost by evaporation. If green water develops in the aquarium, do not discard. It is an excellent source of food for other organisms.

To make a terrarium, place two centimeters of pebbles on the bottom of the container. Add one centimeter of clean sand and three centimeters of topsoil. On top of the soil, place a layer of healthy green moss. Plant several clusters of small ferns and liverworts. Lichens can also be added. Cover the terrarium and place it in filtered light. Keep the plants moist by sprinkling with water occasionally. The pebble and sand layers allow for drainage. If water accumulates in the pebble layer, do not add more water.

Plants can be grown in the laboratory from seeds or cuttings. Bean plants, coleus, geraniums, and wandering jew are easily grown. Mix equal parts of sand and topsoil. Place five centimeters of the mixture in the bottom of a milk carton or plastic sandwich bag. Plant seeds or cuttings from other plants. Keep the soil moist. Seeds should germinate within two weeks. Cuttings should root in two to four weeks. (Some cuttings can be rooted in water alone.) Transplant into pots with coarse sand or pebbles in the bottom for drainage. Water occasionally. Do not overwater. Rotting stems and roots and yellow or brown leaves may indicate overwatering. Place the plants in a warm, lighted area where the air is moist. Leaf curling is a sign of too much heat. Dropping leaves indicate a lack of humidity. Slow-release plant food should be added every two to three months to supply nutrients.

Working with Glass Tubing

It is recommended that all pieces of glass tubing used in the activities be prepared prior to the activity by the teacher only. You may wish to prepare tubing as a class demonstration for students to see how glass is cut, fire polished, heated, and bent.

FIGURES C, D, and E illustrate the proper techniques to be used when heating and working with glass tubing.

CAUTION: *Glass cools slowly. Do not touch glass that has been heated unless sufficient time has been allowed for cooling. Always place hot glass on hot pad, never on a metal or wooden desktop.*

Cutting Glass Tubing

Figure C

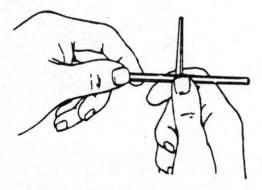

Score the tube once with a triangular file.

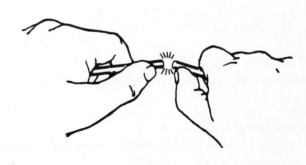

Place your thumbs opposite the scratch. Apply pressure and bend the tubing with a quick motion.

Figure D Fire Polishing Glass Tubing

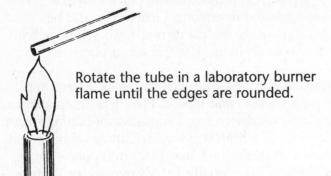

Rotate the tube in a laboratory burner flame until the edges are rounded.

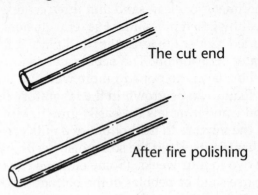

The cut end

After fire polishing

Figure E Bending Glass Tubing

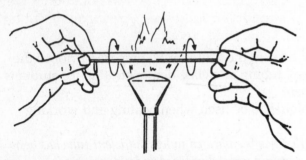

Use a wing top on the laboratory burner. Roll the tube back and forth in the flame until the glass becomes soft. A Meker type high temperature burner with a grid produces excellent results for bending glass.

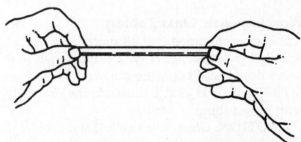

Remove from the flame and hold for a few seconds until the heat is evenly distributed.

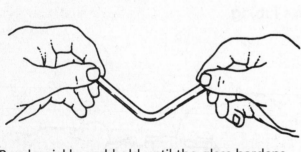

Bend quickly and hold until the glass hardens

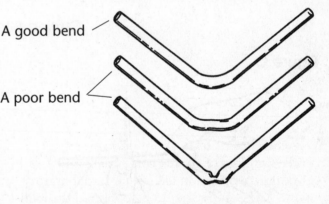

A good bend

A poor bend

Sterilizing Glassware

Clean glassware is extremely important. All glassware should be thoroughly washed and rinsed several times, then rinsed with distilled water. Glassware can be sterilized in several ways.

1. *Dry heat.* Glassware (petri dishes, test tubes, baby food jars, and so on) may be sterilized by placing them in an oven at a temperature of 160° to 190°C for two hours.
2. *Steam under pressure.* Sterilize media and glassware in a pressure cooker or autoclave for 15 minutes.
3. *Boiling.* Small pieces of glassware (droppers, stirring rods, and so on) may be sterilized by boiling them in water for 30 minutes.
4. *Chemicals.* Discarded cultures should be treated with steam under pressure, or the surface of the culture dishes can be covered with a 10 percent solution of household disinfectant. Wear rubber gloves to avoid burns when using strong disinfectants.

EVALUATING ACTIVITY WORK

Evaluation of the activities and of the general outcomes of laboratory work is a difficult task. Pure recognition and recall tests are not usually suitable for evaluating laboratory experience. Evaluation methods that depend on accurate observation, recognition of pertinent data, and ability to reason logically are more suitable for measuring outcomes of laboratory work. This type of evaluation may be done through periodic checking of student notebooks or individual or group conferences. You may also require students to submit laboratory reports. Laboratory reports should include

- a clearly stated problem.
- a procedure outlined in detail.
- data organized in good form and understandable; may include
  a. labeled diagrams.
  b. labeled and titled graphs.
  c. data tables.
- conclusions that answer the problem based on data obtained in the activity.
- a report that is clear enough to serve as a future review of the material.

The following questions should be answered in evaluating an activity report.

- Is the report written clearly enough so that an uninformed person could read it and know exactly what was being attempted, how it was done, and what conclusions were reached?
- Can the student duplicate the experiment using the report alone as a guide?

Achievement tests designed to assess understanding of course content are an important evaluation technique for laboratory work. Knowledge should be obtained through correct laboratory methods.

- You may wish to observe techniques used, correctness of procedures, and results obtained. An observational checklist based on objectives could be used.
- You may wish to direct students to perform a laboratory task in a practical test. Students should be able to satisfactorily complete this test before beginning laboratory work. For this test, set up equipment stations in the classroom. At each station,

provide instructions. Use a checklist like the one following this test to evaluate each student's performance.

Station 1: Lighting a Laboratory Burner
Equipment: laboratory burner, rubber hose, gas outlet, gas lighter, or safety matches
Instructions: Correctly set up and light the burner and adjust the flame.

Station 2: Decanting and Filtering
Equipment: two beakers—one containing a mixture of water and sand, stirring rod, filter paper, funnel, ring stand
Instructions: Decant the clear liquid from the residue. Correctly set up the equipment for a filtration procedure.

Station 3: Using the Balance
Equipment: balance, rubber stopper
Instructions: Correctly carry the balance from Station 3 to your desk and back to Station 3. Determine the mass of the rubber stopper.

Station 4: Measuring Temperature
Equipment: thermometer, beaker of water
Instructions: Position the thermometer correctly and determine the temperature of the water in the beaker.

Station 5: Measuring Volume
Equipment: graduated cylinder containing colored water
Instructions: Determine the volume of water in the graduated cylinder.

Station 6: Identifying Parts of a Microscope
Equipment: microscope, labels
Instructions: Correctly identify the labeled parts of this microscope.

Station 7: Using a Microscope
Equipment: microscope, prepared slide
Instructions: Correctly carry the microscope from Station 7 to your desk and back to Station 7. Place the slide on the stage and bring the slide into sharp focus.

Station 8: Inserting Glass Tubing into a Rubber Stopper
Equipment: glass tubing, glycerol or soapy water, one-hole rubber stopper, cloth towel
Instructions: Insert the glass tubing into the rubber stopper.

Name _____ Date _____

Rating Scale: **1.** Student is careless
2. Student needs to improve
3. Student is proficient

Skill	Proficiency		
lights burner correctly	1	2	3
adjusts air and gas supply correctly	1	2	3
decants correctly using stirring rod	1	2	3
folds filter paper correctly	1	2	3
carries balance properly	1	2	3
determines mass accurately	1	2	3
positions thermometer correctly	1	2	3
records accurate reading	1	2	3
identifies the parts of the microscope	1	2	3
carries microscope correctly	1	2	3
focuses microscope correctly	1	2	3
inserts glass tubing correctly	1	2	3

LABORATORY SAFETY

A major consideration for any school offering a science program is safety. Although posting safety guidelines and procedures has been held by recent court rulings as insufficient safety instruction, it should be done anyway. Post fire drill regulations and a chart of emergency procedures in a prominent place in the laboratory. Remind students of proper safety procedures at the beginning of each laboratory session.

Before each session, check all setups for proper assembly, and make sure each student is wearing proper safety attire. **Students must wear safety goggles and aprons when using any chemical, heat source, or hammer** (to split rocks). Be sure students with long hair secure it, and avoid wearing loose-fitting clothing in the presence of an open flame. Wearing contact lenses, even with safety glasses, should not be permitted. Splashing chemicals could infuse under the lenses causing eye damage.

Familiarize yourself with each activity before the class session. Instruct students to follow directions carefully and not to take shortcuts or switch steps. (Such shortcuts may lead to an unsafe situation.) Allow for sufficient cleanup at the end of each laboratory session. At this time, inspect all materials and equipment. Always be present during the laboratory session. Do not allow students to work unsupervised. Familiarize yourself and your students with emergency and first aid procedures. The Red Cross frequently offers classes in first aid. Contact it to find out when it offers these classes. Demonstrate the parts and proper use of laboratory equipment before the class. Spend time reviewing the laboratory techniques printed in the front of the pupils' laboratory manual. A sample laboratory safety contract is provided. You may wish to have each student contract for safety at the beginning of each semester.

Student Safety Contract

I will:

- Follow all instructions given by the teacher
- Protect eyes, face, hands, and body while conducting class activities
- Carry out good housekeeping practices
- Know the location of first aid and fire fighting equipment
- Conduct myself in a responsible manner at all times in a laboratory situation.

I, _____ , have read and agree to abide by the safety regulations as set forth above and also any additional printed instructions provided by the teacher and/or district. I further agree to follow all other written and verbal instructions given in class.

Signature _____

Date _____

Safety Precautions

1. Do not allow students to perform any activities unless under your direct supervision. They should perform only those activities assigned by you.
2. Modify any activities to comply with local safety regulations. For example, an open flame may not be permitted in your classroom.
3. Safety glasses, aprons, and gloves must be worn when any activity calls for heating, pouring, or mixing chemicals. It is good practice for you and your students to wear safety glasses when conducting any activity.
4. Immediately flush any acid or base chemical spills on clothing or skin with large amounts of water. Chemicals spilled on work areas or floor should be removed immediately.
5. In the event of fire, smother flames with cloth towels or fire blankets. Location of fire extinguisher, fire blanket, and fire alarm box should be pointed out to students.
6. Combustible materials (alcohol, lighter fluid) must be kept away from open flames. Use of electric hot plates should greatly reduce fire hazard.
7. Glass tubing must be wrapped in cloth toweling when inserted into or removed from rubber stoppers.
8. Chemical substances should never be tasted or inhaled.
9. If electrical equipment is used, make sure your classroom has the proper electrical outlets.

Laboratory Equipment and Supplies

The quantities listed are for one class of 30 students working in pairs. Some experiments may require larger groups of students due to equipment and space limitations. Some equipment may be acquired locally, L; or from a commercial supply house, SH.

It is assumed that goggles, laboratory aprons, gloves, tap water, textbooks, paper, calculators, pencils, and pens are available for all activities.

Equipment	Quantity	Source	Experiments used in
alligator clips	60	L	12, 30, 31
balance	15	SH	17, 23, 31, 51
basketball	15	L	35
battery clip for 9-V battery	15	L	12
beaker (250-mL)	75	SH	17, 31
beaker (400-mL)	15	SH	1, 14, 15, 43
beaker (500-mL)	15	SH	16
beaker (600-mL)	15	SH	48, 51
beaker (1000-mL)	15	SH	6
beaker (heat proof)	15	SH	18
beaker tongs	15	SH	7
binoculars or telescope	15	SH	32
bright portable light or flashlight	15	SH	29
bucket	15	L	21
burner	15	SH	14, 15
camera (instant developing)	15	L	26
camera (with time exposure)	1 or 2	L	38
clipboard	15	L	50
compass (directional)	15	SH	52
compass (drawing)	15	L	38
convex lenses (eyepiece, short focal length; objective, long focal length)	15 each size	SH	37
copper wire (fine)	30 cm	L	7
copper wire (insulated)	1 30-m spool	L	12
diode	15	SH	30
dissecting needle	15	SH	46, 47, 49
dissecting pan	15	SH	46, 47
dissecting pins	90	SH	46
dissecting scissors	15	SH	46, 47
dowel (wood, about 50 cm long)	15	L	25
dropper	15	SH	7, 8, 18
dropper/rubber stopper assembly (one-hole)	30	SH	43
drum	15	L	29
Erlenmeyer flask	30	SH	1
eye hook	15	L	22
flashlight	15	L	35
forceps	15	SH	47, 49
glass rod	25	SH	30, 31
globe	15	L	33, 34
graduated cylinder (10-mL)	15	SH	17, 42, 51

Equipment	Quantity	Source	Experiments used in
graduated cylinder (100-mL)	15	SH	2, 5, 16, 31, 43, 51
granite	15 pieces	L	3
granite (crushed)	500 mL	L	3
graphite (pencil lead)	30	L	30
hand lens or magnifier	15	L/SH	3, 7, 13, 44, 46, 47
heat lamp	15	L	36
hemisphere (clear plastic) or terrarium top	15	L	33
hot plate	15	L	3, 7, 15, 17, 18, 48
jars (baby food, with lids)	120	L	42
lamp sockets	30	SH	28, 30
LED (light-emitting diode)	15	SH	12
lightbulbs (25 W)	60	L	28, 30
masses (set)	15	SH	22
masses (set) and materials for creating mass set	15	SH	25
meterstick	15	SH	20, 23, 24, 25, 26, 28, 34
microplate (24-well)	15	SH	12, 15
microplate (96-well)	15	SH	13
microscope	15	SH	7
microscope slide	30	SH	2, 7
multigear bicycle	15	L	24
multimeter or ohmmeter	15	SH	28
nail (iron scraps)	30	L	51
nail (iron)	30	L	14
nails	15	L	30
pan (large, shallow)	15	L	53
paper clip	450	L	30
photo resistor	15	SH	28
pipe (copper)	15	L	30
pipette (plastic microtip)	15	SH	13, 15
pipette (plastic)	150	SH	12, 15
plastic lining	15	L	27
plexiglass or glass	15 sheets	L	27
protractor	15	L	38
ramp (wood, 50-cm-long)	15	L	20
resistor (1000-ohm)	15	SH	12
ring stand	15	SH	28
ruler (metric)	15	L	2, 41
scissors	15	L	5, 18, 25, 35, 39, 41, 47, 52
screw (brass)	15	L	30
spoon	15	L	14, 42
spring scale	15	SH	22
steel barrier (1 m × 4 cm × 1 cm)	15	L	27
stirring rod	15	SH	16
stoppers to fit flasks	30	SH	1

Equipment	Quantity	Source	Experiments used in
sunlamp	15	SH	53
television or other electronic device that is operated by an infrared remote control device	1	L	29
test tubes	300	SH	14, 17, 18, 43, 48
test-tube holders	15	SH	14, 17, 18
test-tube rack	15	SH	17
thermometer (Celsius, alcohol)	60	SH	5, 15, 17, 29, 36, 48
timer, such as watch with second hand or stopwatch	15	L	1, 5, 14, 15, 16, 20, 21, 23, 25, 29, 34, 36, 43, 48
tongs	15	SH	14
toy car, small with free-spinning wheels	15	L	20, 23
toy water rocket and launcher	15	L	21
tripod or support for camera	1 or 2	L	38
ultraviolet light	14	SH	29
utility clamp	15	SH	28
voltmeter	15	SH	31
walkie-talkies (pair)	15	SH	29
washers (iron or lead)	60	L	15
wire strippers	15	L	30
wire, insulated "bell"	30 m	L	31
wire, insulated copper (20-cm lengths)	60	SH	30
wood block (1 foot long)	15 pieces	L	24
wood block (15 cm × 3 cm × 7 cm)	15	L	27
wood block (2 in. × 4 in.)	15	L	22
wood frame (1 m × 1 m × 10 cm)	15	L	27
wood splint	15	SH	14

Chemicals and Consumables List

The quantities listed are for one class of 30 students working in pairs. Some experiments may require larger groups of students due to equipment and space limitations. The chemicals may be purchased from groceries, G; locally, L; or from a commercial supply house, SH.

Chemicals and Consumables	Quantity	Source	Experiments used in
acorn	1 or 2	L	45
aluminum foil	3 rolls	G	14, 30, 41
aluminum foil (heavy gauge)	1 roll	G	31
aluminum nitrate [$Al(NO_3)_2$]	500 g	G	13
aluminum strip	15	SH	31
aluminum strip (1 mm × 10 mm)	15	G	13
apple	1 or 2	G	45
apple juice	1 large bottle	G	18
avocado	1 or 2	G	45
baking soda	1 box	G	14
balloon (rubber)	15	L	8
battery (1.5-V)	30	L	30
battery (9-V)	15	L	12
bean in a pod	1 or 2 pods	G	45

Chemicals and Consumables	Quantity	Source	Experiments used in
Benedict's solution	2 quarts	SH	18
bottle (small medicine, clear, with cap)	15	L	7
bottle (soda water)	15	L/G	16
cardboard (stiff)	75 sheets	L	12, 35, 36
cardboard (thin)	15 sheets	L	52
cardboard mailing tubes (9 cm and 18 cm long—9-cm should be slightly smaller in diameter than 18-cm)	15	L	37
carrots	15	G	44
cereal bowls	15	L/G	53
chocolates (candy-coated)	1 large package	G	10
cobalt nitrate [$Co(NO_3)_2$]	30 g	SH	15
copper nitrate [$Cu(NO_3)_2$]	30 g	SH	13
copper strip	15	SH	31
copper strip (1 mm × 10 mm)	15	SH	13
copper(II) sulfate ($CuSO_4$)	180 g	SH	14
copper(II) sulfate crystals ($CuSO_4$)	60 g	SH	51
corn	1 or 2 ears	G	45
cotton swabs	15	G	42
cups (clear)	15	G	16
cups (paper)	30	G	41
disaccharides	1 container	SH	18
distilled water	20 L	G/SH	12, 13, 17
drinking glass (plastic)	15	G	6
earthworm (preserved)	15	G	46
eraser (rubber)	15	L	30
film (black and white)	2 rolls	L	38
fluorescent crayons or paint	15	L	29
glucose	1 container	SH	12
glue	1 bottle	L	52
granite samples	15	SH	7
graph paper	360 sheets	L	10, 32, 36
grasshopper (preserved)	15	SH	47
honey	1 jar	G	18
hot mitt	30	G/L	16
hydrochloric acid (0.1 M)	2 L	SH	31
iodine	1 bottle	L	18
iron nitrate [$Fe(NO_3)_2$]	30 g	SH	13
iron strip (1 mm × 10 mm)	15	SH	13
labels	300	L	18, 42
lead nitrate [$Pb(NO_3)_2$]	35 g	SH	13
lead strip (1 mm × 10 mm)	15	SH	13
litmus paper (blue)	15	SH	51
magnesium nitrate [$Mg(NO_3)_2$]	2 g	SH	13
matches	1 package	G	14
modeling clay	5 kg	L	23

Chemicals and Consumables	Quantity	Source	Experiments used in
modeling clay (four different colors; one white if possible)	15 sets	L	4
mold source	a moderate amount	L	42
monosaccharides	1 container	SH	18
nickel nitrate [$Ni(NO_3)_2$]	30 g	SH	13
nickel strip (1 mm × 10 mm)	15	SH	13
nutrition labels from foods	60	G	5
oats	1 container	G	18
okra	1 or 2	G	45
olive	5	G	45
owl pellets	15	SH	49
pancake syrup	1 bottle	G	43
pans (potpie, aluminum)	45	G	17
paper (black and white construction)	15 pieces each	L	5
paper (waxed)	1 roll	G	41
paraffin block (10 cm × 6 cm × 1 cm)	30	L	27
paraffin block (4 cm × 4 cm × 1 cm)	15	L	27
pea in a pod	1 or 2	G	45
peach	1 or 2	G	45
peanut	1 or 2	G	45
peanuts (candy-coated, red and green)	1 large package	G	9
pear	1 or 2	G	45
pen (marking)	15	L	33, 53
pen cap (plastic)	15	L	30
pencils (colored)	15 sets	L	28, 36
pie pans (disposable)	30	L	3
plastic bag (clear, large)	15	G/L	53
plastic spoons	15	G	48
plastic storage box and lid (clear)	15	L	36
plum	1 or 2	G	45
polysaccharides	1 container	SH	18
potassium chloride [$KCl(cr)$]	75 g	SH	17
potato	15	G	41
potato flakes	1 package	G	42
rope (100-m long)	1500 m	L	29
rope or clothesline	75 m	L	26
rubber band	30	L	48
salol	100 g	SH	7
salt (rock)	1 bag	L/G	3
sand or soil	1 bag	L	53
sandwich bags (plastic)	45	G	48
shortening (solid) or butter or margarine	1 can	G	48
silver nitrate ($AgNO_3$) solution	15 drops	SH	7
sodium chloride ($NaCl$)	1 box	G/SH	12
sodium chloride (rock, crystalline)	1 package	G	12

Chemicals and Consumables	Quantity	Source	Experiments used in
sodium hydroxide (NaOH)	15 g	SH	12
sodium hypochlorite [NaOCl(aq)]	40 mL	SH	15
soil	1 bag	L	36
spring toy	15	L	26
steel wool	1 large package	L	14
sticks, popsicle	60	L	30
string	5 rolls	SH	14, 23, 25, 33, 34
sugar	2 packages	G	12, 18
sugar (powdered)	1 box	G	18
sugar cubes (sucrose)	2 package	G	12, 16
sulfuric acid [H$_2$SO$_4$(aq)]	10 mL	SH	12
sunflower seeds	5	L	45
tape (adhesive)	1 roll	L	34
tape (black)	2 rolls	L	28
tape (duct)	1 roll	L	27
tape (masking)	10 rolls	L	5, 12, 20, 23, 25, 37, 41
tomato	1 or 2	G	45
towels (paper)	15 rolls	G	12, 13, 14, 16, 31, 42
tracing paper (unlined)	30 sheets	L	38
twist ties	100	L	25
vanilla extract	1 large bottle	L	8
vinegar (white)	1 bottle	G	31
wire coat hangers or bendable wire	30	L	53
yarn (colored)	2 skeins	L	26
yeast (cake type)	3	G	43
zinc nitrate [Zn(NO$_3$)$_2$]	30 g	SH	13
zinc strip (1 mm × 10 mm)	15	SH	13

Suppliers

Company names, mailing addresses, phone numbers, and, when available, e-mail addresses and World Wide Web sites were accurate at the time of publication and are subject to change.

Carolina Biological Supply Co.
2700 York Rd.
Burlington, NC 27215
(800) 334-5551
www.carolina.com

Central Scientific Co.
11222 Melrose Ave.
Franklin Park, IL 60131-1364
(800) 262-3626
cencophys@aol.com

Fisher Science Education
485 S. Frontage Rd.
Burr Ridge, IL 60521
(800) 955-1177
www.fisheredu.com

Flinn Scientific Inc.
P.O. Box 219
Batavia, IL 60510
(800) 452-1261
flinn@flinn.sci.com

Frey Scientific
100 Paragon Parkway
Mansfield, OH 44903
(800) 225-3739
freyscientific.com

Kemtec Educational Corp.
8944 Beckett Rd.
West Chester, OH 45069
(877) 536-8321
prekem@fuse.net

Nasco
901 Janesville Ave.
Fort Atkinson, WI 53538-0901
(800) 558-9595
info@nascofa.com

Sargent-Welch Scientific Co.
P.O. Box 5229
Buffalo Grove, IL 60089
(800) 727-4368
www.sargentwelch.com

Science Kit and Boreal Labs
777 E. Park Dr.
P.O. Box 5003
Tonawanda, NY 14151-5003
(800) 828-7777
sk@sciencekit.com

Wards Natural Science
Establishment, Inc.
P.O. Box 92912
Rochester, NY 14692-9012
(800) 962-2660
customer_service@wardsci.com

GLENCOE

SCIENCE VOYAGES

Exploring the Physical, Earth, and Life Sciences

LABORATORY MANUAL

Student Edition

Glencoe
McGraw-Hill

New York, New York   Columbus, Ohio   Woodland Hills, California   Peoria, Illinois

Glencoe Science Voyages

Student Edition
Teacher Wraparound Edition
Assessment
    Chapter Review
    Standardized Test Practice
    Performance Assessment
    Assessment—Chapter and Unit Tests
    ExamView Test Bank Software
    Performance Assessment in the Science Classroom
    Alternate Assessment in the Science Classroom
Study Guide for Content Mastery, SE and TE
Chapter Overview Study Guide, SE and TE
Reinforcement
Enrichment
Critical Thinking/Problem Solving
Multicultural Connections
Activity Worksheets

Laboratory Manual, SE and TE
Science Inquiry Activities, SE and TE
Home Involvement
Teaching Transparencies
Section Focus Transparencies
Science Integration Transparencies
Spanish Resources
Lesson Plans
Lab and Safety Skills in the Science Classroom
Cooperative Learning in the Science Classroom
Exploring Environmental Issues
MindJogger Videoquizzes and Teacher Guide
English/Spanish Audiocassettes
Interactive Lesson Planner CD-ROM
Interactive CD-ROM
Internet Site
Using the Internet in the Science Classroom

Glencoe/McGraw-Hill

A Division of The McGraw-Hill Companies

Send all inquiries to:
Glencoe/McGraw-Hill
8787 Orion Place
Columbus, OH 43240

ISBN 0-07-824373-4
Printed in the United States of America.
1 2 3 4 5 6 7 8 9 10 009 05 04 03 02 01 00

TO THE STUDENT

Science is the body of information including all the hypotheses and experiments that tell us about our environment. All people involved in scientific work use similar methods for gaining information. One important scientific skill is the ability to obtain data directly from the environment. Observations must be based on what actually happens in the environment. Equally important is the ability to organize these data into a form from which valid conclusions can be drawn. The conclusions must be such that other scientists can achieve the same results.

Glencoe Science Voyages: Laboratory Manual is designed for your active participation. The activities in this manual require testing hypotheses, applying known data, discovering new information, and drawing conclusions from observed results. You will be performing activities using the same processes that professional scientists use. Work slowly and record as many observations and as much numerical data as possible. You will often be instructed to make tables and graphs to organize your data. Using these tools, you will be able to explain ideas more clearly and accurately.

Each activity in *Glencoe Science Voyages: Laboratory Manual* is designed to guide you in the processes scientists use to solve a problem. The introductory section provides information about the problem under study. The **Strategy** tells you what you are expected to learn from the activity. These statements emphasize the most important concept(s) in the activity. **Materials** tells you the equipment and supplies needed to conduct the activity. **Procedure** is the list of steps you follow in doing the activity. **Data and Observations** is the section in which you record your findings. Record all observations, no matter how minor they may seem. In some activities, you will be asked to organize your data into tables or graphs. Organizing data helps you recognize relationships among the data. In **Questions and Conclusions,** you must give written answers to questions and problems. The questions are designed to test your understanding of the purpose and results of the activity. The last section is the **Strategy Check.** If you can answer "yes" to each question, you understand the concepts involved in the activity. If not, reread or repeat the activity to see if you can identify the concept you do not understand.

Remember that the way you approach a problem—collecting data and making observations—is as important as the "right" answer. Good luck in your laboratory experiences.

TABLE OF CONTENTS

TABLE OF CONTENTS *(continued)*

LABORATORY EQUIPMENT

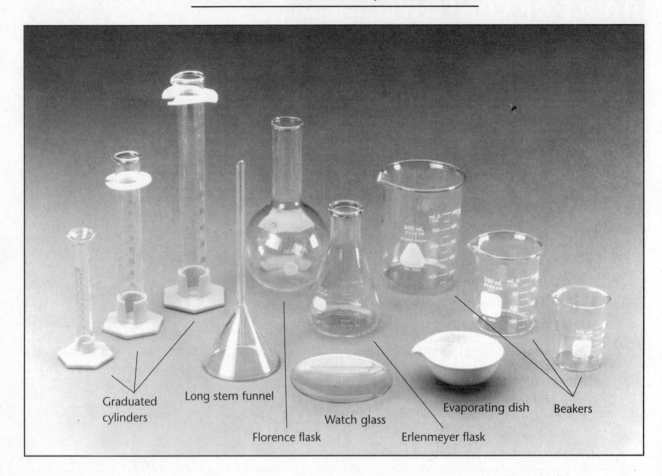

Graduated cylinders

Long stem funnel

Florence flask

Watch glass

Erlenmeyer flask

Evaporating dish

Beakers

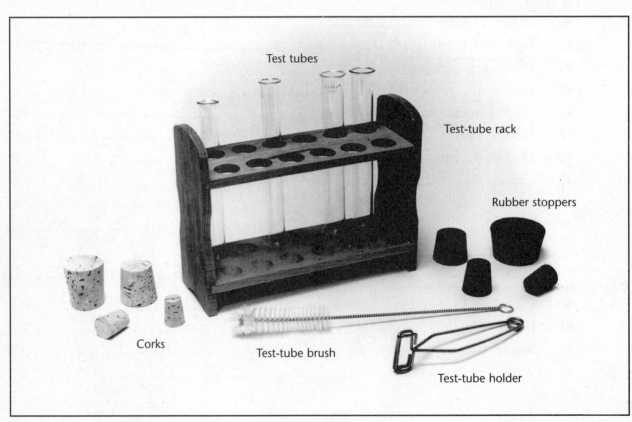

Test tubes

Test-tube rack

Rubber stoppers

Corks

Test-tube brush

Test-tube holder

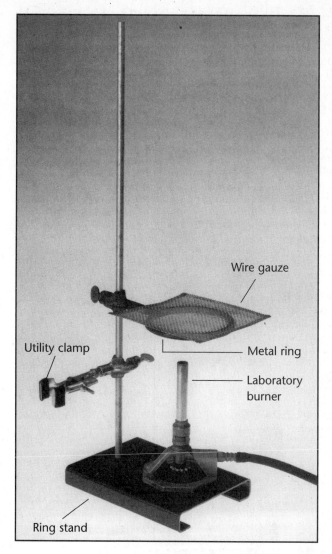

Wire gauze

Metal ring

Utility clamp

Laboratory burner

Ring stand

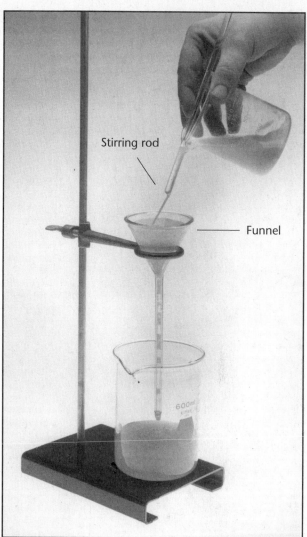

Stirring rod

Funnel

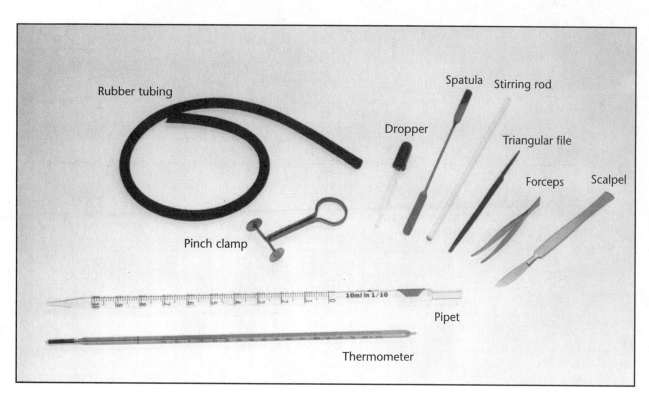

Rubber tubing

Spatula

Stirring rod

Dropper

Triangular file

Forceps

Scalpel

Pinch clamp

10ml in 1/10

Pipet

Thermometer

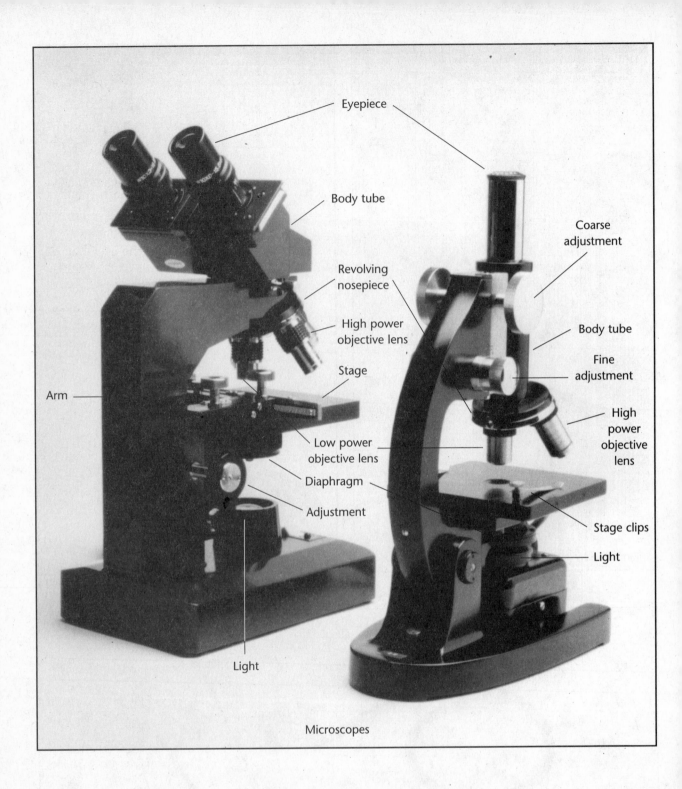

Eyepiece

Body tube

Revolving
nosepiece

High power
objective lens

Stage

Arm

Low power
objective lens

Diaphragm

Adjustment

Light

Coarse
adjustment

Body tube

Fine
adjustment

High
power
objective
lens

Stage clips

Light

Microscopes

Lighting a Laboratory Burner and Adjusting the Flame

Connect the hose of the burner to a gas supply. Partly open the valve on the gas supply, and hold a lighted match to the edge of the top of the burner. See FIGURE A.

The size of the flame can be changed by opening and closing the valve on the gas supply. The color of the flame indicates the amount of air in the gas. The air supply is controlled by moving the tube of the burner. A yellow flame indicates more air is needed, and the burner tube can be turned to increase the amount of air. If the flame goes out, the air supply should be reduced by turning the burner tube in the opposite direction. The gas supply is controlled by the valve on the bottom of the burner. The hottest part of the flame is just above the tip of the inner cone of the flame.

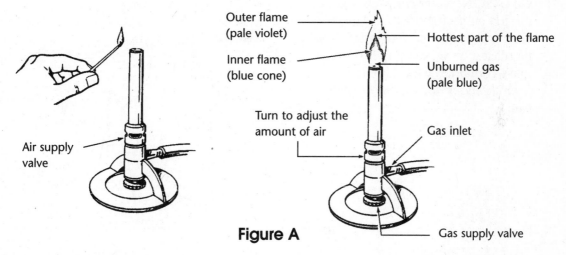

Outer flame (pale violet)
Inner flame (blue cone)
Hottest part of the flame
Unburned gas (pale blue)
Turn to adjust the amount of air
Gas inlet
Air supply valve
Gas supply valve

Figure A

Decanting and Filtering

It is often necessary to separate a solid from a liquid. Filtration is a common process of separation used in most laboratories. The liquid is decanted, that is, the liquid is separated from the solid by carefully pouring off the liquid, leaving only the solid material. To avoid splashing and to maintain control, the liquid is poured down a stirring rod. See FIGURE B. The solution is usually filtered through filter paper to catch any solid that has not settled to the bottom of the beaker. See FIGURE C.

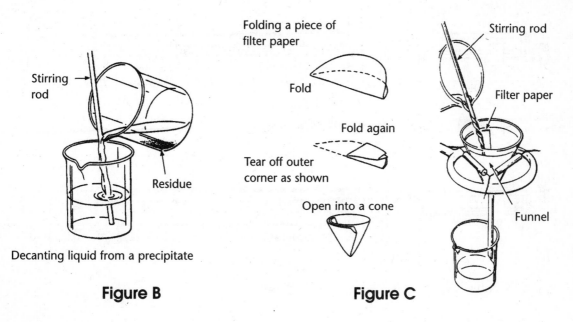

Stirring rod
Residue
Decanting liquid from a precipitate

Figure B

Folding a piece of filter paper
Fold
Fold again
Tear off outer corner as shown
Open into a cone

Stirring rod
Filter paper
Funnel

Figure C

Using the Balance

There are various types of laboratory balances in common use today. The balance you use may look somewhat different from the one in FIGURE D; however, all beam balances have some common features. The following technique should be used in transporting a balance.

(1) Be sure all riders are back to the zero point.

(2) If the balance has a lock mechanism to lock the pan(s), be sure it is on.

(3) Place one hand under the balance and the other hand on the beam's support.

The following steps should be followed in using the balance.

(1) Before determining the mass of any substance, slide all of the riders back to the zero point. Check to see that the pointer swings freely along the scale. You do not have to wait for the pointer to stop at the zero point. The beam should swing an equal distance above and below the zero point. Use the adjustment screw to obtain an equal swing of the beams, if necessary. You must repeat this procedure to "zero" the balance every time you use it.

(2) **CAUTION:** *Never put a hot object directly on the balance pan.* Any dry chemical that is to be massed should be placed on waxed paper or in a glass container. **CAUTION:** *Never pour chemicals directly on the balance pan.*

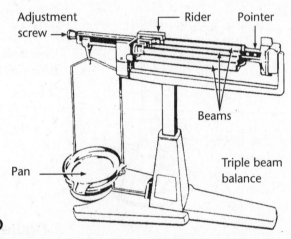

Figure D

(3) Once you have placed the object to be massed on the pan, move the riders along the beams beginning with the largest mass first. If the beams are notched, make sure all riders are in a notch before you take a reading. Remember, the pointer does not have to stop swinging, but the swing should be an equal distance above and below the zero point on the scale.

(4) The mass of the object will be the sum of the masses indicated on the beams. For example:

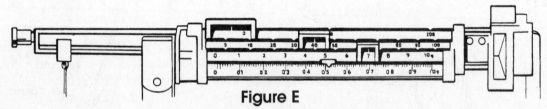

Figure E

The mass of this object would be read as 47.52 grams.

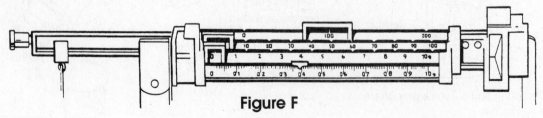

Figure F

The mass of this object would be read as 100.39 grams.

Measuring Temperature

When the temperature of a liquid is measured with a thermometer, the bulb of the thermometer should be in the liquid. When the thermometer is removed from the liquid, the column of mercury or alcohol in the thermometer soon shows the temperature of the air. When measuring the temperature of hot liquids, be sure you use a thermometer that is calibrated for high temperatures.

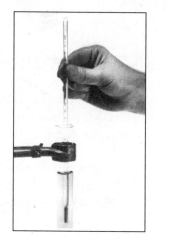

Figure G
Measuring temperature

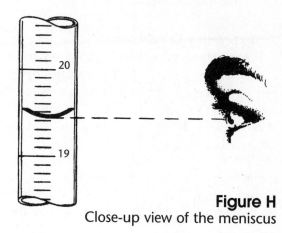

Figure H
Close-up view of the meniscus

Measuring Volumes

The surface of liquids when viewed in glass cylinders is always curved. This curved surface is called the meniscus. Most of the liquids you will be measuring will have a concave meniscus.

(1) The meniscus must be viewed along a horizontal line of sight. Do not try to make a reading looking up or down at the meniscus. Hold the apparatus up so that its sides are at a right angle to your eye.

(2) Always read a concave meniscus from the bottom. This measurement gives the most precise volume, because the liquid tends to creep up the sides of a glass container. Liquid in many plastic cylinders does not form a meniscus. If you are using a plastic graduate and no meniscus is noticeable, read the volume from the level of the liquid.

Inserting Glass Tubing or a Thermometer into a Stopper

This procedure can be dangerous if you are not careful. Check the size of the holes in the rubber stopper to see if they are just slightly smaller than the glass tubing. The rubber stopper should stretch enough to hold the glass tubing firmly.

Place a drop of glycerol or some water on the end of the glass tubing. Glycerol acts as a lubricant to help make the tubing go through the stopper more easily. Wrap the glass tubing and the stopper in a towel. Then push the tubing through the stopper using a gentle force and a twisting motion. Your hands should not be more than one centimeter apart. **CAUTION:** *Never hold the tubing or stopper in such a way that the end of the tubing is pointed toward or pushing against the palm of your hand. If the tubing breaks, you can injure your hand if it is held this way.*

This procedure also is used in inserting thermometers in rubber stoppers. Equal caution should be taken.

Disposal of Biological Materials

In certain laboratory investigations, living and preserved plant and animal tissues will be handled. Once the investigation is completed, these materials should be disposed of immediately. Give all preparations to your teacher for proper disposal unless otherwise instructed by your teacher. Familiarize yourself with the safety symbol for biologicals. Always wash your hands after handling these materials.

Transferring Liquids

Follow these general rules to safely transfer a liquid from one container to another. If the first container has a stopper, remove the stopper and hold it in your fingers as shown in FIGURE I. Put a stirring rod in the second container into which you are pouring the liquid. Hold the stirring rod against the lip of the first container as shown in FIGURE J. Pour the liquid from the first container slowly down the stirring rod into the second container. Replace the stopper in the first container when you are finished.

CAUTION: *Chemicals can be harmful if spilled on skin, clothes, or tabletops. If any liquid runs down the outside of the first container, rinse it with water before returning it to the shelf.* If the container is not rinsed, it may damage the shelf. Also, the next student who handles the container may be burned by the liquid. Remember: *You* might be that student!

Figure I

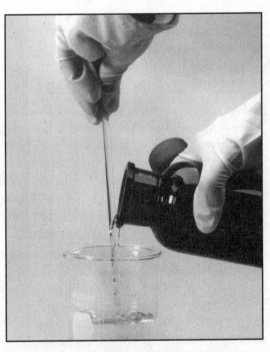

Figure J

Using the Microscope

The microscope is an important tool for life scientists. To use the microscope properly, you should study page viii and learn the name of each part. Whenever you use the microscope, carefully follow these instructions.

Always carry the microscope with both hands. Hold the arm with one hand. Put your other hand under the base as shown in FIGURE K. Place the microscope on a table gently, with the arm facing you. Clear the table of other objects not needed for the activity you are doing.

Turn on the light if the microscope has one. (If the microscope does not have a light, use a lamp as a light source. **CAUTION:** *Never use direct sunlight as a light source. It can damage your eyes.* Look through the eyepiece and adjust the mirror so that light from the lamp is reflected up through the opening in the stage.) Make sure that electric cords from microscopes or lamps do not block aisles. Be careful not to upset a microscope or lamp by running into a cord. Always unplug electric cords by gripping the plug and not the cord itself.

Adjust the diaphragm so that the greatest amount of light comes through the opening. The circle of light that you see is called the field of view. Turn the nosepiece so that the low power objective lens ($10\times$) clicks into place. Focus by turning the coarse adjustment. Turn the nosepiece again until the high power objective lens clicks into place. Turn the fine adjustment to focus. Never turn the coarse adjustment when the high power objective lens is in place. Be sure you do not touch the lenses. Use only special lens paper to clean the lenses.

When you are finished using the microscope, always click the low power objective lens back into place over the field of view. Turn the coarse adjustment to raise the body tube until the low power objective lens is about two or three centimeters above the stage. Carry the microscope properly to its storage place.

Figure K

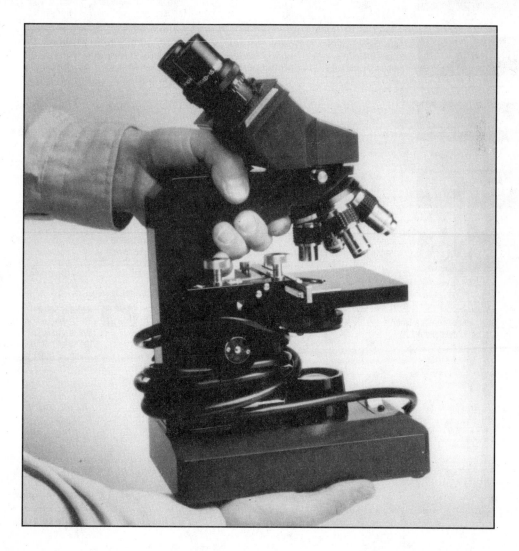

SAFETY SYMBOLS

SAFETY SYMBOLS	HAZARD	EXAMPLES	PRECAUTION	REMEDY
Disposal	Special disposal considerations required	chemicals, broken glass, living organisms such as bacterial cultures, protists, etc.	Plan to dispose of wastes as directed by your teacher.	Ask your teacher how to dispose of laboratory materials.
Biological	Organisms or organic materials that can harm humans	bacteria, fungus, blood, raw organs, plant material	Avoid skin contact with organisms or material. Wear dust mask or gloves. Wash hands thoroughly.	Notify your teacher if you suspect contact.
Extreme Temperature	Objects that can burn skin by being too cold or too hot	boiling liquids, hot plates, liquid nitrogen, dry ice, all burners	Use proper protection when handling. Remove flammables from area around open flames or spark sources.	Go to your teacher for first aid.
Sharp Object	Use of tools or glassware that can easily puncture or slice skin	razor blade, scalpel, awl, nails, pushpins	Practice common sense behavior and follow guidelines for use of the tool.	Go to your teacher for first aid.
Fume	Potential danger to olfactory tract from fumes	ammonia, heating sulfur, mothballs, nail polish remover, acetone	Make sure there is good ventilation and never smell fumes directly.	Leave foul area and notify your teacher immediately.
Electrical	Possible danger from electrical shock or burn	improper grounding, liquid spills, short circuits	Double-check setup with instructor. Check condition of wires and apparatus.	Do not attempt to fix electrical problems. Notify your teacher immediately.
Irritant	Substances that can irritate the skin or mucus membranes	pollen, mothballs, steel wool, potassium permanganate	Dust mask or gloves are advisable. Practice extra care when handling these materials.	Go to your teacher for first aid.
Corrosive	Substances (acids and bases) that can react with and destroy tissue and other materials	acids such as vinegar, hydrochloric acid, hydrogen peroxide; bases such as bleach, soap, sodium hydroxide	Wear goggles and an apron.	Immediately begin to flush with water and notify your teacher.
Toxic	Poisonous substance that can be acquired through skin absorption, inhalation, or ingestion	mercury, many metal compounds, iodine, poinsettia leaves	Follow your teacher's instructions. Always wash hands thoroughly after use.	Go to your teacher for first aid.
Flammable	Flammable and combustible materials that may ignite if exposed to an open flame or spark	alcohol, powders, kerosene, potassium permanganate	Avoid flames and heat sources. Be aware of locations of fire safety equipment.	Notify your teacher immediately. Use fire safety equipment if applicable.

 Eye Safety
This symbol appears when a danger to eyes exists.

 Clothing Protection
This symbol appears when substances could stain or burn clothing.

 Animal Safety
This symbol appears whenever live animals are studied and the safety of the animals and students must be ensured.

Chapter 1

LABORATORY MANUAL

• Solving a Problem with a Scientific Method 1

A method by which a scientist solves a problem is called a scientific method. This method usually includes observation, experimentation, interpretation, and hypothesis formation. Scientific methods are often compared to the procedures a detective uses in solving a crime or problem. The following investigation creates a scientific problem for you and asks you to solve it. You will use scientific methods in attempting to solve the problem.

Strategy
You will use a scientific approach to solve whether or not flasks A and B contain similar or different liquids.
You will make careful observations.
You will record accurate experimental results.
You will use your data as a basis for deciding if the two liquids are similar or different.

Materials
2 Erlenmeyer flasks containing liquids   2 stoppers (to fit flasks)   apron   gloves
clock or watch with second hand   beaker   goggles

Part A Observation
CAUTION: *Use care when handling sharp objects.*
CAUTION: *Do not taste, eat, or drink any materials used in the lab.*
CAUTION: *Inform your teacher if you come in contact with any chemicals.*

Procedure
1. Examine the two flasks. DO NOT remove the stoppers and DO NOT shake the contents.

2. Notice the flasks have been labeled A and B.

3. Record in Table 1 two or three similarities or differences between the two flasks.

   a. Do you think both flasks contain the same liquid? Explain. _____

   _____

   b. Is your answer to question a based on experimentation or guessing? _____

   _____

   c. Would scientists guess at answers to questions or would they experiment first? _____

   _____

   d. Do both flasks contain exactly the same amount of liquid? _____

   _____

Data and Observations

Table 1

Similarities	Differences

Part B Experimentation

Experiment 1—What happens if you shake the liquids?

FIGURE 1

Procedure

1. Give each flask *one hard shake using an up-and-down motion of your hand.* Make sure your thumb covers the stopper as you shake. Use FIGURE 1 as a guide.

2. Observe each flask carefully.

3. Record your observations in Table 2. Again, look for similarities and differences.

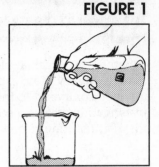

  a. After shaking the flasks, do you think they contain different liquids?

  _____

  b. What was present in flask A that may have been responsible for the change in the liquid?

  _____

Data and Observations

Table 2—Experiment 1

Similarities	Differences

Experiment 2—What happens if you remove some of the liquid in flask B so it appears like flask A?

Procedure

1. Remove the stopper from flask B and pour out half of the contents into a beaker or other suitable container (see FIGURE 1). Make sure that the amount of liquid in flask B is equal to the amount of liquid in flask A.

2. Replace the stopper. Give both flasks *one hard shake using an up-and-down motion of your hand.* Hold stopper in place while shaking.

3. Observe each flask carefully.

4. Record any similarities or differences observed in Table 3.
  a. Do both flasks now appear to contain the same liquid?

  _____

  b. What may have been added to flask B that was not present before?

  _____

Data and Observations

Table 3—Experiment 2

Similarities	Differences

Experiment 3—What happens if you shake the flasks more than once?

Procedure

1. *Shake each flask hard once with an up-and-down motion.*

2. Note the exact time in *seconds* after shaking that it takes for each liquid to return to its original condition. Record the time in Table 4.

3. Shake each flask *hard twice with an up-and-down motion.*

4. Again record in Table 4 the time it takes for the liquids to return to their original conditions.

5. *Shake both flasks hard three times with an up-and-down motion.*

6. Record in Table 4 the time it takes for them to return to their original conditions.
   a. After one shake, are the two liquids generally "behaving" in a similar way? That is, is the time needed for flasks A and B to return to their original conditions about the same?

   _____

   b. After two and three shakes, are flasks A and B generally "behaving" in a way similar

   to each other? _____

   _____

7. Look at your data in Table 4.
   a. Does flask A show an increase or decrease in time needed to return to its original condition as the number of shakes increases from one to three?

   _____

   _____

   b. Does flask B show a similar change? _____

8. Run two more trials for each part of Experiment 3. Be sure to keep track of the amount of time needed for the liquids to return to their original conditions.

9. Consider your recorded results in Table 4 as Trial 1. Record the results of Trials 1, 2, and 3 in Table 5.

10. Do three trials give better evidence than one trial in helping you to determine

   a. the contents of flasks A and B? _____

   _____

   b. the effects of shaking on flasks A and B? _____

   _____

Data and Observations

Table 4—Experiment 3 sample data

Time to Return to Original Condition (s)		
	1 shake	2 shakes	3 shakes
Flask A			
Flask B			

Table 5—Experiment 3

	Time to Return to Original Condition (s)								
	1 shake			2 shakes			3 shakes		
Trial	1	2	3	1	2	3	1	2	3
Flask A									
Flask B									

Questions and Conclusions

Questions 1–4 should help you to make some interpretations of what you have observed. Interpretations are reasonings based on observations and experiments. They are usually the next step in a scientific method.

1. On the basis of your first observations in Part A, could you decide if both flasks contained the same liquid? _____

2. After performing Experiment 1, could you decide if both flasks contained the same liquid? _____

3. Which experiment or experiments may have helped you to decide that the liquids in flasks A and B were similar or different? _____

   Explain. _____

4. Besides the liquid itself, what else seems to be needed in order for the liquid to change color?

   _____

Questions 5–7 should help you to form a hypothesis. In a hypothesis, all facts are joined in an attempt to explain what has been observed.

5. Explain why flask B did not change color when shaken in Experiment 1. _____

   _____

6. Why must the liquids in the half-filled flasks be shaken in order to produce a color change?

   _____

7. Did more shaking increase the amount of time needed for the liquids in flasks A and B to change back to their original color? Why or why not? _____

   _____

8. Why is experimenting a better method of problem solving than guessing?

   _____

9. What is meant by the phrase "solving a problem by using scientific methods"?

   _____

Strategy Check

_____ Can you use a scientific approach to solve whether or not flasks A and B contain similar or different liquids?

_____ Can you make careful observations?

_____ Can you record accurate experimental results?

_____ Can you use your data as a basis for deciding if the two liquids are similar or different?

Chapter 1

LABORATORY MANUAL • **Using SI Units 2**

How many inches equal 1 foot? How many feet equal 1 yard? Almost everybody can answer these questions. But how many yards equal 1 rod?

Is there any one number that is common for changing inches to feet, feet to yards, or yards to rods? A problem with the English system for measuring is that there is no common number for changing one unit to another. As a result, you may have had difficulty remembering that there are 5 ½ yards to a rod.

Scientists use the SI system of measuring rather than the English system. SI is an abbreviation for the International System of Measurement. SI is a more modern version of the old metric system.

Strategy

You will identify and use SI units of length and volume to measure several objects.
You will learn two important rules for converting from one SI unit to another.

Materials

metric ruler   graduated cylinder (50-mL)   microscope slide

Procedure

Part A Measuring Length in SI Units

1. Examine a metric ruler. Starting at the left edge, locate the smallest division or mark. This unit is the millimeter (mm). Ten millimeters are equal to a unit called the centimeter (cm). The ruler will have a longer line and the number 1 marked at the 1 cm length. See FIGURE 1.

   a. How many millimeters equal 1 cm? _____

   b. How many millimeters equal 3 cm? _____

   c. What number is used in changing the number of millimeters to centimeters? _____

   Ten centimeters are equal to 1 decimeter (dm). Ten decimeters are equal to 1 meter (m).

   d. What number is used when changing centimeters to decimeters? _____

   e. What number is used when changing decimeters to meters? _____

2. Measure a microscope slide in millimeters. Use FIGURE 2 as a guide to length, width, and height. Record these values in the column marked "mm" of Table 1.

3. To convert your millimeter numbers to centimeters, divide the millimeter numbers by 10. Record the length, width, and height of your slide in centimeters. Use the column marked "cm" of Table 1.

4. To convert your centimeter numbers to decimeters, divide the centimeter numbers by 10. Record the length, width, and height of your slide in decimeters. Use the column marked "dm" of Table 1.

5. To convert decimeters to meters, divide decimeters by 10. Record your slide measurements in meters on Table 1 in the column marked "m."

FIGURE 1

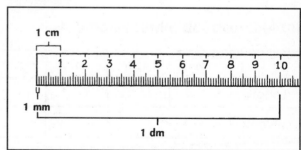

FIGURE 2

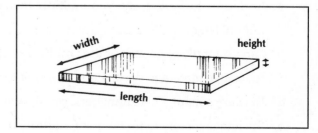

Table 1 Microscope Slide Measurements

	mm	cm	dm	m	km
Length					
Width					
Height					

A unit, kilometers, often is used to measure long distances. One thousand meters (m) equal
1 kilometer (km).

6. To convert meters to kilometers, divide meters by 1000 (not by 10). Record your slide measurements in kilometers in the column marked "km" of Table 1.

    a. Can you divide millimeter figures by 100 to change directly to decimeters? _____

    b. Can you divide millimeter figures by 1000 to change directly to meters? _____

    c. What number do you divide by when changing centimeters to meters? _____

    d. To change millimeters to centimeters, divide by _____

    e. To change millimeters to decimeters, divide by _____

    f. To change millimeters to meters, divide by _____

    g. To change millimeters to kilometers, divide by _____

    h. To change centimeters to meters, divide by _____

    i. To change centimeters to kilometers, divide by _____

7. Measure the length and width of your lab table or desk.

8. Record these dimensions in meters in Table 2. Record your answers in decimals. If your desk or lab table measures 1 m plus 14 cm, record this measurement as 1.14 m. If it measures less than 1 m, such as 83 cm, record this measurement as 0.83 m. Because 1 m equals 100 cm, 83 cm is the same as 83/100 or 0.83 m.

9. Convert your meter measurement to decimeters by multiplying meter figures by 10. Record the decimeter values in the proper column of Table 2. Convert your decimeter values in Table 2 to centimeters by multiplying decimeter figures by 10. Record the centimeter values in the proper column of Table 2.

Table 2 Lab Table Measurements

	m	dm	cm	mm
Length				
Width				

10. To convert your centimeter values to millimeters, multiply centimeter figures by 10. Record the millimeter values in the proper column of Table 2.

    a. According to Table 2, can you multiply meter figures by 100 to change directly to

       centimeters? _____

    b. Can you multiply meter figures by 1000 to change directly into millimeters? _____

    c. To change meters to decimeters, multiply by _____

    d. To change meters to centimeters, multiply by _____

    e. To change meters to millimeters multiply by _____

f. To change centimeters to millimeters, multiply by _____

g. To change kilometers to meters, multiply by (Be careful.) _____

11. When converting from one SI unit to another, you must either multiply or divide. Is there any pattern that will always allow you to decide whether to divide or multiply? Yes, there is.

   a. What operation is used in Table 1 to go from millimeters to centimeters? (Millimeters are small in size, centimeters are larger.) _____

   b. When changing from small SI units to large units, what mathematical operation (multiplying or dividing) is used? _____

   c. Which unit is smaller in size: decimeter or meter? _____

   d. Which unit is smaller in size: centimeter or kilometer? _____

   e. Which unit is smaller in size: meter or kilometer? _____

   f. When changing from larger SI units to smaller units, what mathematical operation (multiplying or dividing) is used? _____

   g. What operation is used in Table 2 to go from meters to centimeters? _____

   h. Which unit is larger in size: kilometer or millimeter? _____

   i. Which unit is larger in size: decimeter or millimeter? _____

   j. Which unit is larger in size: centimeter or decimeter? _____

When changing from one unit to another, you must remember:

• If you are changing from a small unit to a larger unit, you must divide. What number to divide by is determined by what new units are being asked for. For example, if changing millimeters to centimeters, divide by 10; if changing millimeters to decimeters, divide by 100 again.

• If you are changing from a large unit to a smaller unit, you must multiply. What number to multiply by is determined by what new units are being asked for. For example, if changing kilometers to meters, multiply by 1000; changing meters to millimeters, multiply by 1000 again; changing kilometers to centimeters, multiply by 100 000.

12. The meter is the main unit for measuring length or distance in the SI system. All changes from one unit to another involve a change of 10, or some multiple of 10. Fill in the blanks.

   a. 29 mm = _____ cm

   b. 4 dm = _____ m

   c. 44 dm = _____ cm

   d. 1205 cm = _____ dm

   e. 27 km = _____ m

   f. 103 dm = _____ m

   g. 0.29 dm = _____ mm

   h. 1202 mm = _____ cm

   i. 48 mm = _____ m

   j. 7.2 m = _____ cm

Part B Measuring Volume in SI

1. Examine a graduated cylinder with volume markings of 50 units. Each single line represents a unit of volume called a milliliter (mL). DO NOT confuse this word with millimeter (mm).

2. Fill the cylinder with water to the 25-mL line and place the cylinder on your desk.

3. Compare the level of water in your cylinder with FIGURE 3. On close examination, the water rides up along the edges of the cylinder. The proper reading of volume is judged by the bottom level of water.

FIGURE 3

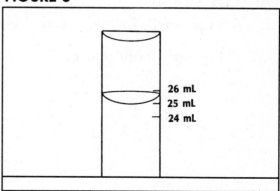

26 mL
25 mL
24 mL

4. Adjust the volume of water if necessary so that it is exactly 25 mL.

5. Convert your 25-mL volume to centiliter (cL) units. Use the same rule as established for length units. Are you changing from small to large units? If yes, then divide.

6. Fill in Table 3 for centiliters, deciliters (dL), and liters (L). There are 10 centiliters in a deciliter, and 10 deciliters in a liter.

7. Complete the chart on the right based on the numbers filled in for you. "kL" stands for kiloliter.

Table 3 Volume of Water in Cylinder

	mL	cL	dL	L
Volume				

	kL	L	dL	cL	mL
Volume	0.032	32			

8. The liter is the main unit for measuring volume in the SI system. Fill in the blanks.

a. 1.4 L = _____ mL

b. 5520 mL = _____ cL

Questions and Conclusions

1. What SI units studied can be used for measuring length? _____

2. What SI units studied can be used for measuring volume? _____

3. Why is it easier to convert meters to centimeters or millimeters than to convert miles to feet or inches?

_____

_____

4. Give the symbol for each of the following units.

millimeter = _____ kiloliter = _____ centimeter = _____ liter = _____

5. What units are represented by each of the following symbols?

dL = _____ km = _____ dm = _____ cL = _____

6. Circle the larger unit in each of the following pairs.

a. kiloliter or liter

b. centimeter or meter

c. decimeter or millimeter

d. centimeter or millimeter

e. millimeter or kilometer

f. centiliter or deciliter

7. Which mathematical process (multiplying or dividing) is used to change

a. centiliters to liters? _____

b. centiliters to deciliters? _____

c. meters to centimeters? _____

d. millimeters to meters? _____

Strategy Check

_____ Can you identify and use SI units of length and volume to measure objects?

_____ Did you learn the rules for converting from one SI unit to another?

Chapter 2

LABORATORY MANUAL

● Mixtures and Compounds 3

Matter is anything that has mass and occupies space. Matter exists in different forms. Three forms of matter are well known to us: elements, mixtures, and compounds. Elements are the basic materials of our world. Elements in a mixture have recognizable boundaries and can be separated by mechanical means. Elements that form a chemical compound can be separated only by a chemical process. Oxygen (O) is an element, which combined with hydrogen forms water, H_2O, a compound. Salt water is a mixture of two compounds, water and salt.

Strategy

You will separate a mixture into its parts.
You will compare the characteristics of a compound and a mixture.

Materials

granite	magnifying glass	sand (coarse)	apron
granite (crushed)	2 pie pans (disposable)	water	goggles
heat source	rock salt		

Procedure

1. Use the magnifying glass to observe the sand and granite. Sketch the shapes of the different minerals found in the granite and the shapes of the sand grains under Sketch A.

2. Sort the crushed granite into separate piles according to color.

3. Sketch the general shape of a piece from each pile of the sorted granite and label it as to color under Sketch B.

4. Mix a spoonful of sand in some water in a pie pan. Sketch what you observed under Sketch C.

5. Examine and sketch the salt crystals under Sketch D. **CAUTION:** *Do not ingest rock salt. It may contain harmful impurities.*

6. Mix a spoonful of salt in some water in the second pie pan. Record your observations.

7. Heat both pans until the water is evaporated. Sketch what is left in each pan under Sketch E.
   CAUTION: *Be careful not to get clothes or hair close to the heat source.*

Data and Observations

Sketch A

Sketch B

Sketch C

Sketch D

Sketch E

Questions and Conclusions

1. Are any of the sand grains similar to any of the granite fragments? _____
   If so, describe them. _____
   _____

2. How are salt and sand similar? _____
   How are they different? _____

3. Is salt water a compound or mixture? _____ Explain. _____
   _____
   _____

4. Is granite a compound or mixture? _____ Explain. _____
   _____
   _____

5. Name some mechanical processes used to separate mixtures. _____
   _____
   _____

Strategy Check

_____ Can you separate components of a mixture?

_____ Can you tell the difference between a compound and a mixture?

Chapter 2

LABORATORY MANUAL

• Constructing Compounds 4

All elements are made of atoms. Compounds are formed when two or more elements combine to form a different type of matter. A chemical formula is a shortcut chemists take to describe a specific compound. It tells the numbers and types of atoms that make up a single unit of a compound. You probably already know the formula for one common compound—water is H_2O. The formula for water tells us that a molecule of water has two hydrogen atoms and one oxygen atom.

Strategy

You will build models of different compounds.
You will use your models to determine how many atoms of each element are in each molecule.

Materials

modeling clay (red, yellow, and blue)
toothpicks
apron
goggles

Procedure

1. Obtain enough clay to make four balls of each color. Each clay ball represents one atom of an element. Blue balls represent hydrogen atoms, red balls represent oxygen atoms, and yellow balls represent carbon atoms.

2. Using toothpicks to connect your clay atoms (FIGURE 1), construct a model of each of the following compounds. After you construct each model, fill in the blanks for that compound in Table 1 in the Data and Observations section. After you finish making the molecules in parts a and b below, take them apart. Then make the molecule in part c.

   a. H_2O—water (Connect two hydrogen atoms to one oxygen atom.)

   b. CO_2—carbon dioxide (Connect two oxygen atoms to one carbon atom.)

   c. CH_4—methane (Connect four hydrogen atoms to one carbon atom.)

FIGURE 1

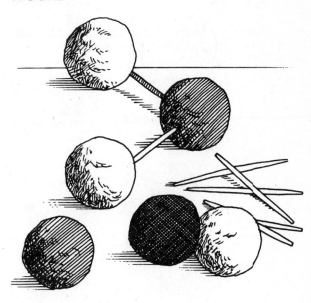

Data and Observations

Table 1

Chemical formula	Number of atoms in compound			
	Hydrogen	Carbon	Oxygen	Total
H_2O (water)				
CO_2 (carbon dioxide)				
CH_4 (methane)				

Questions and Conclusions

1. What would the answers in Table 1 be for a molecule of fruit sugar, $C_6H_{12}O_6$?

_____

2. From the formulas given, identify each of the following as either an element or a compound:

   NaCl, Ag, Co, CO, SO_2, AgBr. _____

_____

3. Each carbon atom can be attached to up to four other atoms. The compound hexane has six carbon atoms joined together in a chain. If only carbon and hydrogen make up the hexane molecule, what is the greatest number of hydrogen atoms that could be in the molecule? Draw a picture of the molecule to help you.

_____

_____

4. Nitrogen in air is in the form of two nitrogen atoms fastened together, N_2. Is nitrogen an element or is it a compound? Explain. _____

_____

Strategy Check

_____ Can you make a simple model of a compound based on its molecular formula?

_____ Based on a compound's molecular formula, can you figure out how many atoms of each element are in a compound?

_____ Do you understand the differences between an element and a compound?

Chapter 3

LABORATORY MANUAL

• Thermal Energy— Radiation 5

Have you ever walked barefoot on pavement on a sunny summer day? The pavement is hot because thermal energy from the sun is transferred to the pavement through radiation. Radiation is the movement of energy in the form of waves. Different materials absorb radiant energy from the sun differently. In today's experiment, you will compare how light-colored materials and dark-colored materials differ in their ability to absorb energy from the sun.

Strategy

You will observe how energy from the sun can increase the temperature of water.
You will determine how color influences the absorption of solar radiation.

Materials

construction paper (black)   scissors
construction paper (white)   tape
containers (2 plastic, 500-mL)   thermometer (alcohol, Celsius)
graduated cylinder (100-mL)   timer
pencils (colored)   water

Procedure

CAUTION: *Use care when handling sharp objects.*

1. Fasten black construction paper on the bottom and sides of one container.

2. Fasten white construction paper on the bottom and sides of the other container.

3. Add 250 mL of room-temperature water to each container.

4. Use a thermometer to find the temperature of the water in each container. Record this data in Table 1.

5. Place the containers side by side in direct sunlight outside or on a sunny windowsill. Be sure both containers receive the same amount of sunshine.

FIGURE 1

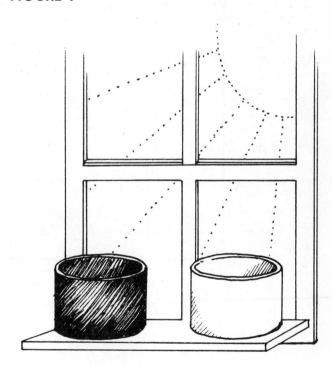

6. Measure the temperature of the water in each container at 5-minute intervals for 30 minutes. Record your data in Table 1.

7. Using FIGURE 2, graph the data from the table, using a line graph. Use one colored pencil to show data for the light container and a different one to show data for the dark container. Draw lines to connect the temperature data for each container of water.

Data and Observations

Table 1

Color of Container	Time (min)						
	0	**5**	**10**	**15**	**20**	**25**	**30**
Temp. (˚C)—Light							
Temp. (˚C)—Dark							

FIGURE 2

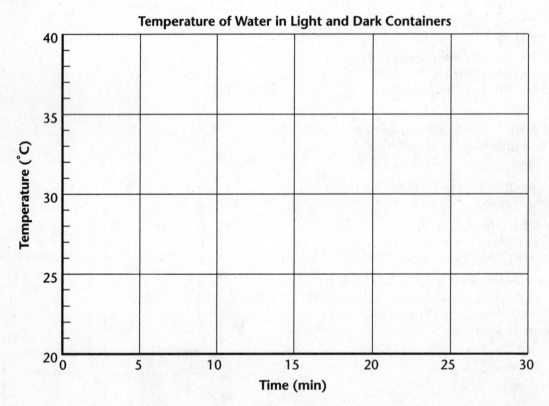

Temperature of Water in Light and Dark Containers

1. What was the final temperature of the water in the dark container? _____

2. What was the final temperature of the water in the light container? _____

3. How many degrees did the temperature of the dark container increase? _____

4. How many degrees did the temperature of the light container increase? _____

Questions and Conclusions

1. Did one container of water heat up more quickly? Which one?

_____

2. How do you think color influences the ability of something to absorb energy
from the sun?

_____

_____

3. Would you get the same results if you placed the containers in the shade? Why or
why not?

_____

_____

4. If you were stranded in a desert, would you rather be wearing a dark-colored or a
light-colored T-shirt? Why?

_____

_____

_____

Strategy Check

_____ Did you observe the influence of solar radiation on water temperature?

_____ Did you determine how color influences the absorption of solar radiation?

Chapter 4

LABORATORY MANUAL

• States of Matter 6

Three common states of matter are solid, liquid, and gas. A fourth state of matter, the plasma state, exists only at extremely high temperatures. Differences among the physical states depend on the distance between the atoms or molecules and on the rate of movement of the atoms or molecules. Pressure and temperature control these two factors.

Strategy

You will observe the characteristics of a solid.
You will change a gas to a liquid.
You will compare the characteristics of a solid, a liquid, and a gas.

Materials

beaker (1000-mL)
ice cubes (frozen from 500 mL of water)
ice cube tray
plastic drinking glass (cold or add an ice cube)
water

Procedure

1. Mark the level of the top of the ice cubes while they are still in the tray. Remove the ice cubes and place them in the beaker. Record the characteristics of ice in Table 1.

2. Let the ice cubes melt. Record the characteristics of the resulting water in Table 1.

3. Pour the water back into the tray. Mark the level of the top of the water on the tray. Under "Other characteristics" in Table 1, record whether this level is higher or lower than that of the ice.

4. Place the cold glass in a warm area. After a few minutes record your observations in Table 1.

5. Place an ice cube in the beaker of water. Observe whether or not it floats. Record your observations in Table 1.

Data and Observations

Table 1

Material	State of matter	Takes shape of container	Other characteristics
Ice cubes		Yes No	Floats Yes No
Water			Higher/Lower in tray than ice
Glass	Observations: Beads of water appear on it.		
Beaker with ice	Observations: Floats		

Questions and Conclusions

1. What is solid water called? _____ Liquid water? _____

   Water as a gas? _____

2. Did the ice cube sink or float in water? _____ Explain. _____

   _____

3. Which occupies more volume, an equal amount of water or ice? _____

   Explain. _____

   _____

   _____

4. Where did the water on the glass come from? _____

   What are the characteristics of water as a gas? _____

   _____

   _____

5. What change caused the water vapor to change to a liquid? _____

   _____

6. If you changed the water to water vapor in a pressure cooker, what volume would the water vapor

   occupy? _____

7. Compare the characteristics of water as a solid, a liquid, and a gas. _____

   _____

   _____

   _____

Strategy Check

_____ Can you observe the characteristics of a solid?

_____ Can you observe a gas change to a liquid?

_____ Can you compare the characteristics of a solid, a liquid, and a gas?

Chapter 4

LABORATORY MANUAL • **Crystal Formation 7**

Early in Earth's history, the crust was produced by the cooling of magma. When this molten rock flows into cracks, its temperature is about 1200°C. As the atoms of the different elements that make up the magma cool and slow down, they group themselves into a regular order to form a solid or crystal. This grouping is always the same for a given substance and is referred to as a mineral. When the magma cools to about 500°C, most of the minerals have crystallized out. The remaining minerals are dissolved in water. As the hot solution cools still more and finds its way to the surface where there is less pressure, the water evaporates and the rest of the minerals crystallize out. If the cooling is slow, large crystals result. If the cooling is fast, small crystals result. If the cooling is very fast, and the atoms do not have time to arrange themselves into regular order, an amorphous substance such as opal or glass results.

Strategy

You will observe crystal growth from a melt.
You will see mineral crystals in a sample of granite.
You will discover the effect that cooling rate has on crystal size.
You will discover processes that result in crystal growth.

Materials

beaker tongs
clear small medicine bottle with cap
dilute silver nitrate solution
eyedropper
fine copper wire
goggles
granite samples
hot plate
magnifying glass
microscope (optional)
microscope slides
salol
apron
gloves

Procedure
Part A

1. Using the magnifying glass, look at the sample of granite. The granite was once molten. The minerals that make up the granite can be recognized by their different colors.

Data and Observations

Table 1

2. Fill in the table below by placing an X in the appropriate box.

Mineral (color)	Having a definite shape	Shapeless
a) White or pink		
b) Black and shiny		
c) Black and dull		
d) Clear		

Questions and Conclusions

Part A

1. The clear material in granite is called quartz. It is nearly the last to crystallize out from a melt (500°C). Why do you suppose quartz is shapeless? _____

_____

2. Were the mineral crystals in granite easy to see with the unaided eye? _____

3. What can you say about the cooling rate of granite? _____

_____

Procedure

Part B

1. Place a clean fine copper wire (you may have to clean it with steel wool) about 1 cm long on a clean microscope slide.

2. Put the slide on the stage of a microscope or on a piece of white paper if you are using a hand lens.

3. From the dropper bottle marked silver nitrate solution, put 1 drop of the dilute silver nitrate on the copper wire and immediately watch what happens. **CAUTION:** *Do not spill the silver nitrate or get any of it on your clothes or hands.*

4. Draw a representative sample of the growth and the copper wire in the box below.

Questions and Conclusions
Part B

1. The pattern you have drawn is called a dendritic pattern and is made of silver. Is there a regular pattern to the growth? _____

2. Is the pattern repeated? _____

3. Are there plane surfaces that might suggest an orderly arrangement of atoms? _____

4. Look up the word *crystal* in your textbook. If this activity were to occur in nature, could the silver dendrite be called a crystal? Explain. _____

    _____

    _____

5. On a very cold day, the water vapor in the air of a warm room contacts the cold windowpane and freezes. The result is a feathery, almost dendritic pattern of ice. Would the dendritic pattern be the result of fast or slow crystallization? What is your evidence? _____

    _____

Procedure
Part C

1. Place a few crystals of salol into a small glass bottle and screw on the lid.

2. Heat the bottle in a water bath. The salol melts at 43°C, which is a little above body temperature.

3. When the salol has melted, lift the bottle out of the water bath using beaker tongs. Pour some of the liquid salol onto a clean microscope slide.

4. Watch the crystal growth using a magnifying glass or microscope.

Questions and Conclusions
Part C

1. The salol melts at 43°C, but when placed in the closed bottle, it melts at a higher temperature. Why? _____
   _____
   _____

2. Where did the crystals begin to form in the "puddle" of salol? _____
   _____

3. Where would you expect to find the irregular shaped crystals? _____
   _____

Strategy Check

_____ Can you recognize different crystals in a rock sample?

_____ Can you list some natural processes that result in crystal formation?

_____ Can you associate crystal size with the rate of cooling?

Chapter 5

• Atoms—Smaller Than You Think! 8

Much matter is composed of atoms, which means that atoms are everywhere. But if atoms are every-where, why haven't you ever seen a single atom? You aren't able to see atoms because they are so small. But you can use other senses to detect some of the small molecules made from atoms. In this experiment, you will study the small size of single vanilla molecules.

Strategy

You will predict what happens when drops of a liquid are placed in a balloon.
You will observe the small size of molecules.

Materials

rubber balloon
closet or locker
dropper
vanilla extract (2 mL)

Procedure

1. Use a dropper to place 20 to 40 drops of vanilla extract into a rubber balloon (FIGURE 1).

2. Blow up the balloon and tie it tightly at the end.

3. Place the balloon in a small, enclosed area such as a closet or locker for at least 30 minutes.

4. What do you think will happen to the molecules in the vanilla extract in the balloon? Record your prediction in the Data and Observations section.

5. After 30 minutes, open the closet or locker. What did you observe? Record your observation in the Data and Observations section.

FIGURE 1

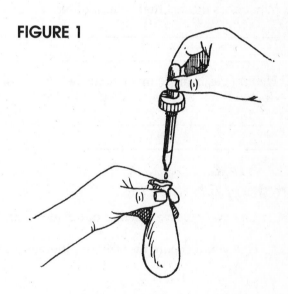

Data and Observations

1. What do you predict will happen to the vanilla in the balloon?

_____

_____

_____

2. What did you observe when you opened the area that held your balloon?

_____

_____

Questions and Conclusions

1. How do you explain the results of this experiment?

_____

_____

2. What do your results tell you about the size of the vanilla molecules?

_____

_____

3. What does the fact that helium-filled balloons deflate tell you about the size of helium atoms?

_____

_____

4. Helium gas is made up of single helium atoms. Vanilla molecules have the formula $C_8H_8O_3$. Which do you think will leak more rapidly from equally inflated balloons—helium or vanilla?

_____

_____

Strategy Check

_____ Can you observe whether or not atoms and molecules are very small?

_____ Can you compare the sizes of different molecules and atoms based on how they behave?

● Isotopes and Atomic Mass 9

A sample of an element, as it occurs in nature, is a mixture of isotopes. All the isotopes of a given element have the same number of protons, but each isotope has a different number of neutrons. Therefore, the atomic masses of elements, as shown on the periodic table, are average atomic masses. In this exercise, you will use a model of isotopes to help you understand the concept of atomic mass.

Strategy

You will model isotopes of two different elements using two colors of candy-coated peanuts and candy-coated chocolate.
You will determine the average mass of the two colors of candy-coated peanuts and candy-coated chocolate.
You will relate your results to the average atomic mass of atoms.

Materials 🖐️ 🥽

4 red and 3 green candy-coated peanuts
2 red and 3 green candy-coated chocolates

Procedure

1. Group together four red candy-coated peanuts and two red candy-coated chocolates. The two different kinds of candy represent two isotopes of the same element.

2. Assume that a red peanut has a mass of 2 candy units, and a red chocolate has a mass of 1 candy unit. Calculate the average mass of the red candy as follows:

   a. Multiply the number of red peanuts by the mass in candy units.

   b. Multiply the number of red chocolates by the mass in candy units.

   c. Add the masses and divide by the total number of candies.

3. Repeat steps 2 and 3, but use three green peanuts and three green chocolates. Assume a green peanut has a mass of 4 units, and a green chocolate has a mass of 3 units.

4. Record your calculations in Table 1.

Data and Observations

Table 1

	Peanut (candy × candy unit)	Chocolate (candy × candy unit)	Average $\dfrac{\text{(total mass)}}{\text{(total candies)}}$
Red			
Green			

Questions and Conclusions

1. There were six red and six green candies. Why were their calculated average masses not the same?

_____

_____

_____

2. If a sample of element Y contains 100 atoms of Y-12 and 10 atoms of Y-14, calculate the average mass of Y.

3. Look at the periodic table and notice that none of the naturally occurring elements have atomic masses that are whole numbers. How does your candy model of atoms help you explain that?

_____

_____

_____

4. An element needed for most nuclear reactors is uranium. Its two major isotopes are U-235 and U-238. Look up the mass of uranium on the periodic table. Infer which isotope is the most common.

_____

_____

5. Compare and contrast mass number and atomic mass.

_____

_____

_____

6. Hydrogen has three isotopes. The most common one, protium, has no neutrons. Deuterium, the second isotope, has one neutron. Tritium has two neutrons. Using this information, calculate the mass number of these isotopes.

_____

Strategy Check

_____ Can you explain how candy-coated peanuts and candy-coated chocolate can be a model for isotopes?

_____ Are you able to find the average mass of two different isotopes of the same element?

Chapter 6

LABORATORY MANUAL

• Relationships Among Elements 10

The periodic table is a wonderful source of information about all of the elements scientists have discovered. In this activity, you will investigate the relationship among the elements' atomic numbers, radii, and positions in the periodic table.

The radii for elements with atomic numbers from 3–38 are given in Table 1. The radii are so small that a very small metric unit called a picometer is used. A picometer (pm) is one trillionth of a meter.

Strategy
You will plot the atomic radii of elements with atomic numbers 3–38.
You will examine the graph for repeated patterns.

Materials 🧤 🥽

copy of the periodic table
graph paper
pencil

Table 1

Name and symbol		Atomic number	Atomic radius (picometers)	Name and symbol		Atomic number	Atomic radius (picometers)
Aluminum	Al	13	143	Magnesium	Mg	12	160
Argon	Ar	18	191	Manganese	Mn	25	127
Arsenic	As	33	121	Neon	Ne	10	131
Beryllium	Be	4	112	Nickel	Ni	28	124
Boron	B	5	85	Nitrogen	N	7	71
Bromine	Br	35	117	Oxygen	O	8	60
Calcium	Ca	20	197	Phosphorus	P	15	109
Carbon	C	6	77	Potassium	K	19	231
Chlorine	Cl	17	91	Rubidium	Rb	37	248
Chromium	Cr	24	128	Scandium	Sc	21	162
Cobalt	Co	27	125	Selenium	Se	34	119
Copper	Cu	29	128	Silicon	Si	14	118
Fluorine	F	9	69	Sodium	Na	11	186
Gallium	Ga	31	134	Strontium	Sr	38	215
Germanium	Ge	32	123	Sulfur	S	16	103
Iron	Fe	26	126	Titanium	Ti	22	147
Krypton	Kr	36	201	Vanadium	V	23	134
Lithium	Li	3	156	Zinc	Zn	30	134

Procedure

1. On the graph paper, label the horizontal axis with the numbers 0–38 to represent the atomic numbers of the elements you will be plotting.

2. Label the vertical axis by ten with numbers from 0–280. These numbers represent atomic radii.

3. Plot the atomic radius for each of the elements with atomic numbers 3–38.

Questions and Conclusions

1. Look at the shape of your graph. What patterns do you observe? _____

_____

2. What family is represented by the high peaks in your graph? _____

3. What family is represented by the low points in your graph? _____

4. What family is represented by the smaller peaks just before the high peaks in your graph?

_____

5. What do you notice about the radii of the elements at the high peaks as you move from left to right on your graph? Look at your periodic table and find the element that represents each high peak.

What does each high peak begin in the periodic table? _____

_____

_____

6. What happens to the radii of the elements between two highest peaks? What does each of these

groups of elements represent? _____

_____

_____

7. How can a graph such as the one you made help to predict the properties of elements that have not been discovered yet?

_____

_____

_____

_____

8. How do the radii of metals in each period compare with the radii of nonmetals in that period?

_____

_____

Strategy Check

_____ Can you plot a graph of the atomic radii of elements?

_____ Can you observe repeating patterns in the graph?

Chapter 6

LABORATORY MANUAL

• Periodicity 11

A periodic event is one that occurs time after time in a regular, predictable way. If you have a table of repeating events, you can use it to predict what might be true in the future. For example, astronomers are able to predict the appearance of a comet if they know the dates of the comet's appearance in the past. A calendar is a good model for the periodic table of the elements.

Strategy
You will determine missing information on the calendar for a month.
You will make predictions about future and past events based on the calendar.

Procedure
1. Label the seven columns of the calendar page in FIGURE 1 with the numbers 1–7. There are seven families, or groups, in this periodic table. They are the days of the week.

2. Label the five rows of the calendar page with the numbers 1–5. There are five periods in this periodic table. Each period is a week.

3. Notice that some information is missing. Fill in the missing information by examining the information in the blocks surrounding the spots where the missing information belongs.

Data and Observations

FIGURE 1

SUN	MON	TUE	WED		FRI	SAT
			1	2	3 Soccer Practice
4	5	6 .	7	8	9	10
11	12	@	#	15	16	17 Soccer Practice
18	19	20	21	22	23	24
25	26	27	28	29	30 Your Birthday	31

Questions and Conclusions
1. Two of the days in Families 3 and 4 are marked with an @ and a #. What dates should go in these positions? _____

2. Family 5 doesn't have a name. What is the correct name for this family? _____

3. What dates are included in the third period of the table? _____

4. Assuming that the previous month had 30 days, what day of the week would the 28th of that month have been? _____

A periodic event is one that occurs time after time in a regular, predictable way. If you have a table of repeating events, you can use it to predict what might be true in the future. For example, astronomers are able to predict the appearance of a comet if they know the dates of the comet's appearance in the past. A calendar is a good model for the periodic table of the elements.

Strategy
You will determine missing information on the calendar for a month.
You will make predictions about future and past events based on the calendar.

Procedure 🔬 🥽

1. Label the seven columns of the calendar page in FIGURE 1 with the numbers 1–7. There are seven families, or groups, in this periodic table. They are the days of the week.

2. Label the five rows of the calendar page with the numbers 1–5. There are five periods in this periodic table. Each period is a week.

3. Notice that some information is missing. Fill in the missing information by examining the information in the blocks surrounding the spots where the missing information belongs.

Data and Observations

Questions and Conclusions

1. Two of the days in Families 3 and 4 are marked with an @ and a #. What dates should go in these positions? _____

2. Family 5 doesn't have a name. What is the correct name for this family? _____

3. What dates are included in the third period of the table? _____

4. Assuming that the previous month had 30 days, what day of the week would the 28th of that month have been? _____

5. What period of this table would it appear in? _____

6. Notice that two dates have been scheduled for regular soccer practice. When would you expect the next two soccer practices to take place? _____

Chapter 7

LABORATORY MANUAL

● Chemical Bonds 12

All substances are made of atoms. The physical and chemical properties of a substance depend on how the atoms that make up the substance are held together by chemical bonds. In this experiment, you will investigate the properties of compounds formed by two types of chemical bonds: covalent bonds and ionic bonds.

In some compounds, called covalent compounds, the atoms are held together by covalent bonds. A covalent bond forms when two atoms share a pair of electrons. In other substances, atoms have either lost or gained electrons to form ions. An ion is an atom that has gained or lost one or more electrons. In these substances, the ions are held together by ionic bonds. These substances are called ionic compounds.

Solutions of ionic compounds can conduct an electric current. Some covalent compounds can also form solutions. However, these solutions do not conduct an electric current. A measure of how well a solution can carry an electric current is called conductivity.

Strategy

You will determine the conductivity of several solutions.

You will classify the compounds that were dissolved in the solutions as ionic compounds or covalent compounds.

Materials

apron
alligator clips (4)
9-V battery and battery clip
cardboard sheet, 10 cm × 10 cm
copper wire, insulated, 20-cm lengths (2)
sucrose solution, 0.1M sucrose
glucose solution, 0.1M glucose
sugar cubes (sucrose)
goggles
LED (light-emitting diode)
microplate, 24-well
paper towels
pipettes, plastic (7)
resistor, 1000-Ω
sodium chloride (rock, crystalline)
sodium chloride solution, 0.1M NaCl
sodium hydroxide solution, 0.1M NaOH
sulfuric acid solution, 0.1M H_2SO_4
tape
water, distilled

CAUTION: *Sulfuric acid and sodium hydroxide can cause burns. Avoid contacting them with your skin or clothing. Do not taste, eat, or drink any materials used in the lab.*

Procedure
Part A Constructing a Conductivity Tester

1. After putting your apron and goggles on, attach the 9-V battery clip to the 9-V battery. Use tape to attach the battery securely to the cardboard sheet, as shown in FIGURE 1.

2. Attach an alligator clip to one of the lead wires of the 1000-Ω resistor. Connect the alligator clip to the *red* lead wire of the battery clip. Tape the resistor and alligator clip to the cardboard sheet as shown in FIGURE 2. **CAUTION:** *Use care when handling sharp objects.*

3. Attach an alligator clip to the *long* lead wire of the LED. Connect this alligator clip to the second wire of the 1000-Ω resistor. Tape the alligator clip to the cardboard sheet.

4. Attach an alligator clip to the *short* lead wire of the LED. Connect this clip to one end of one of the insulated copper wires. Tape the clip to the cardboard sheet as shown in FIGURE 3.

5. Attach the last alligator clip to one end of the second insulated copper wire. Connect the alligator clip to the *black* lead wire of the battery clip. Tape the alligator clip to the cardboard sheet as shown in FIGURE 4.

6. Check to be certain that the alligator clips, resistor, and battery are securely taped to the cardboard sheet and that the clips are not touching one another.

7. Have your teacher check your conductivity tester.

8. Touch the two ends of the two insulated wires and observe that the LED glows.

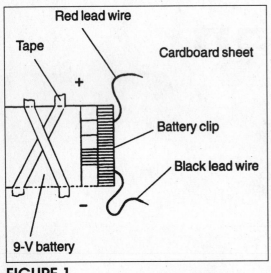

FIGURE 1

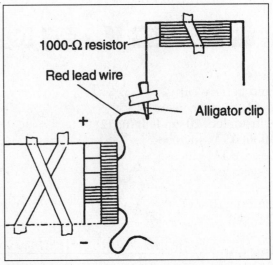

FIGURE 2

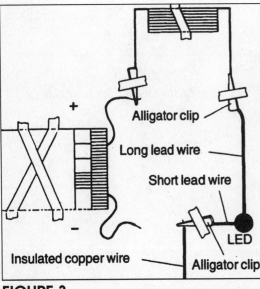

FIGURE 3

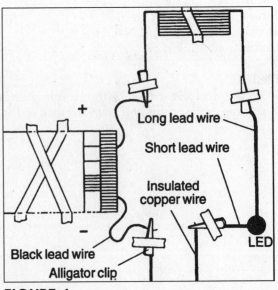

FIGURE 4

FIGURE 5

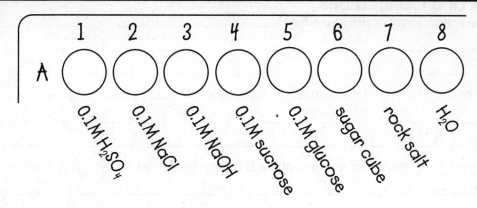

A

1 2 3 4 5 6 7 8

0.1M H₂SO₄   0.1M NaCl   0.1M NaOH   0.1M sucrose   0.1M glucose   sugar cube   rock salt   H₂O

Part B Testing the Conductivity of a Solution

1. Place the microplate on a flat surface. Have the numbered columns of the microplate at the top and the lettered rows at the left. **CAUTION:** *Wash hands immediately after coming in contact with any of the prepared solutions.* **CAUTION:** *Inform your teacher if you come in contact with any chemicals.*

2. Using a clean pipette, add a pipetteful of the sulfuric acid solution to well A1.

3. Using another clean pipette, add a pipetteful of the sodium chloride solution to well A2.

4. Repeat step 3 for each remaining solution or substance. Use a clean pipette for each solution. Add the sodium hydroxide solution to well A3, the sucrose solution to well A4, the glucose solution to well A5, a sugar cube to well A6, and a piece of rock salt to well A7.

5. Using a clean pipette, add a pipetteful of distilled water to well A8.

6. Place the exposed ends of the two insulated copper wires into the solution in well A1, positioning the wires so they are at opposite sides of the well. Be sure that the exposed ends of the wire are completely submerged.

7. Observe the LED. Use the brightness of the LED as an indication of the conductivity of the solution. Rate the conductivity of the solution using the following symbols: + (good conductivity); − (fair conductivity); or 0 (no conductivity). Record your rating in the corresponding well of the microplate shown in FIGURE 6.

8. Remove the wires and dry the ends of the wires with a paper towel.

9. Repeat steps 6, 7, and 8 for each remaining well in the microplate.

Data and Observations

FIGURE 6

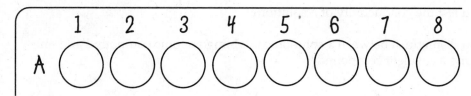

1 2 3 4 5 6 7 8

A

Questions and Conclusions

1. What is the conductivity of distilled water? _____

_____

_____

2. Why was the conductivity of the distilled water measured? _____

_____

_____

3. After studying your results, infer which of the solutions contained an ionic compound.

_____

_____

_____

4. Do your results indicate that any of the solutions contained a covalent compound?

_____

_____

_____

5. How do the conductivities of solutions of ionic compounds and covalent compounds compare?

_____

_____

6. Did the crystal of table salt or the sugar cube conduct electricity? _____

_____

7. How did the conductivities of the crystal of table salt and the 0.1M NaCl solution compare?

_____

8. From your results describe one property of an ionic compound.

_____

_____

Strategy Check

_____ Can you test the conductivity of a solution?

_____ Can you distinguish between a solution containing an ionic compound and one containing a covalent compound?

Chapter 7

LABORATORY MANUAL

• Chemical Activity   13

The atoms of most chemical elements can either gain or lose electrons during reactions. Elements whose atoms lose electrons during reactions are classified as metals. Metals are found on the left side of the periodic table of elements. The tendency of an element to react chemically is called activity. The activity of a metal is a measure of how easily the metal atoms lose electrons.

Strategy

You will observe chemical reactions between metals and solutions containing ions of metals.
You will compare the activities of different metals.
You will rank the metals in order of their activities.

Materials

apron
aluminum nitrate solution, 0.1M Al(NO$_3$)$_3$
copper nitrate solution, 0.1M Cu(NO$_3$)$_2$
goggles
hand lens or magnifier
iron nitrate solution, 0.1M Fe(NO$_3$)$_2$
lead nitrate solution, 0.1M Pb(NO$_3$)$_2$
magnesium nitrate solution, 0.1M Mg(NO$_3$)$_2$
metal strips (8 1-mm × 10-mm strips of each: aluminum, Al; copper, Cu;
  iron, Fe; lead, Pb; magnesium, Mg; nickel, Ni; and zinc, Zn)
microplate, 96-well
nickel nitrate solution, 0.1M Ni(NO$_3$)$_2$
paper, white
paper towels
pipette, plastic microtip
zinc nitrate, 0.1M Zn(NO$_3$)$_2$
water, distilled

CAUTION: *Many of these solutions are poisonous. Avoid inhaling any vapors from the solutions. These solutions can cause stains. Do not allow them to contact your skin or clothing.*

Procedure

1. Wear an apron and goggles during this experiment.

2. Place the microplate on a piece of white paper on a flat surface. Have the numbered columns of the microplate at the top and lettered rows at the left.

3. Using the microtip pipette, place 15 drops of the aluminum nitrate solution in each of wells A1–H1. Rinse the pipette with distilled water.

4. Place 15 drops of copper nitrate solution in each of wells A2–H2 using the pipette. Rinse the pipette with distilled water.

5. Repeat step 4 for each of the remaining solutions. Add the iron nitrate solution to wells A3–H3, the lead nitrate solution to wells A4–H4, the magnesium nitrate solution to wells A5–H5, the nickel nitrate solution to wells A6–H6, and the zinc nitrate solution to wells A7–H7. Leave the wells in column 8 empty.

6. Carefully clean each metal strip with a paper towel.

7. Place one strip of aluminum in each of wells A1–A8.

8. Place one strip of copper in each of wells B1–B8.

9. Repeat step 8 for the remaining metals. Add the iron strips to wells C1–C8, the lead strips to wells D1–D8, the magnesium strips to wells E1–E8, the nickel strips to wells F1–F8, and the zinc strips to wells G1–G8. Do not put strips in the wells in row H.

10. FIGURE 1 shows the metal and the solution that are in each of wells A1–H8.

11. Wait 10 min.

12. Use a hand lens or magnifier to observe the contents of each well. Look for a change in the color of the solution in each well by comparing it with the color of the solution in well H at the bottom of the column. Look for a change in the texture or color of the metal strip in each well by comparing it with the piece of metal in well 8 at the end of that row. Look for the appearance of deposited materials in the bottom of the well. Each change or appearance of deposits is an indication that a chemical reaction has taken place.

13. If you see an indication of a reaction, draw a positive sign (+) in the corresponding well of the microplate shown in FIGURE 2 in the Data and Observations section. If you see no indication of a reaction, draw a negative sign (–) in the corresponding well of FIGURE 2.

14. Count the number of positive signs in each row of wells in FIGURE 2. Record the value under the corresponding metal in Table 1.

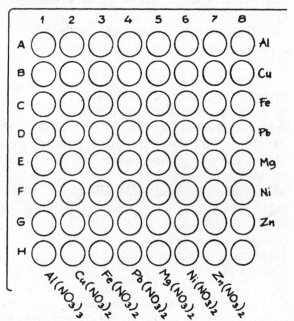

FIGURE 1

Data and Observations
FIGURE 2

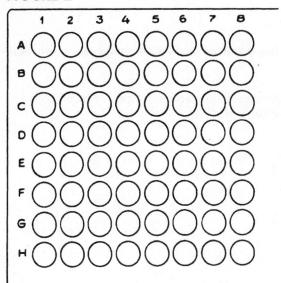

Table 1

Metal	Al	Cu	Fe	Pb	Mg	Ni	Zn
Number of reactions							

Questions and Conclusions

1. Why were solutions but not strips of metal placed in wells H1–H7? _____

_____

_____

2. Why were strips of metal but no solutions added to wells A8–H8? _____

_____

_____

3. Why did you clean the metal strips with the paper towel? _____

_____

_____

4. Using the number of reactions for each metal in Table 1, rank the metals from the most active to

the least active. _____

5. Solutions of dissolved metal compounds contain metal ions. An ion is an atom that has gained or lost electrons. Ions of metals are positively charged because the metals lose electrons when they react. The activity of the ion of a metal is a measure of how easily an ion gains electrons. Use the results of this experiment to rank the activities of ions of metals in solutions.

_____

6. How does the activity of an ion of a metal compare with the activity of the metal?

_____

_____

Strategy Check

_____ Can you identify evidence that a chemical reaction has occurred between a metal and a solution containing metal ions?

_____ Can you interpret evidence of chemical reactions between metals and solutions of metal ions and arrange the metals in order according to their activities?

Chapter 8

LABORATORY MANUAL

● Chemical Reactions 14

The changes that occur during a chemical reaction are represented by a chemical equation. An equation uses chemical symbols to represent the substances that change. The reactants, on the left side of the equation, are the substances that react. The products, on the right side of the equation, are the substances that are formed from the reaction.

In the following reaction, two reactants form one product. Water and oxygen are the reactants. The product is hydrogen peroxide.

$$2H_2O + O_2 \rightarrow 2H_2O_2$$

A chemical reaction may have two products from the breakdown of a single reactant. In this example water is the reactant. Hydrogen and oxygen are products.

$$2H_2O \rightarrow 2H_2 + O_2$$

Two reactants can also combine to make two products. In the following reaction, carbon displaces the hydrogen in water and hydrogen and carbon monoxide are released as gases.

$$H_2O + C \rightarrow H_2 + CO$$

Strategy

You will recognize the reactants and products of a chemical reaction.
You will write a word equation for a chemical reaction.
You will write a balanced chemical equation using chemical symbols.

Materials 🔲 ☠️ 🔥 🥽 ✋ 🧤 🧹

Part A	Part B	Part C
aluminum foil	baking soda, $NaHCO_3$	beaker
apron	matches	copper (II) sulfate solution, $0.1M$ $CuSO_4$
burner	spoon	common nail, Fe
goggles	test tube	paper towel
matches	test-tube holder	string
steel wool	wood splint	watch or clock
tongs		

CAUTION: *Copper (II) sulfate solution is poisonous. Handle with care. Wear goggles and an apron.*

Procedure

Part A Two Reactants→One Product

1. Protect the table with a sheet of aluminum foil. Place the burner in the center of the foil. Light the burner. **CAUTION:** *Stay clear of flames.*

2. Observe the color of the steel wool. Record your observations in the Data and Observations section.

3. Predict changes in the steel wool when it is heated in the flame. Write your prediction in the Data and Observations section.

4. Hold the steel wool (containing iron, Fe) with the tongs over the flame as shown in FIGURE 1. As the steel wool burns, record the changes it goes through.

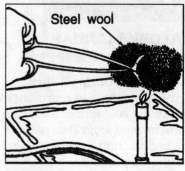

FIGURE 1

Part B One Reactant→Two Products

1. Use the burner set up in Part A.

2. Place a spoonful of baking soda, $NaHCO_3$, in a test tube. Use the test-tube holder to heat the test tube in the flame, as shown in FIGURE 2. Do not point the mouth of the test tube toward anyone. In the Data and Observations section, write your prediction of what will happen as the baking soda is heated.

3. Record the description and colors of the products formed inside the tube as it is heated.

4. Test for the presence of CO_2. Light a wooden splint. Insert the flaming splint into the mouth of the test tube. If the flame of the splint goes out, CO_2 is present. Record your observations of the products of this reaction.

FIGURE 2

Part C Two Reactants→Two Products

1. Carefully rub the nail with a piece of steel wool until the nail is shiny. Tie a string around the nail. Fill a beaker about half full with the $CuSO_4$ solution. Record the colors of the nail and the $CuSO_4$ solution in Table 1. **CAUTION:** *Use care when handling sharp objects. Wash hands immediately after coming in contact with copper (II) sulfate solution.*

2. Dip the nail in the $CuSO_4$ solution. (See FIGURE 3.) Predict what changes will happen to the appearance of the nail and the solution. After 5 min, pull the nail from the solution and place it on a paper towel. Record the colors of the nail and the solution in Table 1.

3. Put the nail back into the solution and observe further color changes.

FIGURE 3

Data and Observations

Part A Two Reactants→One Product

Color of steel wool before burning: _____

Prediction of changes in the heated steel wool: _____

Color of burned steel wool: _____

Part B One Reactant→Two Products

Prediction of changes in the heated baking soda: _____

Description of deposits inside heated test tube: _____

Observations of flaming splint: _____

Part C Two Reactants→Two Products

Prediction of changes in nail and $CuSO_4$ solution: _____

Table 1

Observation time	Color of nail	Color of $CuSO_4$ solution
Before reaction		
After reaction		

Questions and Conclusions

1. Identify the two reactants in the heating of steel wool. _____

_____

2. How does the heat from the flame affect the reactants when steel wool is heated? _____

_____

3. What evidence suggests that at least two reactants were formed when $NaHCO_3$ was heated?

_____

_____

4. Was the heating of $NaHCO_3$ an endothermic or exothermic reaction? Explain your answer.

_____

_____

5. From your observations, does the reaction of an iron nail with the copper (II) sulfate yield more than one product? _____

_____

6. Was the addition of the iron nail to the copper (II) sulfate solution an endothermic or exothermic reaction? _____

Strategy Check

_____ Can you identify the reactants and products of a chemical reaction?

_____ Can you write a word equation for a chemical reaction?

_____ Can you write a balanced chemical equation?

Chapter 8
LABORATORY MANUAL

• Reaction Rates and Temperature   15

Not all chemical reactions occur at the same rate. Some chemical reactions are very fast; others are very slow. The same chemical reaction can happen at several different rates depending on the temperature at which the reaction occurs.

In this experiment, you will investigate the effect of temperature on a decomposition reaction. Household bleach is a solution of five percent sodium hypochlorite (NaOCl). This compound decomposes to produce sodium chloride and oxygen gas.

$$2NaOCl \rightarrow 2NaCl + O_2$$

Strategy

You will observe the amount of oxygen produced from the decomposition of household bleach at various temperatures.

You will graph the reaction data.

You will determine the relationship between reaction rate and temperature for this reaction.

Materials

apron
beaker (400-mL)
clock with second hand
cobalt nitrate solution, $1M$ $Co(NO_3)_2$
goggles
immersion heater or hot plate
microplate (24-well)
pipette, plastic
pipette, plastic microtip
sodium hypochlorite solution, $1M$ NaOCl
thermometer
washers (4 iron or lead)

CAUTION: *Handle both solutions with care. Solutions can stain clothes and skin. Rinse spills with plenty of water.*

Procedure

Part A—Reaction at Room Temperature

1. Safety goggles and a laboratory apron must be worn throughout this experiment. Look at the equation of the decomposition reaction. In the Data and Observations section, write a prediction of what you might observe during this reaction. Write a hypothesis describing how temperature will affect the reaction rate.

2. Allow 400 mL of tap water to come to room temperature.

3. At the top of Table 1, record the temperature of the water to the nearest 0.5°C.

4. Using the microtip pipette, place 30 drops of 2.5 percent sodium hypochlorite solution in well A1 of the microplate.

5. Rinse the microtip pipette twice with distilled water. Discard the rinse water.

6. Using the rinsed pipette, place 10 drops of cobalt nitrate solution into well C1 of the microplate.

7. Rinse the microtip pipette twice with distilled water. Discard the rinse water.

8. Draw up the sodium hypochlorite solution in well A1 into the bulb of the plastic pipette. Be sure that no solution remains in the stem of the pipette.

9. Place three or four iron or lead washers over the top of the stem of the pipette, as in FIGURE 1.

10. Squeeze and hold the pipette to expel the air from the bulb of the pipette.

11. Bend the stem of the pipette over into the cobalt nitrate solution in well C1, as shown in FIGURE 2. Be prepared to start timing the reaction as soon as you complete the next two steps.

12. Release the pipette bulb and draw the cobalt nitrate solution into the pipette. The two solutions will mix. Record any changes you observe.

13. Quickly submerge the pipette and washer assembly in the beaker of water, as shown in FIGURE 3. Begin timing. If necessary, hold the pipette upright.

14. Count the number of bubbles produced by the reaction as they escape from the stem of the pipette. Every 15 s for 3 min, record in Table 1 the total number of bubbles counted.

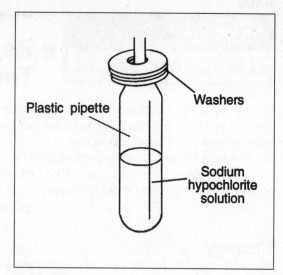

FIGURE 1

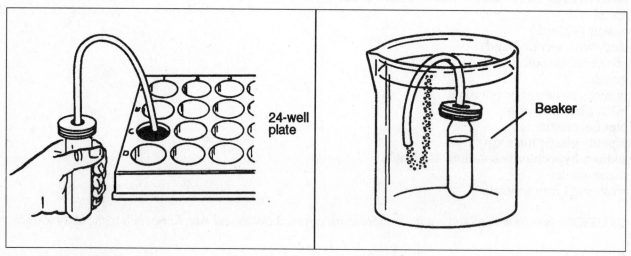

FIGURE 2   **FIGURE 3**

15. Use FIGURE 4 to graph the data from Part A. Plot time on the *x*-axis and the total number of bubbles on the *y*-axis. Draw a line that best fits the data points.

Part B—Reaction at a Higher Temperature
1. Place the beaker of water in the immersion bath or on the hot plate. Heat the water until its Celsius temperature is 10° higher than that of the room temperature water.

2. Repeat steps 3–14 in Part A, using the water bath at this higher temperature.

3. Plot your data from Part B on the same graph as Part A, but use a different colored pen or pencil.

Part C—Reaction at a Lower Temperature
1. Fill the beaker with tap water. Add ice to lower the Celsius temperature of the water 10° below that of the room temperature water.

2. Repeat steps 3–14 in Part A, using the water bath at this lower temperature.

3. Plot your data from Part C on the same graph as Parts A and B, but use a third color.

Data and Observations

Prediction of observations of reaction: _____

Hypothesis relating reaction rate and temperature: _____

Table 1

Time (s)	A. Total number of bubbles (room temperature) _____°C	B. Total number of bubbles (higher temperature) _____°C	C. Total number of bubbles (lower temperature) _____°C
0			
15			
30			
45			
60			
75			
90			
105			
120			
135			
150			
165			
180			

FIGURE 4

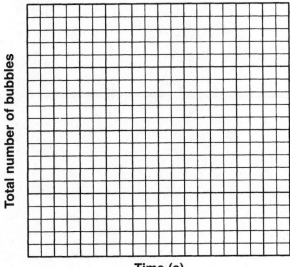

Total number of bubbles

Time (s)

Questions and Conclusions

1. How does raising the temperature affect the shape of the graphs that you plotted in FIGURE 4?

_____

_____

2. Describe the relationship between reaction rate and temperature for the decomposition of sodium hypochlorite. _____

_____

3. Why is it important that there be no sodium hypochlorite solution in the stem of the pipette in step 8 of the procedure? _____

_____

4. Soft drinks contain carbonic acid (H_2CO_3). Carbonic acid decomposes to form water and carbon dioxide.

$$H_2CO_3 \rightarrow H_2O + CO_2$$

Two soft drink bottles are opened, and one is placed in a refrigerator while the other is left at room temperature. The carbonic acid in both bottles decomposes, but one bottle goes "flat" faster than the other. Which bottle will go flat first? Explain. _____

_____

_____

Strategy Check

_____ Do you know how to collect data on the amount of oxygen produced by the decomposition of household bleach?

_____ Can you determine from a graph of the data how the reaction rate differs when the temperature is changed?

Chapter 9

LABORATORY MANUAL ● Solutions 16

If you make a saltwater solution, you can use either table salt or rock salt. As long as the mass of each is the same, the salt with the greater surface area—table salt—will dissolve faster. Other factors affect the rate at which a solute dissolves. For example, temperature and stirring will change the dissolving rate of a solute. In addition, the dissolving rates of gases are affected by changes in pressure.

Strategy
You will explain the effects of particle size, temperature, and stirring on a solid in solution.
You will explain the effects of temperature, stirring, and pressure on a gas in solution.

Materials
beaker (500-mL)
bottle opener
6 cups (transparent plastic)
graduated cylinder (100-mL)
3 paper towels
soda water (bottle)
stirring rod
6 sugar cubes
watch with second hand
water (cold)
tap water (hot) **CAUTION:** *Use care when handling hot liquids.*
apron
goggles
gloves

Procedure
CAUTION: *Do not taste, eat, or drink any materials used in the lab.*
Part A Solid in Solution
1. Label the six plastic cups A through F. Use the graduated cylinder to add 100 mL of cold water to each of cups C, D, E, and F. Add 100 mL of hot water from the tap to each of cups A and B.

2. On three separate paper towels, crush three of the sugar cubes.

3. Add sugar samples to each cup (one at a time) as indicated in Table 1. When adding each sample, observe closely and record the time required for the sugar to dissolve completely. See FIGURE 1. When no sugar particles are visible, record the time in Table 1.

FIGURE 1

Part B Gas in Solution

1. Rinse cups A, B, and C from Part A with water.

2. Observe the unopened bottle of soda water. Open the bottle and observe it again. Compare your observations and record your comparison in Part B of the Data and Observations section.

3. Pour hot water from the tap into the 500-mL beaker until it is about half full.

4. Add 25 mL of soda water to each of the three cups. Stir the soda water in cup B. See FIGURE 2. Place cup C in the beaker of hot water. Leave cup A as your control. Compare the rate of bubbling in each cup. Record your observations in Table 2.

FIGURE 2

Data and Observations
Part A Solid in Solution
Table 1

Cup	Sugar sample	Water conditions	Time	Rating
A	crushed	hot		
B	cube	hot		
C	crushed	cold		
D	cube	cold		
E	crushed	cold, stirred		
F	cube	cold, stirred		

Part B Gas in Solution
Observations of unopened and opened bottle: _____

_____

Table 2

Cup	Soda conditions	Observations and comparison of bubbling
A	control	
B	stirred	
C	heated	

Questions and Conclusions

1. In Table 1 rate the sugar samples from fastest to slowest in dissolving. Give the fastest-dissolving sample a rating of 1. The slowest-dissolving sample should be rated 6.

2. How does particle size affect the rate at which sugar dissolves in water? _____

_____

_____

3. How does temperature affect the rate at which sugar dissolves in water? _____

_____

_____

4. How does stirring affect the rate at which sugar dissolves in water? _____

_____

_____

5. How did you create a pressure change in the bottle of soda water? What happened as a result
   of this pressure change? _____

_____

_____

6. What factors cause the rate of bubbling in soda water to increase? _____

_____

_____

7. Carbonated beverages contain dissolved CO_2 gas. If you shake the bottle and then open it, the beverage may shoot into the air. Explain why this happens. _____

_____

_____

_____

Strategy Check

_____ Can you demonstrate the effect increasing the volume of solvent has on the dissolving rate of solids in solution?

_____ Can you compare and contrast the effect of temperature on the dissolving rate of solids in solution by dissolving sugar in hot tea and iced tea?

Chapter 9

LABORATORY MANUAL • **Solubility   17**

The most familiar kind of solution is a solid dissolved in water. When you add lemon powder to water, you make lemonade, a water solution. Usually, no chemical change takes place when a solid is dissolved in a liquid. If the liquid evaporates, the original solid remains chemically unchanged.

The maximum amount of solute that can dissolve in a solvent is called the solubility of the solution. Solubility is often expressed as grams of solute per 100 grams of solvent. The solubility of a substance is not the same for all conditions. For example, temperature changes can affect the solubility of a solid in water.

Strategy
You will determine the solubility of salt.
You will determine the effect of temperature on the solubility of salt.
You will interpret information from a solubility graph.

Materials
apron
balance
2 beakers (250-mL)
graduated cylinder (10-mL)
goggles
hot plate
ice
hot mitt
potassium chloride, KCl *(cr)*
3 potpie pans (aluminum)
3 test tubes
test-tube holders
test-tube rack
thermometer
water (distilled)

CAUTION: *Wear safety goggles and a laboratory apron throughout this experiment.*

Procedure
1. Fill one beaker about one-third full of tap water. Heat the water on the hot plate until the temperature reaches 55°C–60°C. Use the thermometer to determine the temperature.

2. Fill the second beaker about one-third full of ice water.

3. Label the three test tubes A, B, and C. Also label the three aluminum pans A, B, and C. Find the mass of each pan and record it in Table 1.

4. Add 5.0 g of KCl to each tube.

5. Using the graduated cylinder, add 5.0 mL of distilled water to each test tube. Hold each tube one-fourth of the way down from the top with your thumb and index finger. Flick the bottom of the tube with the index finger of your other hand. In this way, gently shake each tube for 30 s. Be careful to avoid spilling solution.

6. Place test tube B in the test-tube rack.

7. Place test tube A in the beaker of ice water for about 5 min.

8. Slowly pour the liquid from tube A into pan A, and from tube B into pan B. Do not transfer any of the solid. You will need to pour the liquid slowly.

9. Carefully place tube C in the water on the hot plate. Allow the contents to reach the temperature of the water bath, which will take about 5 min. Use the test-tube holder to remove the tube to the test-tube rack. **CAUTION:** *The tube will be hot.*

10. Using the test-tube holder, carefully pour the liquid from tube C into pan C. Do not transfer any of the solid. You will need to pour the liquid slowly. See FIGURE 1.

11. Determine the mass of each pan and its liquid. Record the masses in Table 1.

12. Heat the pans on a hot plate using low heat. When all the liquid evaporates, use a pot holder to remove the pans from the heat. **CAUTION:** *Do not touch the hot pans or the hot plate.* After the pans have cooled, find the mass of each and record this information in Table 1.

FIGURE 1

Data and Observations

Table 1

Object	Mass (g)		
	A	B	C
Empty pan			
Pan and liquid			
Pan after evaporation			
Liquid evaporation			
Salt after evaporation			
Solubility			

13. Determine the mass of the liquid evaporated from each pan by subtracting the mass of the pan after evaporation from the mass of the pan and liquid.

14. Determine the mass of the salt left in each pan after evaporation by subtracting the mass of the empty pan from the mass of the pan after evaporation. Record this information in Table 1.

15. Use the masses of the dissolved salts to determine the solubility per 100 g of water. Use a proportion in your calculations. Record the solubility in Table 1.

Questions and Conclusions

1. What type of solid material settled to the bottom of each test tube? _____

_____

2. What would you expect to happen to the solubility of KCl in each tube if the temperature of the

water were increased to 75°C? _____

3. Look at the solubility graph in FIGURE 2. This graph shows how temperature changes affect the solubility of four common compounds.

   a. How does an increase in temperature affect the solubility of NaCl? _____

   _____

   b. How does an increase in temperature affect the solubility of KNO_3? _____

   _____

FIGURE 2

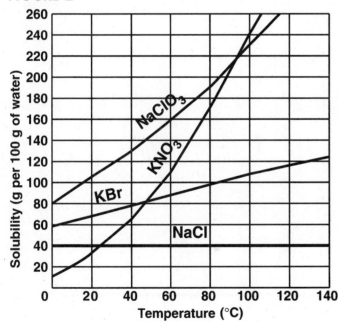

4. Refer to FIGURE 2. At what temperature does KNO_3 have the same solubility as KBr? What is the solubility at this temperature? _____

_____

Strategy Check

_____ Can you demonstrate the increased solubility of a solid in a liquid with temperature?

_____ Can you compare and contrast the amount of solute in saturated and unsaturated solutions?

Chapter 10
LABORATORY MANUAL

• Carbohydrates: Chemistry and Identification 18

Carbohydrates make up a large group of chemical compounds found in cells. Carbohydrates are an energy source or are used in making cell structures. There are three different groups of carbohydrates. They are called monosaccharides, disaccharides, and polysaccharides. *Saccharide* means sugar.

Strategy

You will write simple formulas for several carbohydrates.
You will read structural formulas for several carbohydrates.
You will use models to construct the three main types of carbohydrates.
You will identify the three main types of carbohydrates by using chemical tests.
You will test different food samples to determine what type of carbohydrate they contain.

Materials

beaker (Pyrex)	test-tube holder	oat solution
droppers	apple juice	polysaccharide solution
glass marking pencil or	Benedict's solution	powdered sugar solution
labels	disaccharide solution	table sugar solution
hot plate	honey solution	apron
paper models	iodine solution	goggles
scissors	monosaccharide solution	gloves
test tubes		

Procedure

CAUTION: *Do not taste, eat, or drink any materials used in the lab.*

CAUTION: *Inform your teacher if you come in contact with any chemicals.*

Part A Carbohydrate Models
Group 1. Monosaccharides (single molecule sugars)

1. A single molecule sugar is called a monosaccharide. The prefix *mono-* means one. Glucose, fructose, and galactose are three monosaccharides. Examine the structural formulas of these three sugars in FIGURE 1. What three chemical elements are present in the three monosaccharides?

_____

_____

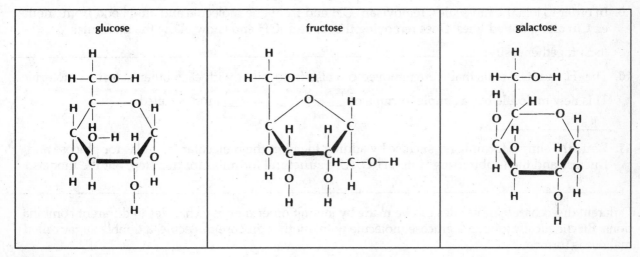

FIGURE 1

2. How many atoms of carbon are present in a molecule of

glucose? _____

fructose? _____

galactose? _____

3. Add subscripts to the following to indicate the correct simple formula. Fill in the blanks by counting the total number of carbon, hydrogen, and oxygen atoms in each molecule.

glucose C__H__O__

fructose C__H__O__

galactose C__H__O__

4. Are there two times as many hydrogen atoms as oxygen atoms in a molecule of

glucose? _____

fructose? _____

galactose? _____

5. Are there two times as many hydrogen atoms as oxygen atoms in a molecule of water?

_____

6. Compare the structural formulas of glucose and fructose. Are the two molecules exactly

the same shape? _____

7. Are both glucose and fructose monosaccharides? _____

Group 2. Disaccharides (double molecule sugars)

Two monosaccharide sugar molecules can join chemically to form a larger carbohydrate molecule called a double sugar, or disaccharide. The prefix *di-* means two. By chemically joining a glucose with a fructose molecule, a double sugar called sucrose is produced. Use the paper models given to you by your teacher to complete this section.

8. Cut out a model of one glucose and one fructose molecule. **CAUTION:** *Use care when handling sharp objects. Always be extremely careful with scissors. Cut along solid lines only.* Try to join the two molecules like puzzle pieces.

Do the glucose and fructose fit together easily to form a sucrose molecule? _____

9. In order to join the molecules, remove an -OH end from one molecule and an -H end from another. Cut along dotted lines. Does removing the -H and -OH ends now allow the molecules

to fit together easily? _____

10. The -H and -OH ends that were removed can also fit together with each other to form a molecule.

This new molecule has a simple formula of _____ and is called

_____.

11. Write the simple formula for sucrose by adding together the molecular formulas for glucose and fructose and then subtracting water, H_2O. (Use structural formulas for this step, not the models.)

_____

Different disaccharide molecules can be made by joining other monosaccharides in different combinations. By chemically joining a glucose molecule with another glucose molecule, a double sugar called maltose is formed.

12. Cut out and attempt to join two new glucose model molecules like puzzle pieces. What must be removed from the glucose model molecules so that they easily fit together?

_____

13. Write the simple formula for maltose. (See question 11.) _____

14. How does the simple formula for sucrose compare to maltose? _____

15. Are there two times as many hydrogen atoms as oxygen atoms in a disaccharide? _____

16. How many monosaccharide molecules are needed to form one sucrose molecule? _____

17. How many monosaccharide molecules are needed to form one maltose molecule? _____

Group 3. Polysaccharides (many molecule sugars)

Just as double sugars were formed from two single sugar molecules, polysaccharides are formed when many single sugars are joined chemically. The prefix *poly-* means many. Starch, glycogen, and cellulose are the three most common polysaccharides. They consist of long chains of glucose molecules joined together.

18. Construct a starch molecule by joining three glucose molecules. This model will represent only a small part of a starch molecule because starch consists of hundreds of glucose molecules. What must be removed from the glucose model molecules in order to have them easily fit together?

_____

Part B Identification of Carbohydrates
Chemical Tests on Known Carbohydrates

Benedict's Test

1. Pour water into a 500-mL beaker until it is half full. Bring the water to a boil on a hot plate. **CAUTION:** *Do not touch hot plate.* The boiling water in FIGURE 2 is called a hot water bath. **CAUTION:** *Water is very hot. Use care when handling hot liquids.*

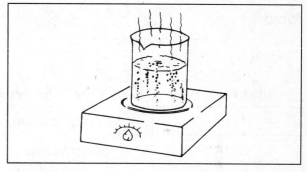

FIGURE 2

2. Number three clean test tubes 1 to 3. Using FIGURE 3 as a guide and a clean dropper for each tube, add the following:

   Tube 1—30 drops of monosaccharide solution
   Tube 2—30 drops of disaccharide solution
   Tube 3—30 drops of polysaccharide solution

3. Add 30 drops of Benedict's solution to each tube. **CAUTION:** *If you spill Benedict's solution, rinse with water and call your teacher.*

4. Place the three test tubes into the hot water bath for 5 min.

5. Use a test-tube holder to remove the tubes from the hot water bath. **CAUTION:** *Water and test tubes are very hot. Handle test tubes only with a test-tube holder.*

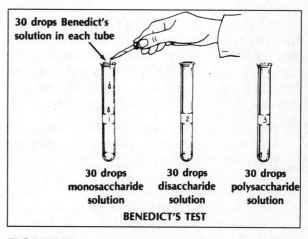

FIGURE 3

6. Observe any color changes in the solutions. NOTE: A color change may or may not occur when Benedict's solution is added to a carbohydrate and then heated. A change from blue to green, yellow, orange, or red occurs if a monosaccharide is present. The original blue color will remain after heating if a disaccharide or polysaccharide is present.

7. Record the colors of the solutions in the test tubes in column three of Table 1.

8. Number three clean test tubes 1 to 3. Using FIGURE 4 as a guide and a clean dropper for each tube, add the following:

   Tube 1—30 drops of monosaccharide solution
   Tube 2—30 drops of disaccharide solution
   Tube 3—30 drops of polysaccharide solution

9. Add 4 drops of iodine solution to each tube. **CAUTION:** *Iodine is poisonous. Do not allow iodine to get on your hands. Wash immediately if iodine comes in contact with your skin. Do not inhale iodine fumes.*

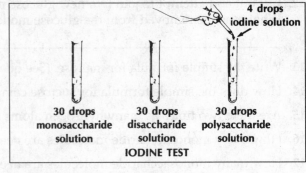

FIGURE 4

10. Mix the contents of each tube by gently swirling.

11. Record in column four of Table 1 the color of the solutions in the three tubes. NOTE: A color change may or may not occur when iodine solution is added to a carbohydrate. A change from its original rust color to deep blue-black occurs if a polysaccharide is present. The original color of the carbohydrate remains if a disaccharide or monosaccharide sugar is present.

Data and Observations
Table 1

Tube number	Carbohydrate type	Change in color after heating with Benedict's	Change in color after adding iodine
1	Monosaccharide		
2	Disaccharide		
3	Polysaccharide		

Chemical Tests on Unknown Carbohydrates

You have tested known carbohydrates, so you are now ready to test some unknown substances. By comparing results of the Benedict's and iodine tests in Table 1, you should be able to classify monosaccharides, disaccharides, or polysaccharides.

12. Number five clean test tubes 1 to 5. Using FIGURE 5 as a guide and a clean dropper for each tube, add the following:
    Tube 1—20 drops of honey
    Tube 2—20 drops of liquid oats
    Tube 3—20 drops of table sugar solution
    Tube 4—20 drops of apple juice
    Tube 5—20 drops of powdered sugar solution

13. Add 30 drops of Benedict's solution to each test tube.

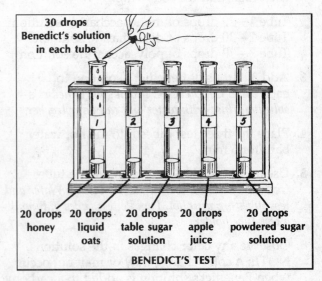

FIGURE 5

14. Place all five test tubes into a hot water bath for 5 min.

15. Remove the test tubes from the bath with a test-tube holder and note any color changes. Record the color of the solutions in Table 2.

16. Using FIGURE 6 as a guide, prepare five more test tubes containing the same substances just used (honey, oats, and so on). *Do not add Benedict's solution.*

17. Add 4 drops of iodine solution to each tube and mix by swirling.

18. Observe any color changes and record them in Table 2.

19. On the basis of your results, classify each carbohydrate as a monosaccharide, disaccharide, or polysaccharide. Record your answers in Table 2.

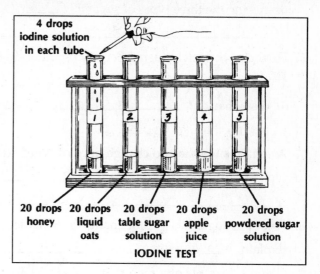

4 drops iodine solution in each tube

20 drops honey | 20 drops liquid oats | 20 drops table sugar solution | 20 drops apple juice | 20 drops powdered sugar solution

IODINE TEST

FIGURE 6

Table 2

Carbohydrate	Benedict's color	Iodine color	Carbohydrate type
Honey			
Oats			
Table sugar			
Apple			
Powdered sugar			

Questions and Conclusions

1. Name the three categories of carbohydrates studied in this investigation. _____

_____

2. What three elements are present in all carbohydrates? _____

_____

3. Give two examples each of sugars that are

   a. monosaccharides. _____

   b. disaccharides. _____

   c. polysaccharides. _____

4. a. How many times larger is the number of hydrogen atoms than oxygen atoms in all

   carbohydrates? _____

   b. In water? _____

5. *Mono-* means one, *di-* means two, and *poly-* means many. Why are these terms used in describing the three types of sugars? _____

_____

6. How can you tell by using Benedict's and iodine solutions if a sugar is a

   a. monosaccharide? _____

   b. disaccharide? _____

   c. polysaccharide? _____

7. A certain sugar has no change in color when tested with Benedict's solution. Can you tell what type of saccharide it is? Explain. _____

_____

8. A certain sugar has a color change in Benedict's solution. Can you tell what type of saccharide it is? Explain. _____

9. Give an example of a food that is a

   a. monosaccharide. _____

   b. disaccharide. _____

   c. polysaccharide. _____

Strategy Check

_____ Can you write simple formulas for some carbohydrates?

_____ Can you read and understand structural formulas for carbohydrates?

_____ Can you make models of the three main types of carbohydrates?

_____ Can you identify monosaccharides, disaccharides, and polysaccharides by means of chemical tests?

_____ Can you test food samples to determine whether they contain carbohydrates and what kind they contain?

Chapter 10

LABORATORY MANUAL

Proteins: Chemistry and Identification 19

Living things are made up of many different molecules. One important group of chemical molecules is proteins. Proteins make up the bulk of all solid material within your body and the bodies of other animals. Your muscle, skin, hair, and inside organs are largely protein. Proteins are essential for body growth and repair. They also make up some hormones that are involved in the chemical control of the body.

Strategy

You will recognize simple formulas for amino acids.
You will use models of different amino acids to construct a protein molecule.
You will use chemical tests to determine if a protein is present in a substance.

Materials

dropper
glass-marking pencil or labels
paper models
scissors
test tubes
test-tube rack (or tin can)
absorbent cotton
cream cheese
dog hair (white)
egg white (hard-boiled)
fingernail clippings
nitric acid
apron
goggles
gloves

Procedure

Part A—Models of Protein:
Amino Acids, Building Blocks of Protein

Proteins are complex molecules made up of smaller molecules called amino acids. There are about 20 different amino acids found in nature. The element nitrogen (N) is present in all amino acids.

1. Examine the structural formulas of the four representative amino acids shown in FIGURE 1, and name the four elements present in these amino acids.

_____

_____

2. What is the simple formula for the amino acid

   a. glycine?   C__ H__ O__ N__

   b. alanine?   C__ H__ O__ N__

   c. valine?   C__ H__ O__ N__

   d. threonine?   C__ H__ O__ N__

FIGURE 1

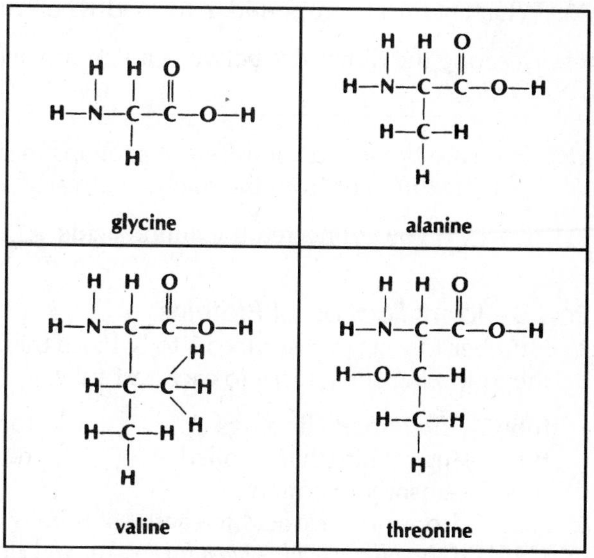

glycine

alanine

valine

threonine

3. How do the simple formulas for all of the amino acids differ?

_____

4. Note the upper right corner of each amino acid. These ends have a special arrangement of carbon, oxygen, and hydrogen atoms. This end arrangement is called a carboxyl group and looks like this:

$$\left(\begin{array}{c} O \\ \parallel \\ -C-O-H \end{array} \right)$$

Circle the carboxyl group on each structural formula in FIGURE 1.

5. Note the upper left hand corner of each amino acid. These ends have a special arrangement of nitrogen and hydrogen atoms. The end arrangement is called an amino group and looks like this:

$$\left(\begin{array}{c} H \\ | \\ H-N- \end{array} \right)$$

Use dashed lines to circle the amino groups on the structural formulas in FIGURE 1.

In the previous lab, you studied carbohydrates.

a. Do carbohydrates have carboxyl groups? _____

b. Do carbohydrates have amino groups? _____

6. How does the number of hydrogen atoms compare with the number of oxygen atoms in each

amino acid? _____

7. Amino acids are not protein molecules. They are only the "building blocks" of protein. Several amino acids must be joined in a chain to form a protein molecule. You can show how amino acids join by using models. Use the paper models given to you by your teacher to complete this section.

8. Cut out the four amino acid models. **CAUTION:** _Always be extremely careful with scissors. Cut along the solid lines only._ Attempt to join the amino acids. Can the amino acid models easily join to form a protein molecule? _____

9. Join the molecules by removing as many —OH groups and —H groups as needed from the amino acids. All four amino acids can be joined in this manner to form a protein. Join them in the order valine—threonine—alanine—glycine.

10. Join the left over —OH and —H ends.

11. What chemical substance is formed with the —OHs and —Hs joined? _____

12. How many molecules of water are formed when four amino acids are joined? _____

13. What chemical compound is formed when the four amino acids are joined? _____

14. Describe the difference between an amino acid molecule and a protein molecule.

_____

15. There are thousands of different proteins in living organisms. Use your models to construct two proteins different from the one you already made. Identify the proteins as _a_ or _b_ and list the order

in which you connected the amino acids. _____

Part B—Identification of Proteins

1. Number five clean test tubes 1 to 5. Place them in a test-tube rack. Using FIGURE 2 as a guide, add the following substances to each test tube:

tube 1—fingernail clippings   tube 4—dog hair, white
tube 2—egg white, hard-boiled   tube 5—cream cheese
tube 3—absorbent cotton

2. Add 5 drops of nitric acid to each test tube.
CAUTION: _Nitric acid is harmful to skin and clothing. Rinse with water if spillage occurs. Call your teacher._

3. A substance containing protein will turn yellow when nitric acid is added to it. No color change to yellow indicates that the substance being tested has no protein. Wait several minutes. Then record the color of the items placed in each tube in Table 1.

4. On the basis of the nitric acid test, indicate in the last column of Table 1 if the substances tested contain protein.

FIGURE 2

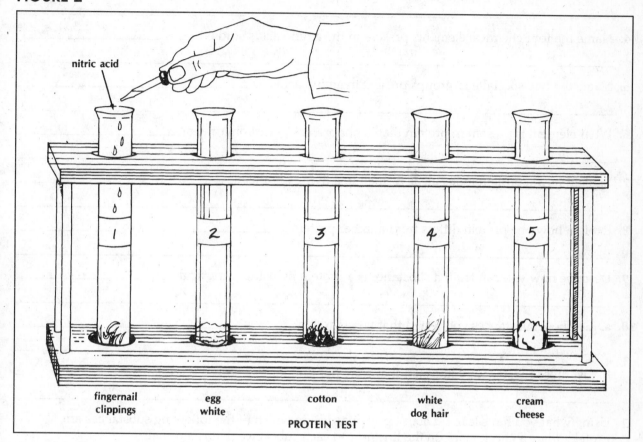

PROTEIN TEST

Data and Observations

Table 1

Substance	Color change due to nitric acid	Substance tested is not a protein (answer yes or no)
Fingernail		
Egg white		
Cotton		
Dog hair		
Cream cheese		

Questions and Conclusions

1. Name four amino acids. _____

2. a. How many amino acids are there? _____

   b. How are amino acids used by living things? _____

3. List several of your body parts that are protein. _____

   _____

4. Name the four chemical elements present in the amino acids studied. _____

   _____

5. Name the two special end groups present in amino acids. _____

   _____

6. What element is present in protein that is not present in carbohydrates? _____

   _____

7. Explain how a protein molecule is formed in a living organism. _____

   _____

8. Explain how one protein differs from another protein. _____

   _____

9. Describe how you can tell if a substance is a protein by using nitric acid. _____

   _____

10. a. List those substances you tested that were protein. _____

    _____

    b. List those substances you tested that were not protein. _____

    _____

11. Using what you have learned about proteins, decide which of the following substances are protein. Place a check mark on the line next to each substance that is a protein.

    a. hamburger   _____   e. liver   _____

    b. chicken   _____   f. human hair   _____

    c. peanut oil   _____   g. stomach   _____

    d. maple syrup _____   h. 207 amino acids joined _____

Strategy Check

_____ Can you identify an amino acid from its formula?

_____ Can you construct a protein molecule using models of amino acids?

_____ Can you explain a test used to determine whether a substance contains a protein?

Chapter 11

LABORATORY MANUAL

● Speed and Acceleration 20

Speed is the distance an object travels divided by the time interval. Speed can be expressed as kilometers per hour (km/h), meters per second (m/s), and so on. In most cases, moving objects do not travel at a constant speed. The speed of an object usually increases and decreases as the object moves. Therefore, the average speed is used to describe the motion. Average speed is a ratio between the total distance and the total time that the object traveled.

$$average\ speed = \frac{total\ distance}{total\ time}$$

In straight line motion in one direction, *acceleration* is the rate at which an object's speed changes. You can express acceleration as meters per second per second (m/s^2). This unit represents the change in speed in meters per second each second. If a car has an average speed of 80 km/h on a hilly road, it probably changes speed many times. If the car is traveling at a constant speed of 80 km/h on a straight and level road, it is not changing speed. The acceleration of the car is zero.

Strategy

You will determine the average speed of a small toy car.
You will study the forces that affect the motion of the car.

Materials 🥽 ✋

books (stack about 20 cm tall)
meterstick
pen or pencil
ramp (wood about 50 cm long)
stopwatch or watch with a second hand
tape (masking)
toy car or ball

Procedure

1. Clear a runway (preferably uncarpeted) about 6 m long.

2. At one end of the runway, set up a launching ramp. Put one end of the wood ramp on the stack of books and the other end on the floor. (See FIGURE 1 on page 58.) You will launch the toy car on its test runs from the top of the ramp.

3. Place a masking tape marker where the ramp touches the floor. Label this marker 0.0 m. Place similar markers at 1.0 m, 2.0 m, 3.0 m, 4.0 m, 5.0 m, and 6.0 m distances from the bottom of the ramp.

FIGURE 1

4. Practice launching the toy car down the ramp several times. Observe the car's motion and path. Add or remove books from the ramp so that the car travels a distance of 5.0 m. Remember that the 5.0-m distance begins at the bottom of the ramp.

5. Measure the time that the car takes to travel the 5.0 m. Record the time in Table 1. Measure and record the times of three more trials.

Data and Observations

Table 1

Trial	Times (s)	Speed (m/s)
1		
2		
3		
4		
Average		

FIGURE 2

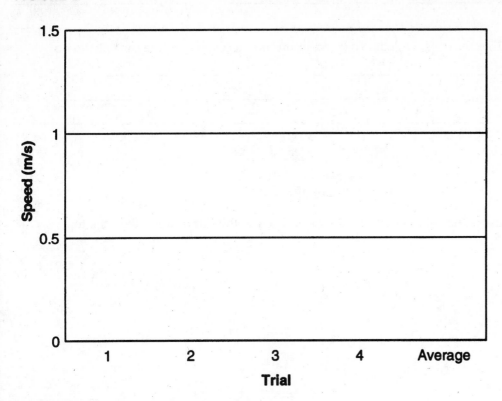

Questions and Conclusions

1. Calculate the speed for each of the four trials by dividing the distance by time. Record the results in Table 1.

2. Calculate the average time for the four trials. Record the results in Table 1.

3. Calculate the average speed of the toy car by dividing the distance by the average time. Record the results in Table 1.

4. Plot the speed of the toy car on the bar graph in FIGURE 2.

5. Describe the motion of the car as it moved across the floor. _____

_____

6. What caused the car to slow down and stop? _____

_____

7. Did the toy car travel at a constant speed? How do you know this? _____

_____

_____

_____

8. How could you change this experiment to make the car accelerate at a faster rate?

_____

_____

9. Consider the 5.0 m that the car traveled. What conditions are necessary for the car to have no acceleration? _____

_____

_____

Strategy Check

_____ Why must all the cars start at the same point on the ramp?

_____ Why do you measure the 5.0 m starting from the bottom of the ramp rather than the top?

Chapter 11

LABORATORY MANUAL

• Projectile Motion 21

The path followed by a projectile is called a trajectory. FIGURE 1 shows the shape of a toy rocket's trajectory. Because the force of gravity is the only force acting on it after the fuel is spent, the toy rocket has an acceleration of 9.8 m/s² downward. However, the *motion of the projectile* is upward and then downward.

   FIGURE 2 shows the velocity vector for a toy rocket at different moments along its trajectory. The rocket's velocity upward begins to decrease after the force exerted by the engine is less than the force of gravity. And then, for an instant at the highest point of its trajectory, its velocity upward is zero because it stops moving upward. The rocket then begins to fall, and its velocity begins to increase downward.

FIGURE 1

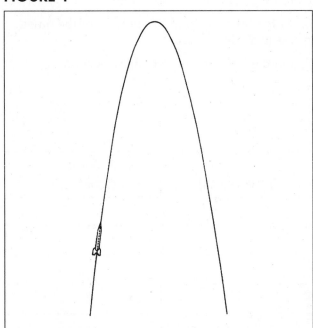

FIGURE 2

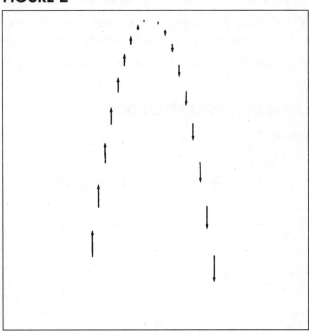

   As you can see, the shape of the upward trajectory of the rocket is a mirror image of the shape of its downward trajectory.

Strategy

You will measure the flight times of a projectile.
You will analyze the flight times of a projectile.

Materials

goggles
3 stopwatches
toy water rocket and launcher
water (bucket)

Procedure

1. Wear goggles during this experiment.

2. Fill the water rocket to the level line shown on the rocket's body. Always fill the rocket to the same level during each flight in the experiment.

3. Attach the pump/launcher to the rocket as shown in the manufacturer's directions.

4. Pump the pump/launcher 10 times. **CAUTION:** *Do not exceed 20 pumps or the maximum number suggested by the manufacturer, whichever is lower. Be sure to hold the rocket and pump/launcher so that the rocket is not directed toward yourself or another person.*

5. At a given signal to the timers, launch the rocket. Your teacher will have timers measure specific parts of the flight using stopwatches. Record the values measured by the timers as Total time, Time up, and Time down in Table 1.

6. Repeat steps 2–6 twice.

7. Repeat steps 2–6 three more times, increasing the number of pumps to 15 for each launch. **CAUTION:** *Do not exceed the maximum number of pumps suggested by the manufacturer.*

8. Calculate the average of the total times, the average of the times up, and the average of the times down for the two sets of launches. Record these values in Table 2.

9. Make a bar graph of the data in Table 2 in FIGURE 3 in the Data and Observations section.

Data and Observations

Table 1

Number of pumps	Total time (s)	Time up (s)	Time down (s)
10			
10			
10			
15			
15			
15			

Table 2

Number of pumps	Average total time (s)	Average time up (s)	Average time down (s)
10			
15			

FIGURE 3

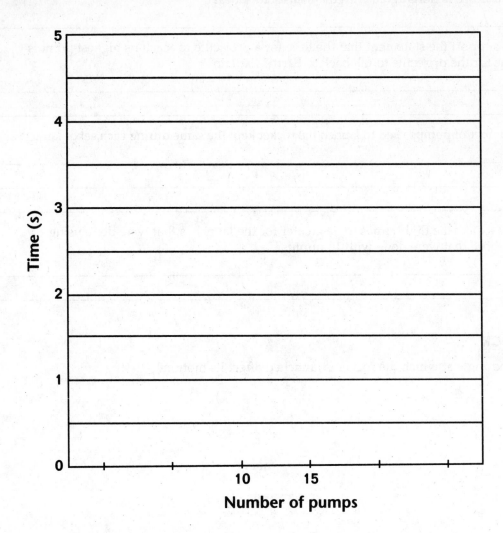

Questions and Conclusions

1. How well did your predictions agree with the measured times?

   _____

2. Do your results support the statement that the time for a projectile to reach its highest point is equal to the time for the projectile to fall back to Earth? Explain.

   _____

   _____

3. Why was the number of pumps used to launch the rocket kept the same during each set of launches?

   _____

   _____

   _____

4. Why would you expect the flight times to be greater for the launches that were done using 15 pumps than those that were done with 10 pumps?

   _____

   _____

Strategy Check

_____ How does the angle at which the rocket is launched affect its motion?

Chapter 12
LABORATORY MANUAL

• Static and Sliding Friction 22

When two objects are in contact, the molecules on their surfaces rub against one another. These surfaces are not smooth; small lumps and grooves exist. When one object slides over the other, the surfaces catch and stick as these lumps and grooves nestle together. The force that results between materials due to the irregularities in their surfaces is called friction. Many factors affect the force of friction, including the nature and conditions of surfaces and how hard the surfaces are pressed together.

For a block sliding on a level horizontal surface, the weight of the block pushes the two surfaces together. The coefficient of friction, symbolized by the Greek letter μ, is the ratio of friction force to the force pushing the objects together. This relationship holds true on a flat horizontal surface when the force that presses the surfaces together is the weight acting on the top object.

When an object is at rest, static friction holds the object in place. This type of friction must be overcome to move the object. When one object is already sliding over another, sliding friction occurs. The force needed to sustain the constant motion of the object must equal the sliding friction force.

Strategy
You will calculate coefficients of static and sliding friction.
You will compare static friction to sliding friction.
You will describe the effect of weight on the force of friction.
You will determine the effect of surface area on friction.

Materials
eye hook
set of masses
spring scale calibrated in newtons
2" × 4" wood block

Procedure
1. Screw the eye hook into the end of the block. Weigh the wood block and eye hook using the spring scale. Record the weight in Table 1.

2. Lay the wood block on a flat surface as shown in FIGURE 1.

3. Find the force required to move the block from rest. Pull on the spring scale and notice the highest reading that occurs before the block moves. That is the static friction.

4. Find the force required to keep the block moving at a constant velocity. As you pull on the spring scale, the reading will not be exact because the friction value will vary. Make the best judgment you can for the value of sliding friction. Record this information in Table 1.

5. Repeat steps 3 and 4 with different weights added on top of the friction block. Be sure to record the new weight of the block and its added weight.

FIGURE 1

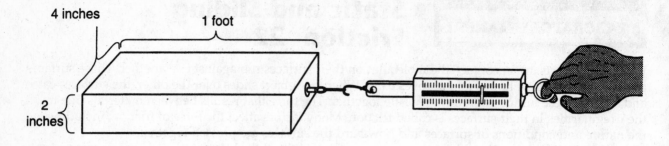

4 inches

1 foot

2 inches

6. Repeat steps 3 and 4 without masses added and with the block resting on a side with a different area.

7. Calculate the coefficient of static friction for each of the trials using the equation below.

$$\mu_{static} = \frac{static\ friction\ force}{weight}$$

8. Calculate the coefficient of sliding friction for each of the trials using the equation below.

$$\mu_{sliding} = \frac{sliding\ friction\ force}{weight}$$

9. Graph the relationship between the weight of the block and each force of friction in FIGURE 2. Use a single graph to compare the data for sliding and static friction.

Data and Observations

Table 1

Friction Coefficients

Force of static friction	Force of sliding friction	Weight of block	μ_{static}	$\mu_{sliding}$	Area of side

FIGURE 2

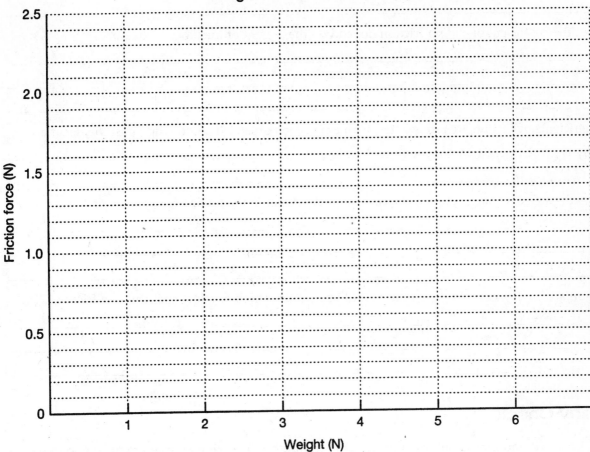

Weight Versus Friction Force

Questions and Conclusions

1. How did the addition of more weight affect the friction? _____

_____

2. How did the change in surface area of the contact between the block and the table affect

the friction? _____

3. How did the force of friction relate to the weight of the block? _____

_____

4. How do static friction and sliding friction relate to each other? _____

_____

5. What could be a source of error in this experiment? _____

_____

_____

6. What happened to the coefficients of friction as the weight increased? _____

_____

7. What happened to the coefficients of friction as the surface area of the contact increased?

_____

8. Does the coefficient of sliding friction depend on the weight of the block? Explain.

_____

_____

_____

9. Coefficients of friction are rarely listed with a precision greater than one digit past the decimal. Why is greater precision not used? _____

_____

10. Does the area of contact between objects make a difference in the friction forces? Explain how you know. _____

_____

_____

11. If you are buying new tires for a car, would you prefer a high or a low coefficient of friction?

_____

_____

_____

Strategy Check

_____ Why is it important that you pull straight forward on the spring attached to the wood block, rather than at an angle?

Chapter 12

LABORATORY MANUAL ● **Newton's Second Law 23**

Newton's second law of motion deals with acceleration, which is how fast something speeds up or slows down. Acceleration depends on the mass of an object and the force pulling or pushing it. One way to write Newton's second law is *force = mass × acceleration*. Another way to think of Newton's second law is that if the same force acts on two objects, the object with the greater mass will accelerate more slowly.

Strategy
You will time the acceleration of a small toy car.
You will observe the effects of increasing mass on acceleration.

Materials
balance
large table
meterstick
modeling clay (about 300 g)
small toy car with free-spinning wheels
stopwatch
string or thread
tape

Procedure
1. Cut a piece of string or thread 110 cm long. Tie a small loop in one end of the string.

2. Make a small ball of clay with a mass of about 2.5 g. Attach this ball of clay to the string by folding the clay around the loop. The loop will prevent the clay ball from falling off the string.

3. Divide the remaining clay into 40-g pieces.

4. Use your balance to measure the mass of the toy car. Write the mass of the car in the Data and Observations section.

5. Use a meterstick to find a spot on the table 1 m from the edge. Mark it with a small piece of tape. This spot will be the starting point for the toy car during the experiment.

6. Put the front of the toy car at the starting point. Hold the piece of string on the table so that the clay ball is about 3 cm over the edge. Tape the other end of the string to the front of the toy car. Trim any excess string so that it does not interfere with the car's wheels. Check that your setup is similar to that shown in FIGURE 1.

FIGURE 1
Experimental setup for
Newton's second law

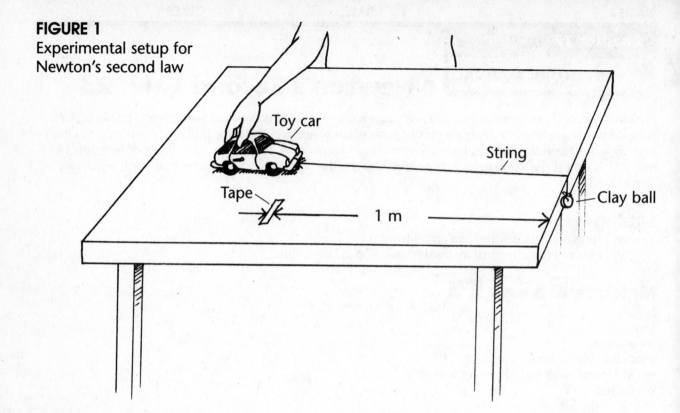

7. Pick someone in your group to be the timer, someone to be the recorder, someone to hold the toy car in place and release it, and someone to catch it as it falls off the table.

8. Release the car. Use a stopwatch to measure the time it takes for the car to reach the table edge.

9. Write the travel time in Table 1.

10. Repeat steps 8 and 9 two more times. Use the data to calculate the average travel time for the car.

11. Add one 40-g piece of clay to the top of the car. Be careful that the clay does not interfere with the car's ability to roll freely.

12. Time three trips of the car. Record the travel times, calculate the average time, and record the average time in Table 1.

13. Repeat steps 11 and 12 until you have timed the car carrying 160 g of clay.

Data and Observations

Mass of car = _____ g

Table 1

Mass (g)		Travel Time (s)			
Total clay on top of car	Total car and clay	Time 1 (T1)	Time 2 (T2)	Time 3 (T3)	Average time (T1 + T2 + T3) ÷ 3
0					
40					
80					
120					
160					

FIGURE 2

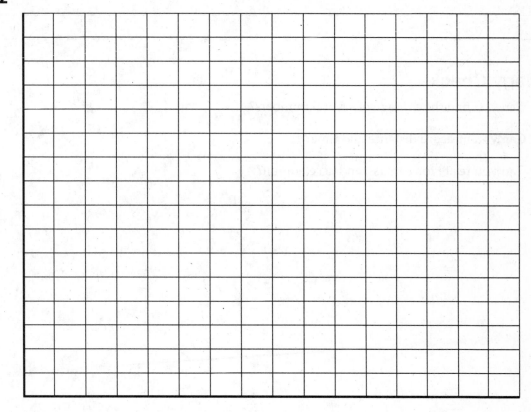

Total mass (g)

Average travel time (s)

Questions and Conclusions

1. Make a graph of total mass versus time on the graph in FIGURE 2.

2. Explain how your data supports Newton's second law of motion.

_____

_____

_____

3. Why is it important to average three travel times for each one of the total masses?

_____

_____

4. What were some possible sources of error in this lab? In other words, what things might have caused differences in travel time for the same mass?

_____

_____

_____

_____

5. Use your graph to predict how much mass would be necessary to cause a travel time of 15 s. Test your prediction. What happened?

_____

_____

_____

Strategy Check

_____ Can you find the average of several numbers?

_____ Can you measure distance and time?

_____ Can you relate force, mass, and acceleration?

Chapter 13
LABORATORY MANUAL

• The Bicycle 24

You have learned about many simple machines that are used in compound machines. The bicycle is a familiar compound machine that uses a wheel and axle.

James Starley designed and manufactured one of the first successful bicycles in 1868. He developed his design so that once it was moving, only a small amount of force would be required to keep the vehicle and driver in motion on level ground.

A multigear bicycle can either multiply its speed or increase the force on the wheels. However, it can never do both at the same time. The bicycle's gears increase or decrease the force pushing the pedals. This results in slower or faster wheel speed. The mechanical advantage of a bicycle is the number of times the force applied by the rider's legs is multiplied. The speed advantage is the number of times the bicycle multiplies the speed for a given effort force. For example, if the bicycle multiplies the force of your legs by a factor of two, the speed is reduced by one-half.

Strategy

You will determine the mechanical advantage and the speed advantage of a multigear bicycle. You will explain the relationship between mechanical advantage and speed advantage. You will describe the distance traveled by a bicycle depending on the gear combination used.

Materials

1 foot-long block of wood
meterstick
multigear bicycle

Procedure

1. Place a block of wood under the bottom bracket of the bicycle's frame so the rear wheel is lifted off the ground. Have your lab partner steady the bicycle by holding the handle bars and the seat as shown in FIGURE 1.

2. **CAUTION:** *Avoid placing your hand or any object near the rear wheel, chain, or gears.* Rotate the forward pedals with one of your hands to make the rear wheel turn. Shift the gears and observe the speed of the rear wheel as you shift through each gear. Be sure to continue rotating the pedal as you switch gears. Switching gears without moving the pedal may result in the chain jumping off the gears. Record your observations in the Data and Observations section.

3. Remove the bicycle from the block of wood and lay it on its side. Count the number of teeth in each gear of both the front section and rear section. Record the data in Table 1.

4. Measure the diameter of the bicycle's rear wheel to the nearest centimeter. Record this in Table 1.

5. Set the bicycle upright. Place the gears in the lowest gear combination, with the chain on the smallest sprocket of the front gears and the largest sprocket of the back gears.

FIGURE 1

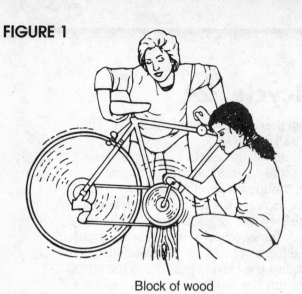

Block of wood

FIGURE 2

Rear gears   Front gears

6. Measure how many centimeters the bicycle travels as the pedal makes one complete revolution. Mark the starting and ending points using the front edge of the front tire and measure the distance between these two points. Record this distance in the Experimental column in Table 1.

7. Repeat steps 5 and 6 for each of the other gear combinations. Record your observations in the data table.

8. Calculate the mechanical advantage (M.A.) for each gear combination using the equation below. Record your answers in Table 1.

$$\text{M.A.} = \frac{\text{number of teeth on rear gear}}{\text{number of teeth on front gear}}$$

9. Calculate the speed advantage (S.A.) for each gear combination using the equation below. Record your answers in Table 1.

$$\text{S.A.} = \frac{\text{number of teeth on front gear}}{\text{number of teeth on rear gear}}$$

10. Find the theoretical distance the bicycle should travel as the pedal makes one revolution for each gear combination using the equation below. Record your answers in the table. ($\pi \approx 3.14$)

$$\text{Distance} = \text{S.A.} \times \text{rear wheel diameter} \times \pi$$

11. Calculate the experimental error between the theoretical and the experimental distance traveled using the equation below. Record your answers in the table.

$$\text{Percent error} = \frac{\text{theoretical} - \text{experimental}}{\text{theoretical}} \times 100$$

12. Graph the mechanical advantage versus the speed advantage.

Data and Observations

Effect shifting gears has on the rear wheel speed: _____

_____

Bicycle's rear wheel diameter: _____

Table 1

Bicycle Data

Front teeth	Rear teeth	M.A.	S.A.	Experimental distance (cm)	Theoretical distance (cm)	Percent error

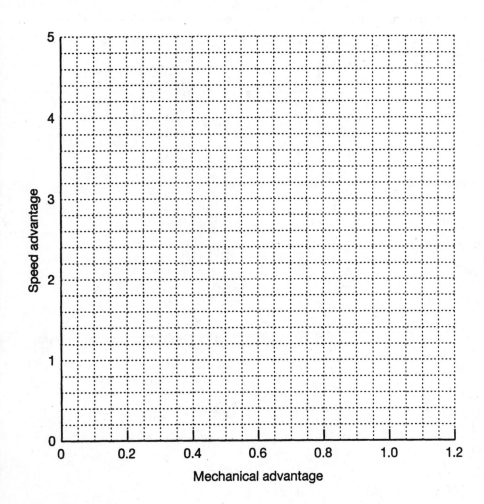

Questions and Conclusions

1. Why is a high mechanical advantage important to bicycle riders? _____
_____

2. Why is a high speed advantage important to bicycle riders? _____
_____

3. What simple machines are involved in a bicycle? _____
_____

4. What is the mathematical relationship between mechanical advantage and speed advantage?
_____

5. Which gear combination produced the greatest mechanical advantage in the bicycle you tested?
_____
_____

6. Which gear combination produced the greatest speed advantage in the bicycle you tested?
_____
_____
_____

7. Under what conditions is it good to increase friction on a bicycle? _____
_____
_____

8. When is it good to reduce friction on a bicycle? _____
_____
_____

Strategy Check

_____ Can you determine how many gear combinations are possible?

● **Work and Power 25**

Work is energy transferred through motion. When a force acts on an object and moves that object a certain distance, work is done on that object. Therefore, work (*W*) is defined by the following equation.

$$W = F \times d$$

In this equation, *F* represents a force acting on the object and *d* represents the distance through which the object moves as that force acts on it. In the metric system, force is measured in newtons (N), and distance is measured in meters (m). If a force of 1 newton acts on an object and the object moves 1 meter while the force is acting on it, the value of $F \times d$ equals 1 newton-meter (N-m). That amount of work is equal to 1 joule (J) of energy being transferred.

Power (*P*) is the rate at which work is done. It can be determined by the following equation.

$$P = W/t$$

In this equation, *W* represents the work done and *t* represents the amount of time required to do the work. In the metric system, the unit of power is the watt (W). If 1 joule of work is done in 1 second, W/t has a value of 1 J/s, which is equal to 1 watt.

Strategy

You will determine the amount of work required to lift an object.
You will determine the power used while lifting the object.

Materials

dowel (wood, about 50 cm long)
mass (1-kg)
meterstick
scissors
spring scale (metric)
stopwatch
string
tape (masking)
wire tie (plastic-coated)

Procedure

1. Weigh the 1-kg mass using the metric spring scale. Record this value in the Data and Observations section.

2. Cut a 1.3-m length of string. Tightly tie one end of the string to the center of the wood dowel. Secure the knot with a piece of masking tape to prevent the string from slipping.

3. Make a small loop at the other end of the string and knot it. Attach the 1-kg mass to the loop with a plastic-coated wire tie.

4. Measure a 1-m distance along the string from the dowel using the meterstick. Mark this distance on the string with a small strip of masking tape.

FIGURE 1   **FIGURE 2**

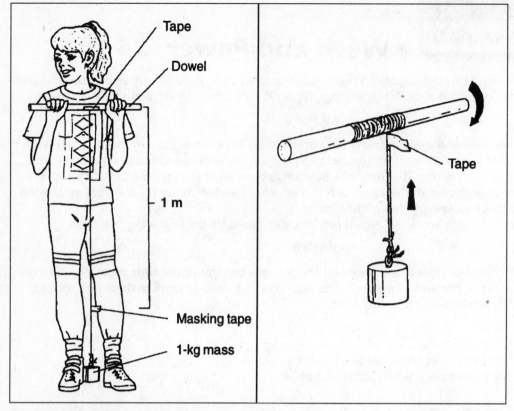

5. Hold the dowel at both ends as shown in FIGURE 1.

6. Raise the 1-kg mass by winding up the string on the dowel as shown in FIGURE 2. Keep the winding motion steady so that the string winds up and the mass rises at a constant speed. Practice raising the mass in this manner several times.

7. You are now ready to have your lab partner measure the time it takes for you to raise the mass a distance of 1 m.

8. Suspend the 1-kg mass from the dowel as before. At a signal from your lab partner, begin to raise the mass at a constant speed by winding the string on the dowel. Have your lab partner use a stopwatch to measure the time required for the piece of masking tape on the string to reach the dowel. Record this value under Student 1 in Table 1.

9. Reverse roles with your lab partner and allow him or her to repeat steps 6–8. Record the time value under Student 2 in Table 1.

10. The size of the force that was needed to raise the 1-kg mass is equal to the weight of 1 kg. The distance that the 1-kg mass was raised is the distance between the dowel and the piece of masking tape, which is 1 m. Record the values for the force and distance under Student 1 and Student 2 in Table 1.

11. Calculate the work you did to raise the 1-kg mass and record this value under Student 1 in Table 2.

12. Calculate the power you developed lifting the 1-kg mass. Record the value under Student 1 in Table 2.

13. Complete Table 2 using your lab partner's data from Table 1.

Data and Observations

Weight of 1-kg mass:

_____

Table 1

Measurement	Student 1	Student 2
Time		
Force (N)		
Distance		

Table 2

Calculation	Student 1	Student 2
Work (J)		
Power (W)		

Questions and Conclusions

1. Compare the amounts of work that you and your lab partner did.

_____

2. Why would you expect both amounts of work to be the same?

_____

_____

3. Compare the amounts of power developed by you and your lab partner.

_____

_____

_____

4. Why would you expect the amounts of power to differ?

_____

_____

_____

5. How do the amounts of work and power depend on the speed at which the 1-kg mass is lifted?

_____

_____

_____

_____

Strategy Check

_____ Can you determine the amount of work required to lift an object?

_____ Can you determine the power used while lifting an object?

Chapter 14

● **Velocity of a Wave 26**

Energy can move as waves through material such as ropes, springs, air, and water. Waves that need a material to pass through are called mechanical waves. Sounds and ripples in flags are examples of mechanical waves. Other energy, such as light, can be transmitted as waves through empty space as well as matter.

   The high part of a transverse wave is the crest. The low part of a transverse wave is the trough. The amplitude of the wave is the distance the crest rises above or the trough falls below the wave's center line.

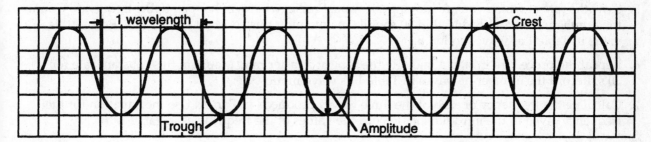

FIGURE 1

The wavelength is the distance between two similar points on successive waves. The number of wavelengths that pass a point in 1 s is the frequency of the wave. Frequency is measured in a unit called the hertz (Hz). A wave with a frequency of 1 Hz indicates that one wavelength is passing a point each second. The frequency can be found using the following equation:

$$frequency = \frac{number\ of\ wavelengths}{1\ s}$$

The velocity of a wave depends upon the material through which the wave passes. The velocity of a wave is equal to the product of its wavelength and its frequency. A wave's velocity is expressed in the same units as any measurement of velocity—meters per second (m/s).

$$velocity = wavelength \times frequency$$

Strategy
You will identify the crest, trough, and amplitude of a wave.
You will determine the wavelength and frequency of a wave.
You will calculate the velocity of a wave.

Materials 🐄 🥽
camera (instant developing)
goggles
apron
meterstick
yarn (20 colored pieces)
rope (about 5 m long)
   or
toy spring

Procedure

CAUTION: *Wear safety goggles throughout the experiment.*

Part A Frequency of a Wave

1. Tie the pieces of yarn to the rope at 0.5-m intervals. Use the meterstick to measure the distances.

2. Tie one end of the rope to an immovable object, such as a door knob. Pull the rope so it does not sag.

3. Make waves in the rope by moving the free end up and down. Continue to move the rope at a steady rate. Observe the crests, troughs, and amplitude of the waves. (See FIGURE 2.)

4. Continue making waves by moving the rope at a constant rate. Observe a particular piece of yarn. Count the number of waves that you produce during a period of 30 s. Record this value in Table 1 as wave motion A.

5. Slow the rate at which you are moving the rope. Predict what will happen to the frequency. Count the number of waves produced in 30 s while maintaining this constant slower rate. Record this value in Table 1 as wave motion B.

6. Repeat the procedure in step 4, moving the rope at a faster rate. Maintain this constant rate for 30 s. Record the number of waves in Table 1 as wave motion C.

7. Calculate the frequency of each of the three waves produced in Part A. Use the equation for the frequency given in the introduction. Record the values of the frequencies in Table 1.

FIGURE 2

Part B Speed of a Wave

1. Use the same rope setup from Part A. Have a classmate move the rope with a constant motion. Record the number of waves produced in 30 s in Table 2 as wave motion A. Photograph the entire length of the moving rope using the instant developing camera. Rest the camera on a table to keep it still.

2. Have your classmate increase the motion of the rope and take another photograph. Predict what will happen to the wavelength. Again count the number of waves produced in 30 s and record these values in Table 2 as wave motion B.

3. Observe the developed photographs. For each photograph, use the yarn markers to determine the length of one wavelength. Record the values in Table 2. You may tape the photographs below.

4. Calculate the frequencies of the two waves produced in Part B. Record these values in Table 2.

5. Calculate the velocities of the two waves using the values of the wavelengths and frequencies in Table 2. Use the equation for velocity of a wave given in the introduction. Record these values of the velocities in Table 2.

Data and Observations
Part A Frequency of a Wave

Table 1

Wave motion	Number of waves in 30 s	Frequency (Hz)
A		
B		
C		

Part B Velocity of a Wave

Table 2

Wave motion	Number of waves in 30 s	Frequency (Hz)	Wavelength (m)	Velocity (m/s)
A				
B				

Attach the wave photographs here.

Questions and Conclusions

1. As you increased the motion of the rope, what happened to the frequency of the waves?

_____

_____

2. As the frequency of the waves increased, what happened to the wavelength?

_____

_____

3. As the frequency of the waves increased, what happened to the velocity of the wave?

_____

_____

4. Do your data indicate that the velocity of a wave is dependent on or independent of its frequency? Explain. _____

_____

_____

_____

Strategy Check

_____ Can you observe transverse waves in a lake or pond?

_____ Can you compare and contrast the frequencies of high-pitched and low-pitched sounds?

Chapter 14

LABORATORY MANUAL

• Wave Reflection, Refraction, and Diffraction 27

Waves enable you to see this page and to hear voices and music. Waves carry energy from one place to another without carrying matter. Waves often bounce off objects, called reflection, change direction when they travel from one medium to another, called refraction, and spread around barriers, called diffraction.

Strategy

You will construct a simple wave tank.
You will observe and study how waves reflect, refract, and diffract.

Materials

steel barrier (1 m × 4 cm × 1 cm)
paraffin blocks, 2 (10 cm × 6 cm × 1 cm)
paraffin block (4 cm × 4 cm × 1 cm)

wood block (15 cm × 3 cm × 7 cm) to use as
  wave generator
wood frame (1 m × 1 m × 10 cm) with plastic
  sheet for lining of wave tank

Procedure

1. Fill the wave tank with water to a depth of 3 cm.

2. Hold the wooden block in the water so that it is just touching the bottom near one end of the wave tank and is parallel with the ledge of the tank. Lift the block out of the water. This entire motion should take about 1 s. Repeat the motion until you can produce uniform waves.

3. Once you are satisfied that you can produce uniform waves, set up the other simulations as illustrated in the diagrams. Each simulation will take at least 5 min. During that period of time, observe the waves and their behavior.

4. After you have finished the simulations, answer the following questions.

Questions and Conclusions

Simulation A

1. Describe the behavior of waves before and after they reflect from the steel barrier. _____

_____

2. Change the angle of the barrier and repeat Simulation A. What happens to the direction of the reflected waves? _____

_____

Simulation B

3. When the waves passed over the glass plate, they entered shallower water. What happened to their speed? _____

_____

4. The change in speed simulates what happens when a wave passes from one medium into another in which its speed is less. How was the direction of the wave affected? _____

_____

5. The change in direction of a wave when it passes from one medium into another is called refraction, and the line drawn perpendicular to the edge of the plate is called the normal. Did the water waves bend away from the normal or toward it when they passed over the plate? _____

_____

6. Describe what happened to the waves after they passed the small paraffin block. _____

_____

7. The bending of the waves around a barrier is called diffraction. How would diffraction affect a boat docked just inside the entrance to a harbor on a seacoast? _____

_____

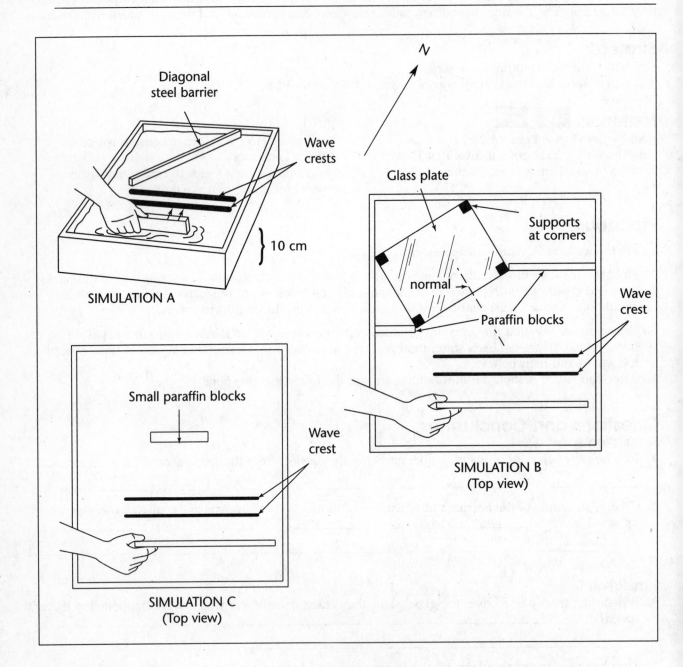

Strategy Check

_____ Can you observe how refraction occurs when you use a magnifying glass to examine a small object?

_____ Can you describe how diffraction enables you to hear someone talking in another room?

Chapter 15

LABORATORY MANUAL

• Light Intensity 28

Have you ever noticed how the brightness of the light from a flashlight changes as you move closer or farther away from it? Likewise, have you ever noticed how the strength of the signals from a radio station fades on a car radio as you move away from the transmitting tower? Both light and radio signals are similar forms of energy. These two examples seem to suggest that the intensity of energy and distance are related. What is the relationship between light intensity and distance? Is there also a relationship between light intensity and direction?

   In this experiment you will use a photo resistor. A photo resistor is a device that changes its resistance to an electric current according to the intensity of the light hitting it. The resistance of a photo resistor is directly related to the intensity of the light striking it. The resistance of a photo resistor is measured in a unit called an ohm (Ω). Photo resistors are often used in burglar alarm systems. A beam of light shines on the photo resistor. If anyone or anything passes through the beam, the intensity of the light striking the photo resistor is changed. This causes the resistance of the photo resistor to change also. Because the photo resistor is in a circuit, the current in the circuit changes, which causes an alarm to sound.

Strategy

You will measure the effect of distance and direction on light intensity.
You will interpret graphs relating light intensity, distance, and direction.

Materials

25-W lightbulb and lamp socket
meterstick
multimeter or ohmmeter
pencil
pencils (colored)

photo resistor
ring stand
tape (black)
utility clamp

Procedure

1. In the Data and Observations section, write hypotheses explaining the relationships between light intensity and distance and between light intensity and direction.

2. Mount the photo resistor on a pencil with tape (see FIGURE 1).

3. Lay the meterstick on a flat, hard surface. Place small pieces of black tape at 10-cm intervals along the meterstick.

4. Set the lightbulb and socket on a smooth, flat surface.

FIGURE 1

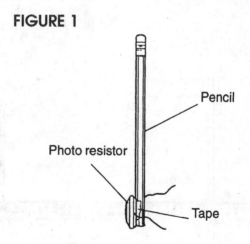

Pencil

Photo resistor

Tape

5. Clamp the meterstick to the ring stand with the utility clamp. Arrange the meterstick so that the lightbulb is at the 0-cm marker (see FIGURE 2).

6. Attach the wires of the photo resistor to the multimeter or ohmmeter. If using a multimeter, set the meter to measure resistance and attach the wires to the appropriate terminals. Darken the room before any measurements are taken.

FIGURE 2

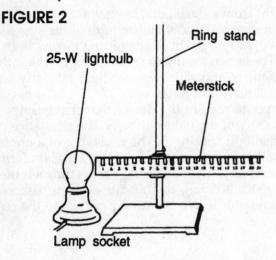

7. Turn off the bulb and place the photo resistor at the 100-cm marker (see FIGURE 3).

8. Turn the bulb on and measure the resistance using the multimeter or ohmmeter. Record the value in Table 1 in the column marked *East*.

9. Move the photo resistor to the 90-cm marker. Measure the resistance and record the value in the same column of the table.

10. Continue advancing the photo resistor to each marker. Record the meter reading at each position. The last reading should be taken at the 10-cm marker.

11. Assume that the meterstick was oriented with the 100-cm marker pointing to the east. Repeat the procedure for each of the three remaining directions shown in FIGURE 4.

FIGURE 3   **FIGURE 4**

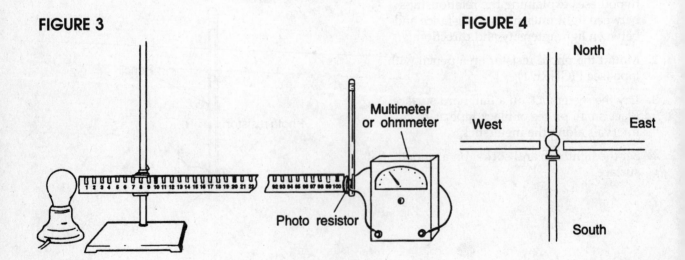

Data and Observations

Hypothesis relating light intensity and distance: _____

Hypothesis relating light intensity and direction: _____

Table 1

Distance (cm)	Resistance (Ω)			
	East	West	North	South
100				
90				
80				
70				
60				
40				
30				
20				
10				

FIGURE 5

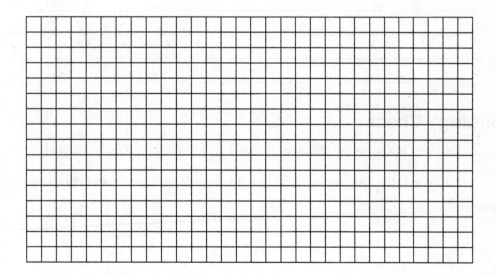

1. Use FIGURE 5 to graph your data. Place the distance values on the *x* axis and the resistance values on the *y* axis. Label the *x* axis *Distance from light source (cm)* and the *y* axis *Resistance (Ω)*.

2. Graph the data for each of the other three directions on the same graph. Use a different colored pencil for each direction.

Questions and Conclusions

1. Look at your graph. Describe how the resistance and distance are related. _____

_____

2. How are light intensity and distance related? _____

_____

3. What does the graph indicate about the relationship between intensity of light and direction?

_____

_____

_____

4. Why was it necessary to darken the room before doing this experiment? _____

_____

_____

_____

5. Do the results of this experiment support your original hypotheses? _____

_____

6. Light from the sun travels to Earth from a distance of almost 150 million kilometers. If Earth were farther away from the sun, what effects would be felt on Earth's surface? What effects would be felt if Earth were closer to the sun?

_____

_____

_____

_____

Strategy Check

_____ Can you measure the effect of distance and direction on light intensity?

_____ Can you interpret graphs relating light intensity, distance, and direction?

Chapter 15

LABORATORY MANUAL

• Investigating Invisible Waves   29

Electromagnetic radiation that has a range of frequencies from 430 trillion to 760 trillion hertz is known as the visible spectrum. Electromagnetic radiation that has frequencies less than 430 trillion hertz or greater than 760 trillion hertz is the invisible spectrum. In this experiment, you will investigate the behavior of some types of electromagnetic radiation in the invisible spectrum. These include radio and infrared waves and ultraviolet light.

Strategy

You will compare the speed of sound in air to the speed of light.

You will examine the behavior of infrared waves used to operate an electronic device from a remote control unit.

You will study fluorescence that results when some materials are exposed to ultraviolet light.

You will determine how certain substances that are added to laundry products are able to whiten and brighten clothes.

Materials

drum
fluorescent materials such as crayons or paints
light (bright, with switch)
rope (100-m)
stopwatch that can measure 0.01 s
television or another electronic device that is operated by an infrared remote control device
thermometer
ultraviolet light
walkie-talkies (pair)

Procedure

Part A Speed of Light and Speed of Sound

1. This part of the activity is done with a partner outdoors. Select an open area such as a field.

2. Use the rope to measure a distance of 100 m in a straight line.

3. First partner—stand at one end of the measured distance with the drum and one walkie-talkie.

4. Second partner—stand at the other end of the measured distance with the stopwatch and the other walkie-talkie.

5. First partner—create a loud, short noise by striking the drum.

6. Second partner—use the stopwatch to time the interval between when you hear the drum on the walkie-talkie and when you hear the drum through the air. Record this time in Table 1 in the Data and Observations section. Carry out a total of three trials.

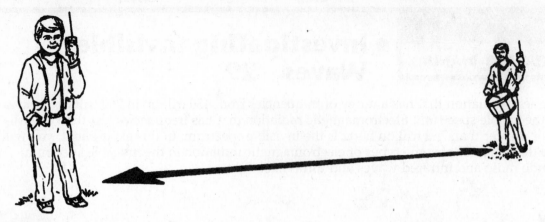

FIGURE 1

7. Switch places and repeat the experiment. This will eliminate any effect of wind in one direction. After three trials record your results in Table 2 in the Data and Observations section.

8. Determine the functioning range of the walkie-talkies by seeing how far apart they can be and still transmit. See what types of obstacles, such as buildings or trees, will block the radio transmission. Record your observations.

9. First partner—stand at one end of the functioning range with the bright light and a walkie-talkie. Signal on the walkie-talkie when you turn on the light.

10. Second partner—time the difference between when you hear the signal and when you see the light. Record the time and distance in the Data and Observations section.

Part B Infrared Remote Control

1. Set up the TV or other electronic device you are using in a long room. Determine the maximum distance at which the infrared remote control device will still operate the electronic device. Record that distance in the Data and Observations section.

2. Hold the remote control device about 5 m from the electronic device. Have someone stand between the remote control device and the electronic device. See if the remote control device will operate the electronic device. Record your observations in the Data and Observations section.

3. Determine if the remote control device can operate the electronic device at angles other than pointing straight at the device. Try "bouncing" the infrared beam off a wall, the floor, or the ceiling. See if the beam will bounce off a person or some other object and still operate the electronic device. Record your observations.

FIGURE 2

Part C Ultraviolet Waves and Fluorescence

1. When some substances absorb ultraviolet light, they can emit light waves that have a lower energy and frequency than the absorbed light. This is called fluorescence.

2. Test the fluorescent substances under the ultraviolet lamp (sometimes called a "black light") to see if they glow. This glow is called fluorescence. Record your results in the Data and Observations section.

3. Use the ultraviolet lamp to test various powdered laundry products that advertise that they whiten and brighten clothes. Shine the ultraviolet lamp on the boxes that these laundry products come from. Record your observations in the Data and Observations section.

Data and Observations

Part A

Table 1 With the Wind

Distance (m)	Time (s)	Speed (m/s)
100		
100		
100		

Table 2 Against the Wind

Distance (m)	Time (s)	Speed (m/s)
100		
100		
100		

Range of walkie-talkies from step 8: _____

Observations of obstacles from step 8: _____

Speed of light data from step 10: _____

_____

Part B
Observations from step 1: _____

Observations from step 2: _____

_____

Observations from step 3: _____

_____

Part C
Observations from step 2: _____

Observations from step 3: _____

Questions and Conclusions

1. Why is there a difference between the time it takes you to hear the drum on the walkie-talkie and the time it takes you to hear it through the air? _____

_____

2. How can you explain the results from step 8 of Part A, when you tested to see if buildings or trees affected the walkie-talkie reception? _____

3. How can you explain the results from step 10 of Part A, when you tried to time the speed of light?

_____

_____

4. How can you explain the results of step 2 of Part B, when someone blocked the infrared wave?

_____

5. How can you explain the results of step 3 of Part B, when you tried to operate the infrared remote control at angles other than pointing straight at the device?

_____

6. What type of substance is added to laundry detergents to make clothes whiter and brighter?

_____

_____

Strategy Check

_____ Can you compare the speed of sound in air to the speed of light?

_____ Can you examine the behavior of infrared waves?

_____ Can you observe the fluorescence that results when some materials are exposed to ultraviolet light?

_____ Can you determine how certain substances whiten and brighten clothes?

Chapter 16

LABORATORY MANUAL

• Conductivity of Various Metals 30

Some materials are excellent conductors of electricity, while other materials do not conduct electricity at all. For example, metals are generally good conductors of electricity, whereas materials like wood and rubber do not conduct electricity. That is why electricians generally wear rubber gloves to protect their hands from electric shock. You will investigate how well various materials conduct electricity.

Strategy

You will determine how well different materials conduct electricity.
You will observe the behavior of a diode.

Materials

testable materials
aluminum foil
brass screw
copper pipe
diode
glass rod
graphite (pencil lead)
nail
paper clip
plastic pen cap
rubber eraser
wooden stick

circuit parts
2 alligator clips
4 20-cm lengths of insulated copper wire
2 lightbulbs
2 lightbulb holders
2 1.5-volt batteries
wire strippers

Procedure

CAUTION: *Be careful working with sharp objects.*

1. Set up a test circuit as shown in FIGURE 1 and described below.

2. With wire strippers, carefully scrape off 1 cm of insulation at the end of each wire.

3. Attach two wires to each of the lightbulb holders.

4. Attach one wire from each of the lightbulb holders to one exposed terminal of the batteries.

5. Leave the other wire from each lightbulb holder unattached. Attach an alligator clip to the free ends of the wires.

6. Put a lightbulb in each lightbulb holder.

FIGURE 1

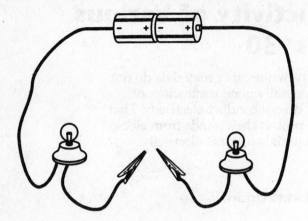

7. Before testing each material, predict whether it will allow the lightbulbs to light. Record your prediction in Table 1.

8. Test each material by attaching the alligator clips to each end as shown in FIGURE 2. Record your observations in Table 1.

9. Reverse the direction of current in each material by switching the alligator clips. Record your observations in Table 1.

10. After testing all the materials, dismantle the circuit and place the components where instructed by your teacher.

FIGURE 2

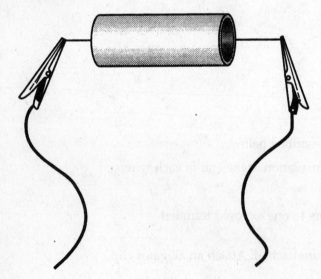

Data and Observations

Table 1

Conductivity of Various Materials

Material	Prediction before connecting	Observations when initially connected	Observations when connected in reverse
Aluminum foil			
Brass screw			
Copper pipe			
Glass rod			
Graphite			
Nail			
Paper clip			
Plastic pen cap			
Rubber eraser			
Wooden stick			
Diode			

Questions and Conclusions

1. From the data in Table 1, prepare a list of the materials that are conductors of electricity.

_____

_____

2. From the data in Table 1, prepare a list of materials that are not conductors.

_____

_____

3. Did any of the materials appear in both lists? _____

_____

4. How can you tell when there is a current in the circuit? _____

_____

_____

5. Were all of the metal materials good conductors of electricity? _____

_____

_____

6. Of the materials that conducted electricity, were there any nonmetals? _____

_____

7. Which materials would make good insulators? _____

_____

8. How could a diode be used in a circuit? _____

_____

Strategy Check

_____ Can you determine how well different materials conduct electricity?

_____ Can you observe the behavior of a diode?

Chapter 16

LABORATORY MANUAL • **Batteries 31**

A wet-cell battery converts chemical energy into electrical energy. Chemical reactions taking place at each of the battery terminals cause electrons to pile up at the negative terminal. Voltage is a measure of the force that causes electrons to flow from the negative terminal to the positive terminal through a conductor. The flow of charges through a conductor is current.

   The amounts of voltage and current produced by a battery depend on the nature and the concentration of the chemicals in the battery. For example, a car battery produces more current and voltage than a flashlight battery does. A car battery also contains chemicals that differ in nature and concentration from the chemicals in a flashlight battery.

Strategy
You will build wet-cell batteries.
You will measure the voltage of the batteries.

Materials

2 alligator clips
aluminum foil, heavy gauge
aluminum strip
apron
beaker (250-mL)
copper strip
glass rod
goggles

graduated cylinder (100-mL)
0.1 M hydrochloric acid
paper towels
vinegar
voltmeter
gloves
water
2 wires

FIGURE 1

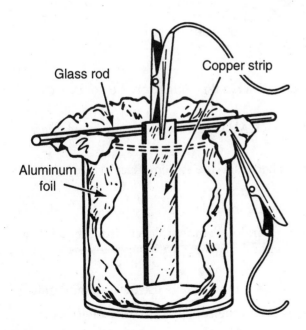

Glass rod

Copper strip

Aluminum
foil

Procedure

1. Line the inside of a 250-mL beaker with aluminum foil. The foil should hang over the outside edges of the beaker as shown in FIGURE 1.

2. Place a glass rod across the mouth of the beaker.

3. Using an alligator clip, hang a copper strip from the glass rod into the beaker. The copper strip should hang near one side of the beaker, but the copper strip should NOT touch the aluminum foil.

4. Attach a wire to the alligator clip. Then attach the other end of the wire to the positive (+) terminal of the voltmeter.

5. Attach a second alligator clip to the aluminum foil hanging over the edge of the beaker. This second alligator clip should be attached across from the copper strip as shown in FIGURE 1.

6. Attach a wire to the second alligator clip and connect the other end of this wire to the negative (−) terminal of the voltmeter as shown in FIGURE 2.

FIGURE 2

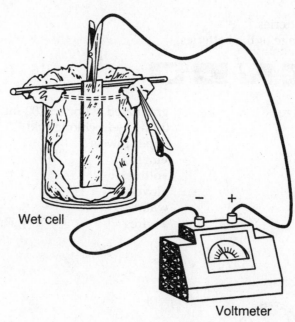

Wet cell

Voltmeter

7. Observe the wet cell and record any changes in Table 1. Observe the voltage on the voltmeter and record it in Table 1.

8. Carefully add 75 mL of 0.1 M HCl to the foil-lined beaker. **CAUTION:** *HCl can cause burns. Rinse any acid spills immediately with water.*

9. After adding HCl, observe the wet cell and notice any changes to the system. Record your observations in Table 1.

10. Observe the voltage on the voltmeter and record the reading in Table 1.

11. Disconnect the wires. Under your teacher's supervision, carefully empty the acid from the beaker. Thoroughly rinse the beaker and copper strip with water and dry them with paper towels. Discard the aluminum foil.

12. Repeat steps 1 through 10 using vinegar instead of HCl. Be sure to always use new aluminum foil.

13. Repeat steps 1 through 10 using an aluminum strip instead of the copper strip. Be sure to use fresh hydrochloric acid and fresh aluminum foil.

Data and Observations

Table 1

Battery conditions	Changes to system	Voltage reading
Without liquid		
HCl, copper, aluminum		
Vinegar, copper, aluminum		
HCl, aluminum, aluminum		

Questions and Conclusions

1. From the data in Table 1, determine which battery conditions produced the largest voltage.

_____

_____

_____

2. Which liquid—HCl or vinegar—produced a higher voltage? Explain.

_____

_____

3. How do you know that a chemical reaction took place in the battery after the vinegar was added?

_____

_____

4. What metals were used to produce the batteries? How did they affect the results?

_____

_____

5. How did the effect of hydrochloric acid on the copper strip differ from its effect on the aluminum foil?

_____

_____

_____

Strategy Check

_____ Can you build a wet-cell battery?

_____ Can you measure the voltages produced by different wet-cell batteries?

Chapter 17

LABORATORY MANUAL • **Star Colors 32**

In 1665, Isaac Newton demonstrated that sunlight was composed of many colors. Today the spectra of a star is one of the most important tools scientists use to determine the star's surface temperature and composition. The Draper system of spectral classification is used in this activity.

Strategy

You will define the term *star*.
You will observe and record star colors.
You will classify stars based on their color.

Materials

binoculars or telescope (optional)
graph paper

Table 1—Star Classification Chart

Star spectral type	Color	Surface temperature (K)
M	red	2000–4000
K	red to orange	3500–5000
G	yellow	5000–6000
F	yellow-white	6000–7500
A	white	9000
B	bluish-white	11 000–25 000
O	bluish-white	60 000

Procedure

1. On a clear, bright night observe the stars with your eyes or with the binoculars or telescope.

2. Use some landmarks and divide the sky into four sections. Label the landmarks in the diagram under Data and Observations.

3. Observe and record the color of each star in each section. Record your observations on your diagram under Data and Observations.

4. Compile your data showing the star color, class, and number of stars in each section in a table. Set up your table on one end of your graph paper.

5. Draw a bar graph showing the star classes and the number of stars in each class under the table on the graph paper.

Data and Observations
Diagram night sky here.

<table>
<tr><td></td><td></td></tr>
<tr><td></td><td></td></tr>
</table>

Questions and Conclusions

1. What property did you use to classify a celestial body as a star? _____
   _____
   _____

2. Which star class is the most abundant? _____
   _____

3. Which star class does our sun belong to? _____

4. What is the surface temperature of our sun? _____

5. The temperature of stars is given in Kelvins. Changing from the Celsius scale to the Kelvin
   scale is very easy: K = °C + 273°. What is the temperature of the sun in Celsius degrees?

   _____

Strategy Check

_____ Can you define the term *star*?

_____ Can you observe and record the colors of the stars?

_____ Can you classify stars based on their color?

Chapter 17

LABORATORY MANUAL ● Star Positions 33

When you watch the stars on a clear night, do you get the impression that you are in an upside-down bowl? The ancient Greeks believed that the stars were fixed to a clear bowl that slowly rotated around Earth. Although today we know that Earth rotates, the celestial sphere is still a good model to use to locate stars and other celestial bodies.

Strategy
You will construct a model of the north celestial hemisphere.
You will plot the stars on the celestial sphere.

Materials
globe (mounted)
hemisphere (clear plastic or terrarium top)

pen (felt-tip)
string to go around celestial equator

Procedure

1. The celestial sphere appears to move around a line that is an extension of Earth's axis. The north and south celestial poles are the points where Earth's geographic axis intersects the celestial sphere (see FIGURE 1). Label the north celestial pole with a dot on the inside of the hemisphere.

2. The celestial equator is the intersection of a plane that passes through Earth's equator and the celestial sphere. Place the clear hemisphere over the globe so that the north pole and the north celestial pole are in line. Mark the celestial equator on the hemisphere. The celestial equator is 90° from the celestial poles (see FIGURE 1).

3. Planes comparable to latitude on Earth are called *declination* on the celestial sphere. Positions north of the celestial equator are called *plus declination* and measured in degrees. Positions south of the celestial equator are called *minus declination*, also measured in degrees.

4. The celestial circle that corresponds to the prime meridian of longitude on Earth is called *right ascension*. Right ascension is measured from the point where the sun crosses the celestial equator about March 21 (the vernal equinox).

5. Right ascension is measured in hours, minutes, and seconds. On the equator, 15 degrees of arc equals 1 hour. Take a length of string and measure the distance around the celestial equator in centimeters. Record. Divide this distance by 24. Measure and mark these spaces around the celestial equator. Each mark represents 1 hour. Start at the prime meridian and move eastward around the celestial equator (see FIGURE 1).

6. Now you have a grid system similar to latitude and longitude.

7. Map the locations of the stars in Table 1 on the celestial sphere.

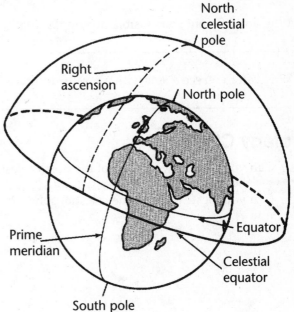

FIGURE 1

Table 1

Common name	Scientific name	R.A. hr	R.A. min	Dec. (°)
Vega	Lyrae	18	35	38
Arcturus	Bootes	14	13	19
Altair	Aquilae	19	48	8
Betelgeuse	Orionis	05	52	7
Aldebaran	Tauri	04	33	16
Deneb	Cygni	20	40	45
Regulus	Leonis	10	06	12
Castor	Geminorum	07	31	32

Data and Observations

Celestial equator = _____ cm

Questions and Conclusions

1. How is right ascension like longitude? _____

   How is it different? _____

2. Compare declination to latitude. _____

   _____

3. What does the vernal equinox on the celestial sphere correspond to on geographic maps?

   _____

4. Why are different stars visible during the year? _____

   _____

5. Why can't you see a star with a minus declination from the northern hemisphere? _____

   _____

Strategy Check

_____ Can you construct a model of the north celestial hemisphere?

_____ Can you locate stars on the celestial sphere?

Chapter 18

LABORATORY MANUAL ● **Earth's Spin 34**

The speed at which Earth turns on its axis can be described in two ways. The velocity of rotation refers to the rate at which Earth turns on its axis. Velocity of rotation refers to Earth as a whole. For any point on Earth's surface, the speed of Earth's rotation can be described as its instantaneous linear velocity. This velocity is the speed of the point as it follows a circular path around Earth.

Strategy
You will determine the instantaneous linear velocity of some points on Earth.
You will compare the linear velocities of points at different locations on Earth.

Materials
globe (mounted on axis)   stopwatch   tape (adhesive)
meterstick   string

Procedure
Part A
1. Place small pieces of adhesive tape on the Prime Meridian, at the equator, at 30° N latitude, at 60° N latitude, and at the north pole.

2. Line up the tape with the metal circle above the globe; see FIGURE 1.

3. With your finger on the globe, move it west to east for one second; see FIGURE 2.

4. For each location marked by tape, measure the distance from the Prime Meridian to the metal circle. Use the string and the meterstick to get accurate distances. Record the distances in Table 1.

5. Realign the metal circle with the pieces of tape. Move the globe west to east for 2 s. Record the distances from the tapes to the metal circle in Table 1.

6. Repeat step 5, moving the globe for 3 s. Record your results in Table 1.

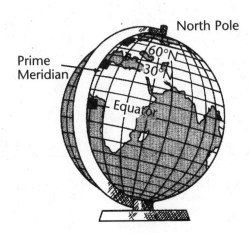

FIGURE 1

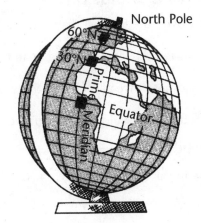

FIGURE 2

Part B

Calculate the speed of each point for each trial. Record in Table 2. Use the formula:

$$velocity\ (cm/s) = \frac{distance\ (cm)}{time\ (s)}$$

Data and Observations

Table 1

Latitude	Distance moved (cm)		
	1 s	2 s	3 s
Equator			
30° N			
60° N			
North Pole			

Table 2

Latitude	Velocity (cm/s)		
	Trial 1	Trial 2	Trial 3
Equator			
30° N			
60° N			
North Pole			

Questions and Conclusions

1. Which point moved the farthest distance in all three trials? _____

2. Which point moved the least distance in all three trials? _____

3. Which point did not move at all in the three trials? _____

4. On what does the linear velocity of a point depend? _____

_____

5. How does the linear velocity change as you move from the equator to the poles? _____

_____

Strategy Check

_____ Can you determine instantaneous linear velocity?

_____ Can you see that the linear velocity is not the same for all points on Earth?

Chapter 18

LABORATORY MANUAL • **Earth's Shape 35**

You've probably seen photographs of Earth taken by satellites in space. Such photographs clearly show Earth's round shape. Early astronomers didn't have spacecraft to help them study Earth. They had to rely on observation and measurement. In this activity, you'll explore some methods used by early astronomers to determine Earth's true shape.

Strategy

You will demonstrate evidence of Earth's shape.
You will describe the type of shadow cast by Earth during a lunar eclipse.

Materials

basketball
small piece of cardboard
flashlight
textbook
scissors

Procedure

1. Cut out a triangular piece of cardboard so that each side measures approximately 6 cm.

2. Hold a basketball at eye level about 33 cm from your eye. Have your partner slowly move the cardboard up and over the basketball from the opposite side.

3. In the space below, sketch the cardboard as it appears when the top of the cardboard first comes in sight over the basketball. Make another sketch of the cardboard as it appears when fully visible above the basketball.

4. Darken the room. Use a flashlight to cast a shadow of a textbook against the wall. Do the same for the basketball. In the space below, draw the shadows of the textbook and the basketball.

Data and Observations

Cardboard drawings

Shadow drawings

Questions and Conclusions

1. Compare and contrast your three drawings of the cardboard.

_____

_____

_____

2. How were your different views of the cardboard similar to the view of a ship on the horizon approaching shore?

_____

_____

3. How did the cardboard activity demonstrate evidence of Earth's shape?

_____

_____

_____

4. Compare and contrast your drawings of the shadows cast by the basketball and the textbook.

_____

_____

5. During a lunar eclipse, Earth casts a shadow on the moon. What type of shadow would Earth cast if it were flat? What type of shadow does Earth cast on the moon during a lunar eclipse?

_____

_____

6. How do the shadows you observed demonstrate evidence of Earth's shape?

_____

_____

_____

7. Can you think of any other evidence that demonstrates Earth's round shape? Describe this evidence.

_____

_____

Strategy Check

_____ Can you demonstrate evidence of Earth's shape?

_____ Can you describe the type of shadow cast by Earth during a lunar eclipse?

Chapter 19

LABORATORY MANUAL

• Venus—The Greenhouse Effect 36

Because Venus is closer to the sun, it receives almost twice the amount of solar radiation received by Earth. Venus reflects more radiation to space than Earth because of its clouds. We might expect Venus, therefore, to have surface temperatures similar to Earth. However, the *Pioneer* Venus vehicles have measured surface temperatures of 460°C. Some scientists explain this high temperature as the "greenhouse effect." When the solar energy strikes the surface of Venus, the energy is absorbed and changed into heat energy. This heat energy is reflected back to the atmosphere where it is trapped.

Strategy

You will build a model to show the greenhouse effect.
You will compare this model to Earth.
You will form a hypothesis about temperatures on Venus using data collected from this model and from the *Pioneer* spacecraft.

Materials

cardboard (stiff)	pencils (colored)	thermometer
graph paper	plastic storage box and lid, clear	watch
heat lamp (mounted)	soil	

Procedure

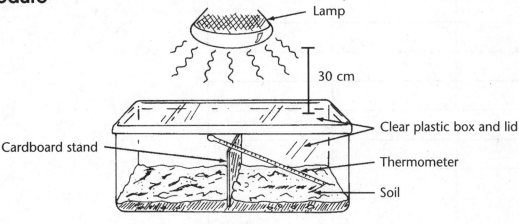

FIGURE 1

1. Place about 3 cm of soil in the bottom of the clear plastic box.

2. Thoroughly moisten the soil with water.

3. Cut the piece of cardboard so that it makes a divider for the box. The cardboard should not quite reach the top of the box. Insert the divider into the box.

4. Lean the thermometer against the divider with the bulb end up (see FIGURE 1). Put the lid on the box.

5. Position the box and lamp in an area of the room where no direct sunlight reaches. **CAUTION:** *Use care when handling heat lamp.*

6. Place the heat lamp about 30 cm above the box and direct the light so it shines on the thermometer bulb.

7. Turn off the lamp and allow the thermometer to return to room temperature. Record room temperature in Table 1.

8. Turn on the lamp and measure the temperature every minute for 20 min. Record the temperatures in Table 1.

9. Turn off the lamp and allow the thermometer to return to room temperature. Remoisten the soil and repeat step 8 with the lid off the box. Record your data in Table 1.

Data and Observations

Table 1

Time (min)	Temperature (°C) Lid off	Lid on
1		
2		
3		
4		
5		
6		
7		
8		
9		
10		
11		
12		
13		
14		
15		
16		
17		
18		
19		
20		

Graph the data using two different colors. Plot Temperature on the vertical axis and Time on the horizontal axis.

Questions and Conclusions

1. Did the temperature increase the most with the lid on or off? _____

   Why? _____

   _____

   _____

2. Draw a diagram of Earth showing its atmosphere and what occurs to solar radiation in the
   atmosphere. List the components of Earth's atmosphere on your diagram. Write a brief explanation
   of the greenhouse effect on Earth. _____

   _____

   _____

   _____

   _____

3. Compare the activity to the greenhouse effect on Earth. How are they similar? How are they
   different? _____

   _____

   _____

   _____

   _____

4. Venus's atmosphere is composed mainly of carbon dioxide, carbon monoxide, water, nitrogen, and sulfuric acid. Venus's atmosphere is 100 times as dense as Earth's atmosphere. From the surface of Venus up to 20 km, there appears to be a clear region of atmosphere. A thick layer of clouds extends from about 50 km to 80 km above the surface of Venus. These clouds are composed of drops of sulfuric acid. Above and below these clouds are other thinner layers of haze. Venus's ionosphere extends from 100 km to 200 km above the surface. Like the ionosphere of Earth, it has layers. The temperature in the ionosphere of Venus is cooler than the temperature in Earth's ionosphere.

Draw a diagram of Venus showing its atmosphere and what happens to solar radiation in the atmosphere. List the components of Venus's atmosphere on your diagram. Write a brief explanation of the greenhouse effect on Venus. _____

_____

_____

_____

5. Compare the greenhouse effect on Earth and Venus. Can you think of a reason why the surface of Venus is so much hotter than the surface of Earth? _____

_____

_____

_____

Strategy Check

_____ Can you build a model to show the greenhouse effect?

_____ Can you compare this model to Earth?

Chapter 19

LABORATORY MANUAL • Jupiter and Its Moons 37

Jupiter and its moons are similar to a model of the solar system. Four of the moons are called the Galilean moons since Galileo first observed them in 1610. The moons are called Io, Ganymede, Callisto, and Europa.

Strategy
You will build an astronomical telescope.
You will observe the Galilean moons of Jupiter.
You will place the four moons in order outward from Jupiter.

Materials
2 cardboard mailing tubes, 9-cm and 18-cm (9-cm one should be slightly smaller in diameter than the 18-cm one)
2 convex lenses
    eyepiece, short focal length
    objective, long focal length
tape (masking)
Star and Sky, *Astronomy*, or *Sky and Telescope*, current issue

Procedure
1. Tape the objective lens to one end of the larger, longer tube.

2. Tape the eyepiece lens to one end of the smaller, shorter tube.

3. Slide the small tube inside the large tube.

4. View a book through the telescope. Move the small tube back and forth to focus. Record your observations under Data and Observations.

5. Look up the position of Jupiter in a current issue of one of the magazines.

6. After dark, take the telescope outside and locate Jupiter. Observe and sketch the four visible moons. Sketch the moons in Table 1.

7. Repeat this observation every clear night for two weeks. Record all data in Table 1.

Data and Observations
Observations of book using the telescope: _____

_____

_____

_____

Table 1

Date/Time	Moon	Sketch

Questions and Conclusions

1. Why is the book upside down when you view it through the telescope? _____
_____
_____

2. List the four Galilean moons of Jupiter in order outward from Jupiter. _____
_____

3. Write a brief description of each moon. Use magazines such as *Newsweek, Time, Science, Scientific American,* or *Astronomy* as sources for your material. _____
_____
_____
_____
_____

Strategy Check

_____ Can you build an astronomical telescope?

_____ Can you place Jupiter's moons in order outward from the planet?

Chapter 20

LABORATORY MANUAL   ● **Star Trails 38**

As Earth rotates on its axis, the stars appear to move also. The north star, Polaris, is a fixed reference point because it is almost directly above the north pole of Earth's axis of rotation. The pole position does not appear to move.

Strategy

You will photograph Polaris in a time exposure.
You will determine how many degrees Earth has rotated during the time exposure.

Materials

camera with time exposure   paper (tracing)
compass (drawing)   protractor
film (black and white)   tripod or support for camera

Procedure

1. Load the camera and mount it on the tripod.

2. On a clear, moonless night, set up the camera outside. Aim the camera so that Polaris is in the center of the viewing field.

3. Set the focus on infinity and open the shutter for a time exposure. Record the time and the landmark that is right under Polaris in Table 1.

4. Three hours later, close the shutter. Record the landmark that is under Polaris in Table 1. Have the film developed. Explain to the developer what you photographed, and ask for special care in the developing.

5. Trace several of the arcs on your developed print on the tracing paper. Be sure to include the arc traced by Polaris. Label the end points.

6. Use the compass to determine the center of the circle of which the arc of Polaris is a part. **CAUTION:** *Use care when handling sharp objects.* Mark the center of the circle with a dot.

7. Draw a line from the center of the circle made by Polaris to the ends of five star curves you traced. Measure the angles between each pair of lines with a protractor. Record each angle in Table 2.

Data and Observations

Table 1

	Landmark
Start	
Finish	

Table 2

Star pairs	Angle (°)
Polaris and Star 1	
Polaris and Star 2	
Polaris and Star 3	
Polaris and Star 4	
Polaris and Star 5	

Questions and Conclusions

1. Did the landmarks change? _____ In what direction do the stars appear to move?

   _____

2. What does your print show? _____

   _____

3. What is the central point in the picture? _____

   Explain. _____

   _____

4. How far did the stars appear to move per hour in degrees? _____

5. How long does it take Earth to make one complete rotation based on your average arc?

   _____

6. How long could you have left the shutter open? _____ Explain.

   _____

   _____

7. Do the stars actually move as the print seems to prove? _____ Explain.

   _____

   _____

8. If the shutter had been left open for 4 hours, how many degrees would Earth have rotated?

   _____

Strategy Check

_____ Can you photograph Polaris?

_____ Can you determine how far Earth rotates during a time exposure?

• Spectral Analysis 39

The photograph of the spectrum of a star, sorted by color across a plate, will reveal spectral lines upon close examination. The lines are produced by elements in a star at high temperature. These lines represent the chemical composition of the star. Each element has its own "fingerprint." To analyze the spectra of stars, scientists collected spectra of all the known elements. If we compare the spectral lines of an unknown star with the spectral lines of elements, we can determine the chemical composition of the star. More recently, we have discovered not only the composition of the stars but also their temperatures, their rotational rate, and their relative motion with regard to Earth.

Strategy
You will construct a simple spectral analyzer.
You will determine the composition of a star using the spectral analyzer.
You will determine other characteristics of a star by comparing the spectral lines with a standard.

Materials
scissors

Procedure
1. Turn to the third page of this lab. Cut out the pull tab card; the spectroscope fingerprints card; and Stars B, C, and D along the dashed lines.

2. Make five slits along the dashed lines A, B, C, D, and E on the fingerprints card.

3. From left to right, insert "Pull Tab Out" up through slit E, down through slit D, up through slit C, down through slit B, and up through slit A.

4. Keeping the sodium doublets aligned, compare the lines of each known element with the lines of Star A. If lines match, then that element is present in Star A. Record your findings in Table 1.

5. Star B, Star C, and Star D are provided for further study and comparison. Each can be placed over Star A.

Data and Observations

Table 1

Star	Chemical composition	Other characteristics
A		
B		
C		
D		

Questions and Conclusions

1. When we say that the neon colored lights look beautiful at night, what color comes to mind?
    _____ What color is suggested by the "fingerprints" of neon? _____
    _____

2. Did any of the stars have the same chemical composition? Look at the table.
    _____
    _____
    _____

3. Sometimes scientists see spectral lines that do not fit the usual pattern. The lines might be shifted
    from their usual positions. This may suggest that the star is moving either toward the observer
    (shift toward the blue) or moving away from the observer (shift toward the red). Look at the
    spectral lines for Star B and Star D. Star B is the standard for comparison. How is Star D different?
    What is a possible explanation for the difference? _____
    _____
    _____

4. If the scientist sees the spectral lines wider than usual, he or she relates this spectral broadening to
    either rotational speed (the broader the faster), temperature (the broader the hotter), or pressure
    (the broader the greater pressure). Look at the spectral lines for Star B and Star C. Star B is the
    standard. How is Star C different? What could be a possible explanation? _____
    _____
    _____

5. Complete Table 1 by filling in the Other characteristics column.

Strategy Check

_____ Can you construct a simple spectral analyzer?

_____ Can you determine the composition of a star using the spectral analyzer?

_____ Can you determine other characteristics of a star by comparing the spectral lines with a
standard?

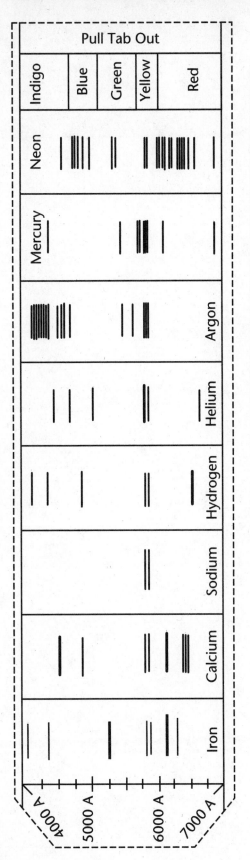

Pull Tab Out

| Indigo | Blue | Green | Yellow | Red |

Neon

Mercury

Argon

Helium

Hydrogen

Sodium

Calcium

Iron

4000 A   5000 A   6000 A   7000 A

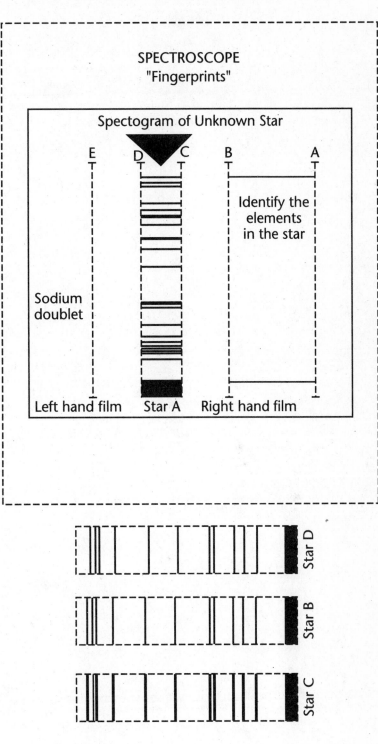

SPECTROSCOPE
"Fingerprints"

Spectogram of Unknown Star

E   D   C   B   A

Identify the elements in the star

Sodium doublet

Left hand film   Star A   Right hand film

Star D

Star B

Star C

Chapter 21

LABORATORY MANUAL

• Shapes of Bacteria 40

Thousands of different types of bacteria are known and have been observed, and there are possibly many more that have not yet been observed. How can a scientist tell those organisms apart when they are so small? One way is by their characteristic shapes, or patterns of joining together in groups.

Strategy

You will identify bacteria by using their shape and other characteristics as clues.
You will discover a process of elimination or "key" that will be used to help in the identification.

Materials

key on the next page

Procedure

1. Examine FIGURE 1 in Data and Observations, which shows bacteria magnified 2000 times their natural size.
2. Use the key to identify each type of bacterium (singular for bacteria). Start at the top, following the directions. The key will allow you to identify each bacterium by name. Each bacterium has a first name that describes its shape in scientific language, and a last name that may also describe some special characteristic. The key also lists in parentheses the disease caused by the bacterium or type of food in which the bacterium may be found. Label each bacterium in Data and Observations.

Data and Observations

Identify and label each bacterium in FIGURE 1.

FIGURE 1

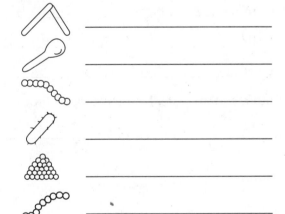

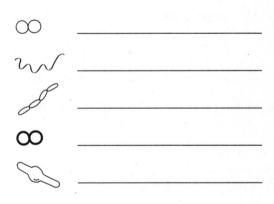

KEY

If the general shape of a bacterium is round, go to I, skip II and III.
If the general shape of a bacterium is rod (long and straight), go to II, skip I and III.
If the general shape of a bacterium is spiral, go to III, skip II and I.

Section I

If in pairs, go to a or a' only.
If in chains, go to b or b' only.
If in clumps, go to c only.
a—without a heavy cover-*Diplococcus meningitidis* (spinal meningitis)
a'—with a heavy cover (capsule)-*Diplococcus pneumoniae* (Pneumonia)
b—large in size-*Streptococcus pyogenes* (Tonsillitis)
b'—small in size-*Streptococcus lactis*-(Buttermilk)
c—*Staphylococcus aureus* (Boils)

Section II

If in chains, go to d only.
If in pairs, go to e only.
If single, go to f or f' or f".
d—*Bacillus anthracis* (Anthrax)
e—*Bacillus lactis* (Sauerkraut)
f—with hairs (flagella)-*Bacillus typhosa* (Typhoid fever)
f'—with a bulge (spore) in the middle-*Bacillus botulinum* (Botulism poisoning)
f"—with a bulge at the end-*Bacillus tetani* (Tetanus)

Section III

Treponema palladium (Syphilis)

Questions and Conclusions

1. What part of the word is the same for all bacteria found in Section I?_____

This word refers to the shape of a bacterium. The shape is _____

2. The word "diplo-" when placed in front of a bacterium name must mean _____

3. The word "strepto-" when placed in front of a bacterium name must mean _____

4. The word "staphylo-" when placed in front of a bacterium name must mean _____

5. What word is the same for all bacteria found in Section II? _____

This word refers to the shape of a bacterium. The shape is _____

6. Some bacteria produce chemicals that provide food with a certain taste. Name two such foods.

_____

Strategy Check

_____ Can you use the key to identify bacteria by their shape and other characteristics?

_____ Can you understand how the use of scientific names helps to describe certain features of bacteria?

Chapter 21

LABORATORY MANUAL • **Bacterial Growth 41**

Bacteria are supposed to be everywhere. But have you ever seen them? If a bacterium (singular of *bacteria*) has good growing conditions, this single cell will grow and quickly multiply. If enough cells get together, you may be able to see the colony (group of bacterial cells) that forms.

Strategy

You will prepare a growth chamber for bacteria.
You will test an object to see if bacteria are present on it.
You will determine whether or not bacteria were present on the object tested upon examination of your growth chambers.

Materials

aluminum foil	ruler	tape (adhesive or masking)
paper cups	scissors	wax paper
potato (raw)		

Procedure

Part A—Preparing Growth Chambers

1. Prepare two growth chambers. For each chamber, cut out a circle of aluminum foil 12 cm in diameter and a circle of wax paper 8 cm in diameter. Cut off the top 3 cm of a paper cup (see FIGURE 1). **CAUTION:** *Always be careful when using scissors.*
2. Mold the foil around the top of the paper cup to form a dish.
3. Cut a slice of potato and put it in your foil dish (see FIGURE 2A).
4. Cover the foil dish with the circle of wax paper, crimping the edges of the aluminum foil and wax paper together. Do not close the dish completely; leave one side open (see FIGURE 2B). Close the opening with tape and print your name on the tape (see FIGURE 2C). Your teacher will sterilize your growth chambers before you add bacteria to the potato.

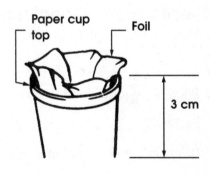

FIGURE 1

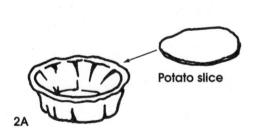

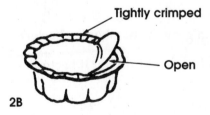

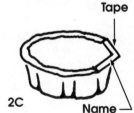

FIGURE 2

Part B—Adding Bacteria to the Potato

1. Set one of your growth chambers aside. This chamber is your control. Label it C, for control.
2. Open the taped end of the second growth chamber. Using your fingertips, touch the potato in this chamber.
3. Reseal the second chamber with tape after touching the potato. Set this chamber aside with the first growth chamber.

Part C—Examining the Potatoes for Bacteria

1. Open both growth chambers after two days. **CAUTION:** *Do not touch the potato surface with your hands.* Examine the potatoes for bacterial growth. Small white, cream, or yellow dots are colonies of bacteria resulting from one bacterium that has multiplied and grown very rapidly to form millions of bacteria cells.
2. Count the number of bacteria colonies on the surface of the treated (touched) potato. Compare the number of colonies on the untreated (control) potato with the number of colonies on the treated potato. If separate colonies cannot be counted, compare the surface of the untreated potato with the surface of the treated potato.
3. **CAUTION:** *Give all growth chambers and potato pieces to your teacher for disposal.*

Data and Observations

1. Record your observations in Table 1.

Table 1

Untreated potato	
Treated potato	

Questions and Conclusions

1. How do you explain finding more bacteria on the treated potato than on the untreated potato?

_____

2. Bacteria requires food in order to live and increase in number. What supplied the food to the

bacteria? _____

3. Why isn't everything on Earth covered with bacteria colonies if they are so easy to grow?

_____

_____

Strategy Check

_____ Did you prepare a growth chamber for bacteria?

_____ Did you test an object and find out if bacteria are present on it?

Chapter 22

LABORATORY MANUAL   • **Molds 42**

Molds are fungi that need food for energy. They contain no chlorophyll, so they cannot make their own food. Will molds grow on almost any surface that provides them with food? Will they grow only on surfaces that provide certain conditions?

Strategy

You will build an apparatus to test for mold growth.

You will test the conditions in which mold will grow by using different foods, different light conditions, and different amounts of moisture.

You will observe and record the conditions in which molds grow.

Materials

8 baby food jars (with lids)   potato flakes (dried)
cotton swab   paper towels
graduated cylinder (10-mL)   spoon
labels   water
mold source

Procedure

1. Your teacher will assign a group with which you will work. Your group will prepare eight jars for testing mold growth.
2. Put a spoonful of dry potatoes in each of four baby food jars. Put a crumpled paper towel in each of the other four jars.
3. Observe and record in Data and Observations the appearance of mold your teacher supplies to you.
4. Rub a cotton swab over the surface of the mold and then rub it over the surface of the towels in the four jars. Rub the swab over the surface of the mold again. Then rub it over the surface of the potato flakes in the other four jars. **CAUTION:** *Give all swabs to your teacher for proper disposal. Always wash your hands after handling microbes.*
5. Put 5 mL of water into each of two potato jars and two paper towel jars.
6. Seal all of the jars with lids. Label the jars with your name and the date. Also write the growth conditions for the jar on each label: dry-dark, dry-light, wet-dark, wet-light.
7. Place one dry potato jar in the light and the other dry potato jar in the dark. Your teacher will tell you the best places to put your jars. Place one wet potato jar in the light and the other in the dark. Do the same for the wet and dry paper towel jars.
8. Observe the jars every day for one week. Record your daily observations in Table 1 in Data and Observations. **CAUTION:** *Give all jars to your teacher for proper disposal.*

Data and Observations

1. Record the appearance of the mold provided by your teacher.

_____

2. Record your daily observations in Table 1.

Table 1

Conditions	Day 1	Day 2	Day 3	Day 4	Day 5	Day 6	Day 7
Potato-dry-light							
Potato-dry-dark							
Potato-wet-light							
Potato-wet-dark							
Towel-dry-light							
Towel-dry-dark							
Towel-wet-light							
Towel-wet-dark							

3. If mold is observed growing in any jar after several days, describe its appearance here.

_____

Questions and Conclusions

1. Is the new mold growing in the jar similar to the original mold? _____

   Give evidence of this. _____

2. Does mold require food in order to grow? _____

   Give evidence of this. _____

3. Does mold require water to grow if food is supplied? _____

   Give evidence of this. _____

4. Does mold grow better in light or dark conditions if food and moisture are supplied? _____

   Give evidence of this. _____

Strategy Check

_____ Can you build an apparatus for testing mold growth?

_____ Can you test mold growth in different conditions?

_____ Can you determine from your results if mold needs food to grow?

_____ Can you determine from your results if mold needs water to grow?

_____ Can you determine from your results if mold grows better under light or dark conditions?

Chapter 22

LABORATORY MANUAL   ● **Yeasts 43**

Yeast are fungi that need food for life. When yeast use food for energy, they give off carbon dioxide as a waste product. The production of carbon dioxide is evidence that yeast are converting food to energy. You can demonstrate that yeast produce carbon dioxide.

Strategy

You will build an apparatus to show that yeast produce carbon dioxide.
You will provide some yeast with food and some yeast with no food.
You will observe yeast producing carbon dioxide gas.

Materials

beaker (large)   graduated cylinder
pancake syrup   watch or clock
2 dropper/rubber stopper   water
  (one hole) assemblies   yeast (cake type)
2 test tubes

Procedure

1. Work with a partner. Fill two test tubes ¼ full of water. Push a 1-cm cube of yeast into each tube.
2. Add 5 mL of pancake syrup to one of the test tubes. Do not add syrup to the other test tube. Put your finger over the mouth of the test tube and mix the contents by shaking the tube slightly.
3. Obtain two dropper/rubber stopper assemblies from your teacher. Then push a stopper into the mouth of each test tube as shown in FIGURE 1. NOTE: Make sure the bottom end of the dropper is *not* below the level of the liquid in the tube. If it is below that level, pour some of the liquid out. This is very important.
4. Fill a large beaker nearly full with warm, but not hot, water. Submerge both tubes in the beaker. NOTE: The tops of the stoppers in each of the tubes must be just below the surface of the water in the beaker. If the tube floats, add a plug of clay to the outside.
5. Wait 4 min, then begin to count the number of bubbles that come from the top of each tube. You can watch one tube while your partner watches the other.
6. Count the number of bubbles rising from the tubes for 2 min. Record this number in Table 1. Continue to count and record the number of bubbles that rise during each of ten 2-min intervals.

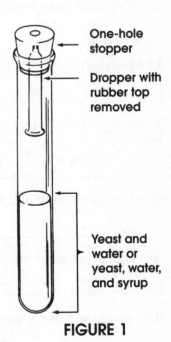

One-hole
stopper

Dropper with
rubber top
removed

Yeast and
water or
yeast, water,
and syrup

FIGURE 1

Data and Observations

1. Record your observations in Table 1.

Table 1

	Tube	
	Water and yeast	**Water, yeast, and syrup**
First 2 minutes		
Second 2 minutes		
Third 2 minutes		
Fourth 2 minutes		
Fifth 2 minutes		
Sixth 2 minutes		
Seventh 2 minutes		
Eighth 2 minutes		
Ninth 2 minutes		
Tenth 2 minutes		

Questions and Conclusions

1. In which tube were more bubbles of carbon dioxide given off?

_____

2. In which tube was little or no carbon dioxide gas given off?

_____

3. What does the tube that makes the most carbon dioxide have in it that the other tube does not have?

_____

What do yeast do with this substance?

_____

4. Does the experiment tell you what specific type of food is best for yeast? _____

Explain. _____

5. Why were the tubes placed in warm water?

_____

6. Design an experiment that tests how different temperatures of water in the beaker change the speed of carbon dioxide production by yeast cells.

_____

_____

_____

_____

_____

7. Which tube is the control?

_____

8. Does the activity prove that the gas being given off by yeast is carbon dioxide? Explain.

_____

_____

9. Does the activity prove that it is actually the yeast and not the syrup that is giving off carbon dioxide? Explain.

_____

Strategy Check

_____ Did you build an apparatus to show that yeast produce carbon dioxide?

_____ Do you know that gas bubbles given off means that food is being used by yeast?

_____ Do you know that the more gas given off, the more food the yeast is using?

_____ From your results, can you determine if food is needed by yeast?

• Root Structure and Functions 44

Roots hold a plant in the ground. They also absorb, store, and transport water and minerals. They have small threadlike side roots with root hairs that absorb water and minerals from the soil.

Strategy

You will examine a dissected carrot root.
You will label a diagram of a root and list the function of each part.

Materials

carrot sliced crosswise
carrot sliced lengthwise
hand lens

Procedure

1. Your teacher will prepare a crosswise slice of a carrot for you.
2. Hold the slice up to the light. Compare what you see with FIGURE 1 under Data and Observations.
3. Examine the lengthwise slice of the carrot. Use the hand lens. Look at both the inner and outer parts.
4. The outside layer of the root is the epidermis. Lateral roots grow from the epidermal cells and root hairs grow from them. Label the epidermis, lateral roots, and root hairs if all of these structures are present.
5. Inside the epidermis, you will find several layers of large, loosely packed cells that store food. This is the cortex. Food stored in the cortex can be used by other cells of the plant. Label the cortex.
6. Inside the cortex are tubelike xylem cells that carry water and minerals in the plant. Label the xylem cells.
7. Other tubelike cells inside the xylem carry food in the plant. These cells are called phloem cells. Label the phloem cells.

Data and Observations

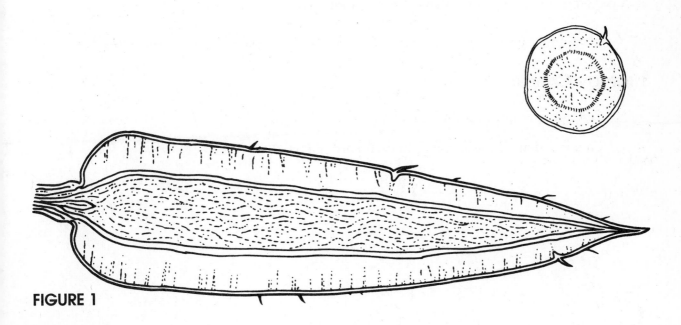

FIGURE 1

Questions and Conclusions

1. What type of root is the carrot?

_____

2. What is the function of the root hairs?

_____

3. How many different kinds of cells did you see in the carrot slice?

_____

4. What is the name and function of the outer ring of cells?

_____

5. What is the green part at the top end of the carrot?

_____

6. What is the name and function of the thicker layer of cells next to the epidermis?

_____

7. What cells are found in the inner core?

_____

8. What is the function of these cells?

_____

9. Why do you think taproots are used as food more often than fibrous roots?

_____

_____

10. List some other food plants that have a taproot.

_____

Strategy Check

_____ Can you examine a carrot root?

_____ Can you identify the locations of each part of a root?

Chapter 23

LABORATORY MANUAL

• Parts of a Fruit 45

Some of the plants that we call vegetables are actually fruits. Fruits are formed inside flowers that have been pollinated and fertilized. After fertilization takes place, the petals fall off and the ovary begins to develop into the fruit.

Strategy

You will study the structure of typical fleshy and dry fruits.
You will examine several fruits and classify the fruits as fleshy or dry.

Materials

acorn	bean in a pod	peanut	olive	sunflower seed
apple	corn	pear	pea in a pod	tomato
avocado	okra	plum	peach	

Procedure

1. Read the following paragraphs and study the diagrams.

The peach is a fleshy fruit. A fleshy fruit consists of a single ripened ovary with a soft fleshy ovary wall when ripe. Three kinds of fleshy fruits are the drupe, pome, and berry. The peach is a drupe. The exocarp is the covering of skin. The mesocarp is fleshy. The endocarp is hard and encloses the seed.

The apple is a pome. The stem is the stalk by which the flower was attached. At the other end are the remains of the sepals, petals, and a ring of dried stamens. The thin skin is the epidermis. The fleshy part inside the skin developed from the receptacle, or flower stalk. The papery core is the ovary wall. Within the ovary are the seeds.

The grape is a berry. The entire ovary is soft.

Dry fruits have an ovary wall that is dry and brittle when ripe. They are classified as dehiscent or indehiscent. A dehiscent fruit splits along a definite seam when ripe. The bean has a dehiscent fruit called a legume. It splits along two seams.

Fruits that do not split along a definite seam when ripe are indehiscent. Grains are indehiscent.

2. Examine each of the fruits listed in Table 1 and determine if they are fleshy or dry. Determine the type of fruit (drupe, pome, or berry and dehiscent). Record your answers in the table.

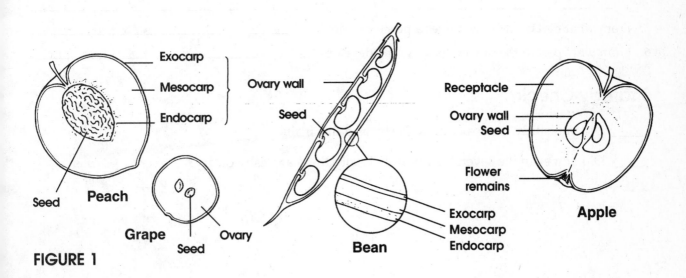

FIGURE 1

Data and Observations

Table 1

Fruit	Fleshy or Dry	Type
Plum		
Tomato		
Apple		
Peach		
Peanut		
Acorn		
Okra		
Olive		
Pear		
Pea		
Avocado		
Sunflower		
Corn		

Questions and Conclusions

1. What part of a flower becomes the fruit? _____

2. What part of a flower becomes the seed? _____

3. What are some fruits that we call vegetables? _____

4. What are some seeds that people eat? _____

_____

5. From what part of the flower does a peach develop? _____

6. From what part of the flower does a grape develop? _____

Strategy Check

_____ Did you study the structure of fleshy and dry fruits?

_____ Did you examine several fruits and classify them as fleshy or dry?

Chapter 24

LABORATORY MANUAL

• Earthworm Anatomy 46

The earthworm is an invertebrate that has a segmented body and specialized body parts. Oxygen from the air moves into its body through its moist skin. Carbon dioxide moves out of its body through the skin. The earthworm has a series of enlarged tubes that act as hearts. The tubes pump blood through the blood vessels of an earthworm's body. The segmented body plan makes an earthworm's anatomy easy to study.

Strategy
You will observe the external parts of an earthworm.
You will dissect an earthworm.
You will identify the internal organs and organ systems of an earthworm.

Materials
dissecting needle
dissecting pan
dissecting pins
earthworm (preserved) **CAUTION:** *Wash hands thoroughly after handling worm.*
hand lens
dissecting scissors

Procedure

Part A External Structure
1. Place a preserved earthworm lengthwise on a paper towel in the dissecting pan with the darker side up. This is the dorsal or top side.
2. Examine the external structure and identify the parts shown in FIGURE 1.
3. Run your fingers lightly along the top, bottom, and sides of the earthworm. The bristles that you feel are setae. Examine the setae with a hand lens. Estimate the number of setae on each segment.
4. Locate the mouth. The part that hangs over the mouth is called the prostonium.
5. Find the thickened band circling the body. This is the clitellum. It forms a cocoon for depositing the eggs during reproduction.
6. Locate the anus (see FIGURE 1).

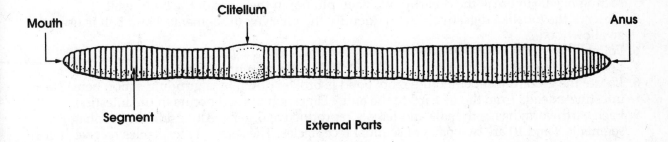

Mouth   Clitellum   Anus

Segment   External Parts

FIGURE 1

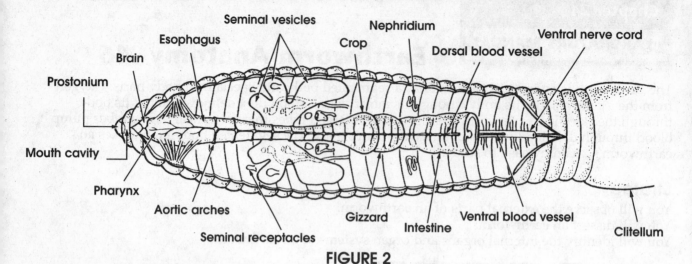

FIGURE 2

Part B Internal Structure

Read the instructions carefully and study FIGURES 1 and 2 before you begin to cut. Identify structures to be cut before you begin. **CAUTION:** *Always be careful with all sharp objects.*

1. With the dorsal side up, pin both ends of the worm to the wax in the dissecting pan.
2. With scissors, begin about 2 cm in front of the clitellum and cut forward through the body wall just to the left of the dorsal blood vessel. Use care to cut through only the body wall (see FIGURE 3).
3. Separate the edges of the cut. Observe the space between the body wall and the intestine. This is the body cavity or coelom.

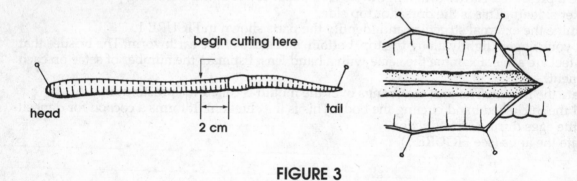

FIGURE 3

4. Observe the partitions between the segments from the body wall to the intestines. Use a dissecting needle to break these partitions. Then pin down the sides of the body wall.
5. Observe the tubelike digestive system. Identify the pharynx in segments 4 and 5. It is used to swallow food.
6. Follow the esophagus to segment 15.
7. Locate the large thin-walled crop. Food is stored in the crop until it is digested.
8. Locate the gizzard just behind the crop. Food is broken down by a grinding action here. The intestine extends from the gizzard to the anus. Digestion of food occurs in the intestine.
9. Each earthworm has both male and female reproductive organs. Alongside the esophagus in segments 9 and 10 are two pairs of seminal receptacles. The seminal receptacles receive sperm from another worm. In front of the receptacles in segments 10, 11, and 12 are seminal vesicles where sperm is stored.
10. Use a hand lens to find the small ovaries where eggs are produced. They are located under the seminal vesicles.

11. Locate the dorsal blood vessel. It carries blood forward to the heart. Carefully remove the white seminal vesicles from the left side of the body. Find the aortic arches, which branch from the dorsal blood vessel and pass around the esophagus. They join the ventral blood vessel below the esophagus. These aortic arches contract and function as hearts. The ventral blood vessel carries blood toward the skin and intestine.
12. Use a hand lens to observe the small white tubes along each side of the digestive tract. These tubes are excretory organs called nephridia. They are found in all segments except the first three and the last. They remove the waste from the body cavity.
13. Find the double nerve ganglion, or brain, of the earthworm near segment 2. The brain connects with the ventral nerve cord, which extends the length of the body. The nerve cord is a white line on the ventral body wall.
14. **CAUTION:** Give all dissected materials to your teacher for disposal. *Always wash your hands after a dissection procedure.*

Data and Observations

1. Record the organs found in each system in Table 1.

Table 1

Systems and Organs of an Earthworm	
System	**Organs**
Digestive	
Reproductive	
Circulatory	
Excretory	
Nervous	

Questions and Conclusions

1. How many setae were located on each segment?_____

2. What is the function of the setae? _____

3. Describe the function of the following organs.

a. pharynx _____

b. crop _____

c. gizzard _____

d. aortic arches _____

e. dorsal blood vessel _____

f. ventral blood vessel _____

g. clitellum _____

h. nephridia _____

i. seminal vesicles _____

j. intestine _____

k. ganglia _____

4. Why is it said that the earthworm has a "closed" circulatory system?

_____

Strategy Check

_____ Can you dissect an earthworm?

_____ Can you identify the external and internal parts of the earthworm?

Chapter 24

LABORATORY MANUAL **• Grasshopper Anatomy 47**

A grasshopper is well adapted to its way of life. Its features are representative of the insect group.
A grasshopper is large enough that its features can be seen easily.

Strategy
You will observe and identify the specialized body parts of the grasshopper.
You will examine and identify the internal structure of the grasshopper.

Materials

dissecting needle   grasshopper (preserved)   scissors
dissecting pan   hand lens
forceps

Procedure

Part A—External Structure

1. Place the grasshopper in the dissecting pan.
   Locate the head, thorax, and abdomen. (See
   FIGURE 1.) Use your hand lens to observe the
   grasshopper carefully. As you observe, record
   your data in Data and Observations.
2. Observe the parts of the head. The grasshopper
   has two compound eyes and three simple eyes.
   The sensory parts located on the head are the
   antennae.
3. Identify the mouth parts. (Refer to FIGURE 2.)
   With your forceps remove the parts. The labrum
   is the hinged upper lip that is used to hold
   food. The mandibles are crushing jaws. The
   maxillae are used to chew and taste food. The
   labium is the broad fat lower lip used to hold
   food while it is being chewed.
4. Locate the eardrums or tympana, small drum-
   shaped structures on either side of the thorax.
5. All insects have six legs. In the grasshopper, the
   front pair is used for walking, climbing, and
   holding food. The middle legs are used for
   walking and climbing. The hind legs are large
   and enable the grasshopper to jump.
6. Locate the two pairs of wings.
7. Use the hand lens to look at the tiny openings
   along the abdomen. These are breathing pores
   called spiracles through which oxygen enters
   and carbon dioxide leaves.

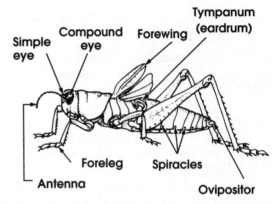

FIGURE 1

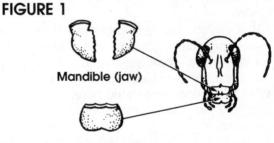

Mandible (jaw)

Labrum (upper lip)

Labium (lower lip)   Maxillae

FIGURE 2

8. A female grasshopper has a much longer abdomen than a male. It ends in a four-pointed tip called an ovipositor through which eggs are laid.

Part B—Internal Structure

1. Remove the three left legs. Insert the point of your scissors under the top surface of the last segment of the abdomen. Make a cut to the left of the mid-dorsal line. Be careful not to cut the organs underneath. In front of the thorax, cut down the left side to the bottom of the grasshopper. Cut down between the next to the last and last abdominal segments. (See FIGURE 3.)

   CAUTION: *Always be careful when using scissors.*

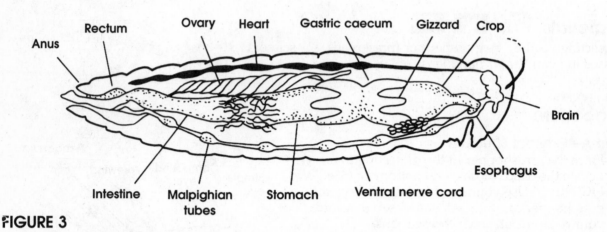

FIGURE 3

2. Use your forceps to pull down the left side. Locate the large dorsal blood vessel.
3. Use your scissors to cut the muscles close to the exoskeleton. Locate the finely-branched trachea leading to the spiracles.
4. Cut through the exoskeleton over the top of the head between the left antenna and left eye to the mouth. Remove the exoskeleton on the left side of the head. Find the dorsal ganglion or brain.
5. Cut away the tissue to show the digestive system. Refer to FIGURE 3 and identify the mouth, esophagus, crop, gizzard, and stomach. Note that the gizzard and stomach are separated by a narrow place. The digestive glands that secrete enzymes into the stomach are attached here.
6. Another narrow place separates the stomach from the intestine. Tubules that collect wastes from the blood are located here.
7. Observe the colon, which enlarges to form the rectum. Wastes collect here before passing out the anus.
8. In the female, the ovary is located above the intestines. In the male, a series of whitish tubes, the testes, are located above the intestine.

Data and Observations

1. What are the three sections of a grasshopper's body? _____

   _____

2. Record your observations of grasshopper body parts in Table 1. Complete the table by listing the function of each part.

Table 1   **Structure of the Grasshopper**

Body part	How many?	Function
Eyes		
Antennae		
Labrum		
Mandibles		
Maxillae		
Labium		
Eardrums		
Legs		
Wings		
Spiracles		
Ovipositor (if female)		
Digestive glands		
Tubules		
Rectum		

Questions and Conclusions

1. How is a grasshopper's mouth adapted for plant eating? _____
   _____

2. What is the difference between a grasshopper's skeleton and yours? _____
   _____

3. How is a grasshopper's digestive system different from yours? _____
   _____

4. How do a grasshopper's legs help it to survive? _____
   _____

5. To which phylum does the grasshopper belong? _____

6. List three characteristics common to all animals in the phylum. _____

_____

7. To which class does the grasshopper belong? _____

8. List three characteristics of this class. _____

_____

Strategy Check

_____ Did you observe specialized parts of the grasshopper?

_____ Can you identify the internal and external parts of the grasshopper?

Chapter 25

LABORATORY MANUAL • **Whale Insulation 48**

Mammals are endotherms that have adaptations, such as hair, that conserve and maintain body temperature. Whales are mammals that are nearly hairless, yet they live in cold seawater. How do whales maintain body temperature? Whales have a layer of fat called blubber beneath their skin. Blubber helps insulate the whale so it can survive in cold water.

Strategy

You will measure and compare the rate of cooling of insulated and uninsulated test tubes.
You will relate the results to the effectiveness of blubber as a means to maintain body temperature in whales.

Materials   Use gloves when working with ice or heated materials to protect your hands.

test tubes (3)
solid food shortening
plastic sandwich bags
plastic spoons
beakers (600-mL)
ice water
heat source
thermometers
rubber bands
watch with a second hand
apron
goggles
gloves

Procedure

CAUTION: *Do not taste, eat, or drink any materials used in the lab.*

1. Place a beaker on a hot plate, filled with approximately 400 mL of water. **CAUTION:** *Do not touch hot plate.* Heat the water to 80°C. **CAUTION:** *Use care when handling hot liquids.*

2. Place one test tube into a plastic bag. Seal the top of the bag around the test tube using a rubber band.

3. Place a spoonful of shortening into a second plastic bag. Place a second test tube into this plastic bag. Spread the shortening over the test tube by moving it with your fingers on the outside of the plastic bag. Seal the top of the plastic bag with a rubber band.

4. Place several spoonfuls of shortening into a third plastic bag. Place a third test tube into this plastic bag. Spread this thick layer of shortening around the test tube and secure the top of the plastic bag.

5. Fill three beakers with ice water.

6. Fill all three test tubes three-quarters full with the heated water and take the temperature of each. Record this temperature in Table 1 under Data and Observations.

7. Place one test tube into each of the three beakers filled with ice water.

8. Measure and record the temperatures of each test tube every 5 minutes for 30 minutes.

9. Graph your results using a line graph with the temperature on the *y*-axis and time on the *x*-axis. Use a different color for each test tube.

Data and Observations
Table 1

Temperature (in °C)	Test tube in plastic bag alone	Test tube in plastic bag and thin layer of shortening	Test tube in plastic bag and heavy layer of shortening
0			
5			
10			
15			
20			
25			
30			

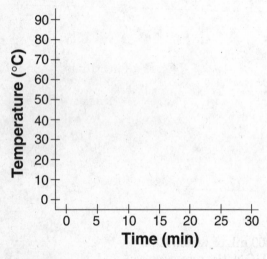

FIGURE 1

Questions and Conclusions

1. How did the temperature change in each of the test tubes? _____

_____

2. How did the rate of cooling of the uninsulated test tube compare to the others? Explain.

_____

_____

3. Infer whether blubber is a good insulator for mammals that swim in cold water.

_____

Strategy Check

_____ Can you measure and compare the rate of cooling of insulated and uninsulated test tubes?

_____ Can you relate your results to the effectiveness of blubber as a means to maintain body temperature in whales?

Chapter 25

LABORATORY MANUAL • **Owl Pellets 49**

The barn owl usually feeds on small mammals such as rodents, moles, and shrews. These mammals are swallowed whole. Some parts of the mammals dissolve in the owl's stomach. The indigestible parts, such as bones, hair, and feathers, are regurgitated in an owl pellet. You can find out what an owl eats by examining the owl pellet in this laboratory.

Strategy
You will dissect an owl pellet and identify animal skulls found in the owl pellet.
You will construct a chart of the numbers and kinds of prey eaten by owls.

Materials
owl pellet
white sheet of paper
forceps
dissecting needle
plastic gloves

Procedure
1. Use the forceps to place the owl pellet on the white paper.
2. Break the owl pellet apart. Carefully separate the bones of the animals from the feathers and fur.
3. Use the forceps and dissecting needle to clean skull bones. **CAUTION**: *Use sharp objects with care.*
4. Identify the skulls of the animals that the owl has eaten, using the drawings on this page. You will also need to use a Field Guide to Small Mammals. Record the number of skulls of different animals in Table 1.
5. Make a class record of the kinds and numbers of animals found in the owl pellets.

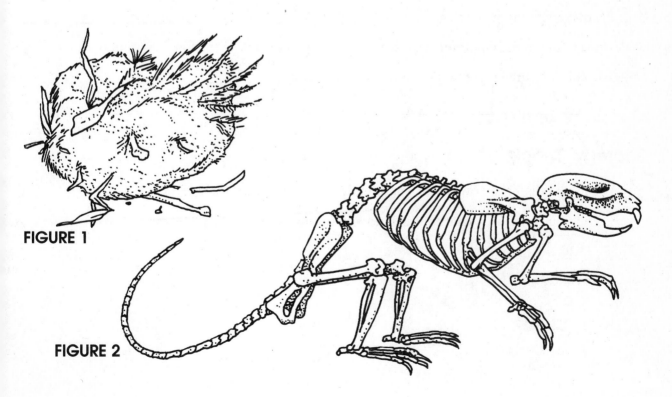

FIGURE 1

FIGURE 2

Data and Observations

Table 1

Animal	Number—individual	Number—class
Shrew		
Mole sparrow		
Vole		
Deer mouse		
Rat		
Other		
Total		

Questions and Conclusions

1. What was the outside covering of the owl pellet? _____

_____

2. An owl regurgitates one pellet a day. How many animals did your owl eat in one day?

_____

3. What animals did you find in the owl pellet? _____

_____

4. What is the owl's role in the environment? _____

5. Is the owl an herbivore or a carnivore? _____

6. Poisons found in the environment often accumulate in the bodies of small mammals. How

would this affect the owl that preys on these animals? _____

_____

Strategy Check

_____ Did you dissect an owl pellet and identify animal skulls?

_____ Did you construct a chart of the kind and numbers of prey eaten by owls?

Chapter 26

LABORATORY MANUAL

• Human Impact on the Environment 50

Human beings are agents of change, and the rate at which they are changing the environment increases rapidly as population increases. Only recently have people become aware of their impact on the atmosphere, water, and the crust of Earth.

Strategy
You will make a survey of your neighborhood or town to observe people's impact on the environment.

You will use the accompanying matrix to estimate the ways in which humans have affected your local environment.

You will suggest some ways people can change their impact on the environment.

Materials
clipboard
environmental impact check sheet, Table 1
pencil

Procedure
1. Look over the check sheet on the next two pages. A, B, C, and D are general categories for the way people change the environment. Across the top are the various areas of the environment that may be affected by the processes and materials that people use.

2. Walk through your neighborhood (in the city, at least a 10-block square) taking the sheet with you.

3. Place a check after each type of environmental influence found in your neighborhood. For example, if new houses are being built, put a check after "houses" in category A.

4. In the boxes to the right, put a diagonal slash under the area(s) affected by this influence. If the effect is good, put a plus in the lower right part of the box. If you think the effect is bad, place a minus in this position.

5. In the upper left of the box, place a number from 1 to 10 to indicate how much impact you think the change has or will have. If you think the change is small, write in 1; if you think it is or will be very large, write in 10. Use your judgment and observations to assign numbers 2 through 9 on this impact scale.

6. Find your total for each influence and for each affected area. Record your totals in the chart.

7. Find the class total for each influence and for each affected area. Record those totals in the chart.

Data and Observations

Table 1—Environmental Impact Check Sheet

	Biological	Scenic	Recreation	Temperature	Air	Water	Eutrophi-cation	Other	Totals
A. Construction—									
(Example) ✔		2 / +				3 / –	1 / –		2 / –
Houses									
Roads									
Transmission lines									
Fences or other barriers									
Canals									
Dams									
Shore structures									
Cut and fill									
Tunnels									
Mines									
Industrial plants									
Landscaped lawns									
B. Traffic—									
On roads									
Pipelines									
C. Chemicals—									
Fertilization									
Weed and insect control									
Deicing highways									

	Biological	Scenic	Recreation	Temperature	Air	Water	Eutrophi-cation	Other	Totals
D. Waste disposal—									
Litter and dumps									
Sewage									
Stack and exhaust emissions									
Cooling water discharge									
Used-lubricant dumping				.					
Totals									
Class Totals									

Questions and Conclusions

1. List three ways in which the construction of concrete pavement (roads) changes the environment.

   _____

   _____

2. How does an automobile affect the atmosphere? _____

   _____

3. What other ways could people use to travel that would have less adverse effects on the

   environment? _____

   _____

   _____

4. If there is smog in your local area, what is its source? _____

   _____

5. What can be done to reduce or eliminate the smog? _____

   _____

   _____

6. What resources are being used in local construction? _____

   _____

   _____

7. What resources are lost to humans when cities move into the surrounding countryside? _____

_____

_____

_____

8. Are there alternatives? _____

_____

_____

9. Discuss the drawbacks of the alternatives you have listed in the questions above. _____

_____

_____

_____

_____

_____

_____

Strategy Check

_____ Can you recognize human influence on your local environment?

_____ Can you estimate the impact, good or bad, using the matrix?

_____ Can you suggest and evaluate alternatives?

Chapter 26

LABORATORY MANUAL

• Reclamation of Mine Wastes 51

Mine wastes, which seem to be worthless, can be made profitable. For example, copper metal can be reclaimed from copper mine waste. When open pit copper is crushed and smelted, copper(II) sulfate is left in the waste rock. The copper(II) sulfate can be dissolved in water. Then more metallic copper can be removed by reacting the copper(II) sulfate with iron ores.

Strategy

You will investigate a process by which copper is reclaimed from open pit waste.

Materials

apron	copper(II) sulfate crystals, $CuSO_4$	litmus paper (blue)	apron
balance	goggles	nails (iron scraps)	gloves
beaker (500-mL)	graduated cylinder (50-mL)	water	

Procedure

1. Place 3 g of copper(II) sulfate in the beaker. **CAUTION:** *Copper(II) sulfate is poisonous. Avoid contact with skin.*

2. Cover the copper(II) sulfate crystals with 50 mL of water. Record the color of the solution in Table 1. Test with litmus; record your results in Table 1.

3. Place the iron scrap in the solution. Observe and record what happens in Table 1.

4. Test the solution with blue litmus paper and record your results in Table 1.

Data and Observations

Table 1

Solution	Color	Litmus	Other observations
Copper(II) sulfate			
Copper(II) sulfate and iron			

Questions and Conclusions

1. Why did you add water to the copper(II) sulfate crystals? _____

_____

2. What happens to the copper in the solution when iron is added? _____

_____

3. Is this a chemical or physical method of reclaiming the copper? _____

_____

4. What happened to the water in which the copper(II) sulfate is dissolved? _____

_____

5. Does this method use up all the waste material? _____

6. What might happen to a stream if large amounts of the water used in this reclaiming process were flushed into it? _____

_____

_____

7. What might happen to an abandoned copper mine in a humid climate? _____

_____

_____

Strategy Check

_____ Can you recognize the copper deposit on the iron?

_____ Could copper be reclaimed from waste using this method?

_____ Would reclaiming the copper be profitable?

Chapter 27

LABORATORY MANUAL ● **Smoke Pollution 52**

In 1967, the former U.S. Bureau of Mines adopted the Ringelmann Chart as a basic scale for measuring smoke pollution. Using an adapted version of the Ringelmann Chart, you can recognize smokestacks that may be polluting your environment.

Strategy

You will observe an industry that is sending out smoke.
You will keep track of this industry for a week to see how often you observe it emitting smoke.

Materials

cardboard (thin)   Ringelmann Chart
compass   (adapted), FIGURE 1
glue or paste   scissors

Procedure

1. Cut out FIGURE 1 and glue it to the cardboard. **CAUTION:** *Use care when handling sharp objects.*

2. When the glue is dry, cut out the center window by cutting along the dotted lines.

3. Go outside and observe a source of industrial smoke.

4. View the smoke through the window while holding the chart at arm's length.

5. Match the color of the darkest part of the smoke plume to one of the examples on the chart.

6. Continue observing the smoke plume for about 5 min. Record the wind direction, wind speed, time of day, and the number of the matching smoke column in Table 1.

7. Repeat these observations every day for a week. Make your readings the same time each day.

Data and Observations

Table 1

Day	Wind direction (north, south, southeast)	Wind speed (light, strong, gusty)	Time of day	Darkness of smoke (from chart)
1				
2				
3				
4				
5				

Questions and Conclusions

1. If accidental air pollution occurred, what kinds of readings would you expect? _____

_____

2. What does Number 5 on the Ringelmann Chart indicate about the relative amount of pollution

entering the atmosphere? _____

_____

3. What effect does wind have on air pollution in your local area? _____

_____

_____

_____

4. What processes are involved in the industry that is emitting smoke? _____

_____

_____

5. How might the smoke pollution be reduced? _____

_____

6. Some industries emit invisible gases. Might these gases also be pollutants? Explain. _____

_____

_____

_____

Strategy Check

_____ Can you determine an average Ringelmann Number for smoke emission you observed?

_____ Can you see how wind influences smoke?

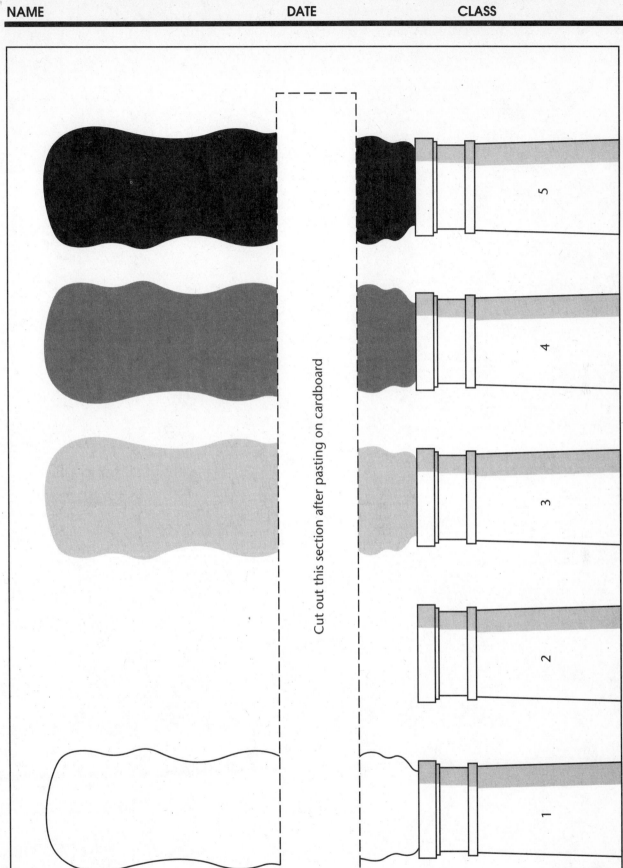

Cut out this section after pasting on cardboard

FIGURE 1

Chapter 27

LABORATORY MANUAL

• Water Purification 53

Pure water is essential to all life forms. But what about a situation in which you do not have pure water available? Life rafts on boats are equipped with an apparatus that can be used to distill water from salt water. Desert safety survival rules provide another means to distill water.

Strategy

You will purify water by using a simple distillation process.
You will discuss how this process could be used in an emergency situation.

Materials

cereal bowl
2 coat hangers, or bendable wire
pan (larger than the circumference of the bag)
pen (felt-tip)

plastic bag (clear)
sand (fine) or soil
sunlamp or bright sunshine
water

Procedure

1. Bend the coat hangers into a frame (see FIGURE 1).

2. Mix the sand or soil into water in the cereal bowl. Mark the water level on the inside with the pen.

3. Place the cereal bowl in the pan and place the wire frame over it.

4. Pull the plastic bag over the frame until it touches the pan. Record the appearance of the water.

5. Set the apparatus in direct sun or under a sunlamp.

6. Allow the apparatus to stand undisturbed. Observe and record your observations after about 10 min and again after 30 min in Table 1.

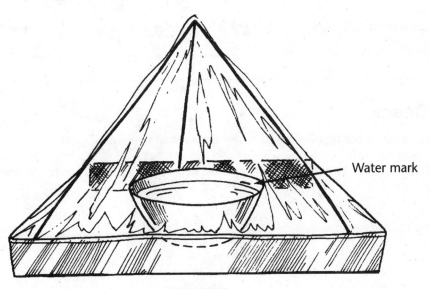

Water mark

FIGURE 1

Data and Observations

Table 1

Time (min)	Observations
0	Water color _____ Inside of plastic bag _____
10	Water level _____ Inside of plastic bag _____
30	Water level _____ Inside of plastic bag _____

Questions and Conclusions

1. What happened to the water level in the cereal bowl? _____

2. Why did water form on the inside of the plastic bag? _____
_____

3. What two processes are involved in this activity? _____
Identify the energy source. _____

4. How could you prove that the water that forms on the inside of the plastic bag is pure? _____
_____
_____

5. What equipment should you carry in a vehicle in order to have pure water if you are going to
cross a desert? _____
_____

Strategy Check

_____ Can you observe the distillation of water by natural processes?

_____ Can you understand how this process could be used in an emergency situation?

Chapter 1

• Solving a Problem with a Scientific Method 1

A method by which a scientist solves a problem is called a scientific method. This method usually includes observation, experimentation, interpretation, and hypothesis formation. Scientific methods are often compared to the procedures a detective uses in solving a crime or problem. The following investigation creates a scientific problem for you and asks you to solve it. You will use scientific methods in attempting to solve the problem.

Strategy

You will use a scientific approach to solve whether or not flasks A and B contain similar or different liquids.

You will make careful observations.

You will record accurate experimental results.

You will use your data as a basis for deciding if the two liquids are similar or different.

Materials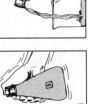

2 Erlenmeyer flasks containing liquids	2 stoppers (to fit flasks)	gloves
clock or watch with second hand	beaker	apron
		goggles

Part A Observation

CAUTION: *Use care when handling sharp objects.*
CAUTION: *Do not taste, eat, or drink any materials used in the lab.*
CAUTION: *Inform your teacher if you come in contact with any chemicals.*

Procedure

1. Examine the two flasks. DO NOT remove the stoppers and DO NOT shake the contents.

2. Notice the flasks have been labeled A and B.

3. Record in Table 1 two or three similarities or differences between the two flasks.

a. Do you think both flasks contain the same liquid? Explain. _____ **Answers will vary. Students are making a hypothesis that they will test.**

b. Is your answer to question a based on experimentation or guessing? _____
At this stage students have guessed.

c. Would scientists guess at answers to questions or would they experiment first? _____
Scientists would experiment.

d. Do both flasks contain exactly the same amount of liquid? _____
Flask B contains more.

Data and Observations

Table 1

Similarities	Differences
Both are liquids.	more liquid in B
Colorless	more space in A
Clear	
White film on bottom	

Part B Experimentation

Experiment 1—What happens if you shake the liquids?

Procedure

1. Give each flask one hard shake using an *up-and-down motion of your hand.* Make sure your thumb covers the stopper as you shake. Use FIGURE 1 as a guide.

2. Observe each flask carefully.

3. Record your observations in Table 2. Again, look for similarities and differences.

a. After shaking the flasks, do you think they contain different liquids? _____
Most students will suggest that the liquids are different.

b. What was present in flask A that may have been responsible for the change in the liquid? _____
Students will likely suggest that the upper half of flask A contains a gas.

Data and Observations

Table 2—Experiment 1

Similarities	Differences
Both are liquids.	A turns blue when shaken.
	B does not change.
	Volumes are different.

Experiment 2—What happens if you remove some of the liquid in flask B so it appears like flask A?

Procedure

1. Remove the stopper from flask B and pour out half of the contents into a beaker or other suitable container (see FIGURE 1). Make sure that the amount of liquid in flask B is equal to the amount of liquid in flask A.

2. Replace the stopper. Give both flasks *one hard shake using an up-and-down motion of your hand.* Hold stopper in place while shaking.

3. Observe each flask carefully.

4. Record any similarities or differences observed in Table 3.
a.ᐧ Do both flasks now appear to contain the same liquid? _____
Most students will suggest that the liquids are the same.

b. What may have been added to flask B that was not present before? _____
Flask B now has space that could contain a gas.

Data and Observations

Table 3—Experiment 2

Similarities	Differences
Both are liquids.	Intensity and duration of the blue
Volumes are the same.	color may vary.
Blue color appears after shaking.	

FIGURE 1

Experiment 3—What happens if you shake the flasks more than once?

Procedure

1. *Shake each flask hard once with an up-and-down motion.*
2. *Note the exact time in seconds after shaking that it takes for each liquid to return to its original condition. Record the time in Table 4.*
3. *Shake each flask hard twice with an up-and-down motion.*
4. *Again record in Table 4 the time it takes for the liquids to return to their original conditions.*
5. *Shake both flasks hard three times with an up-and-down motion.*
6. Record in Table 4 the time it takes for them to return to their original conditions.
   a. After one shake, are the two liquids generally "behaving" in a similar way? That is, is the time needed for flasks A and B to return to their original conditions about the same? **Students should observe similar times although some variation is likely.**
   b. After two and three shakes, are flasks A and B generally "behaving" in a way similar to each other? **Students should observe similar times although some variation is likely.**
7. Look at your data in Table 4.
   a. Does flask A show an increase or decrease in time needed to return to its original condition as the number of shakes increases from one to three? **Students should observe an increase in time that corresponds to an increase in number of shakes.**
   b. Does flask B show a similar change? **A similar change will likely be observed in flask B.**
8. Run two more trials for each part of Experiment 3. Be sure to keep track of the amount of time needed for the liquids to return to their original conditions.
9. Consider your recorded results in Table 4 as Trial 1. Record the results of Trials 1, 2, and 3 in Table 5.
10. Do three trials give better evidence than one trial in helping you to determine
    a. the contents of flasks A and B? **Comparing the averages of three tests will likely show more similarity between flasks A and B.**
    b. the effects of shaking on flasks A and B? **Comparing the averages of three tests will likely show similar effects on both flasks.**

Data and Observations

Table 4—Experiment 3 sample data

	Time to Return to Original Condition (s)		
	1 shake	2 shakes	3 shakes
Flask A	40	62	73
Flask B	43	57	80

Table 5—Experiment 3 sample data

	Time to Return to Original Condition (s)								
	1 shake			2 shakes			3 shakes		
Trial	1	2	3	1	2	3	1	2	3
Flask A	40	44	40	62	65	59	73	88	82
Flask B	43	50	39	57	64	58	80	91	84

Questions and Conclusions

Questions 1–4 should help you to make some interpretations of what you have observed. Interpretations are reasonings based on observations and experiments. They are usually the next step in a scientific method.

1. On the basis of your first observations in Part A, could you decide if both flasks contained the same liquid? **No**
2. After performing Experiment 1, could you decide if both flasks contained the same liquid? **No**
3. Which experiment or experiments may have helped you to decide that the liquids in flasks A and B were similar or different? **Experiment 3** Explain. **Averages for three tests should show close similarity.**
4. Besides the liquid itself, what else seems to be needed in order for the liquid to change color? **air or a component of air such as oxygen**

Questions 5–7 should help you to form a hypothesis. In a hypothesis, all facts are joined in an attempt to explain what has been observed.

5. Explain why flask B did not change color when shaken in Experiment 1. **There was no space for air in the flask.**
6. Why must the liquids in the half-filled flasks be shaken in order to produce a color change? **Air must mix with the liquid in order for a color change to occur.**
7. Did more shaking increase the amount of time needed for the liquids in flasks A and B to change back to their original color? Why or why not? **Each additional shake mixes more air into the liquid and the blue color stays longer.**
8. Why is experimenting a better method of problem solving than guessing? **Experimentation provides evidence and data with which a problem can be solved.**
9. What is meant by the phrase "solving a problem by using scientific methods"? **using observation, experimentation, interpretation, and hypothesis formation to solve a problem**

Strategy Check

___ Can you use a scientific approach to solve whether or not flasks A and B contain similar or different liquids?

___ Can you make careful observations?

___ Can you record accurate experimental results?

___ Can you use your data as a basis for deciding if the two liquids are similar or different?

Chapter 1

LABORATORY MANUAL • Using SI Units 2

How many inches equal 1 foot? How many feet equal 1 yard? Almost everybody can answer these questions. But how many yards equal 1 rod?

Is there any one number that is common for changing inches to feet, feet to yards, or yards to rods? A problem with the English system for measuring is that there is no common number for changing one unit to another. As a result, you may have had difficulty remembering that there are 5 ½ yards to a rod. Scientists use the SI system of measuring rather than the English system. SI is an abbreviation for the International System of Measurement. SI is a more modern version of the old metric system.

Strategy

You will identify and use SI units of length and volume to measure several objects.
You will learn two important rules for converting from one SI unit to another.

Materials

metric ruler   graduated cylinder (50-mL)   microscope slide

Procedure

Part A Measuring Length in SI Units

1. Examine a metric ruler. Starting at the left edge, locate the smallest division or mark. This unit is the millimeter (mm). Ten millimeters are equal to a unit called the centimeter (cm). The ruler will have a longer line and the number 1 marked at the 1 cm length. See FIGURE 1.
   a. How many millimeters equal 1 cm? __10__
   b. How many millimeters equal 3 cm? __30__
   c. What number is used in changing the number of millimeters to centimeters? __10__
   Ten centimeters are equal to 1 decimeter (dm). Ten decimeters are equal to 1 meter (m).
   d. What number is used when changing centimeters to decimeters? __10__
   e. What number is used when changing decimeters to meters? __10__

2. Measure a microscope slide in millimeters. Use FIGURE 2 as a guide to length, width, and height. Record these values in the column marked "mm" of Table 1.

3. To convert your millimeter numbers to centimeters, divide the millimeter numbers by 10. Record the length, width, and height of your slide in centimeters. Use the column marked "cm" of Table 1.

4. To convert your centimeter numbers to decimeters, divide the centimeter numbers by 10. Record the length, width, and height of your slide in decimeters. Use the column marked "dm" of Table 1.

5. To convert decimeters to meters, divide decimeters by 10. Record your slide measurements in meters on Table 1 in the column marked "m."

FIGURE 1

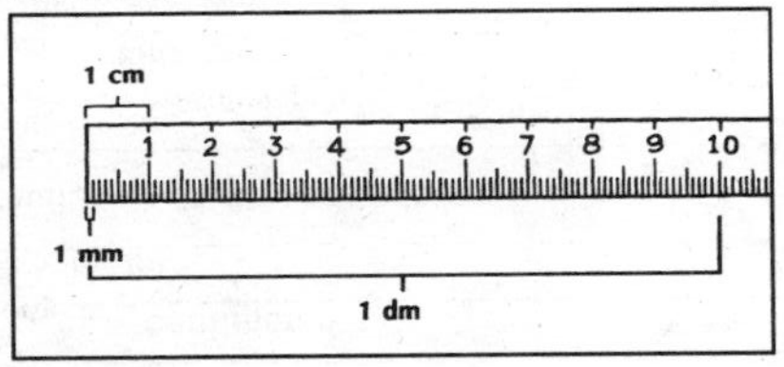

FIGURE 2

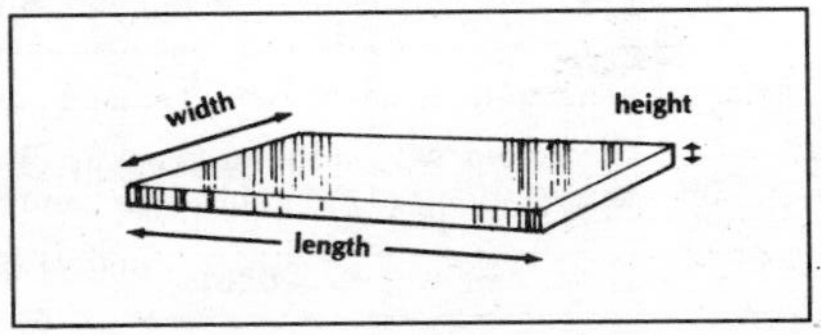

Table 1 Microscope Slide Measurements

	mm	cm	dm	m	km
Length	76	7.6	0.76	0.076	0.000 076
Width	25	2.5	0.25	0.025	0.000 025
Height	1	0.1	0.01	0.001	0.000 001

A unit, kilometers, often is used to measure long distances. One thousand meters (m) equal 1 kilometer (km).

6. To convert meters to kilometers, divide meters by 1000 (not by 10). Record your slide measurements in kilometers in the column marked "km" of Table 1.
   a. Can you divide millimeter figures by 100 to change directly to decimeters? __yes__
   b. Can you divide millimeter figures by 1000 to change directly to meters? __yes__
   c. What number do you divide by when changing centimeters to meters? __100__
   d. To change millimeters to centimeters, divide by __10__
   e. To change millimeters to decimeters, divide by __100__
   f. To change millimeters to meters, divide by __1000__
   g. To change millimeters to kilometers, divide by __1 000 000__
   h. To change centimeters to meters, divide by __100__
   i. To change centimeters to kilometers, divide by __100 000__

7. Measure the length and width of your lab table or desk.

8. Record these dimensions in meters in Table 2. Record your answers in decimals. If your desk or lab table measures 1 m plus 14 cm, record this measurement as 1.14 m. If it measures less than 1 m, such as 83 cm, record this measurement as 0.83 m. Because 1 m equals 100 cm, 83 cm is the same as 83/100 or 0.83 m.

9. Convert your meter measurement to decimeters by multiplying meter figures by 10. Record the decimeter values in the proper column of Table 2. Convert your decimeter values in Table 2 to centimeters by multiplying decimeter figures by 10. Record the centimeter values in the proper column of Table 2.

Table 2 Lab Table Measurements
Sample data

	m	dm	cm	mm
Length	4.5	45	450	4500
Width	2.78	27.80	278	2780

10. To convert your centimeter values to millimeters, multiply centimeter figures by 10. Record the millimeter values in the proper column of Table 2.
   a. According to Table 2, can you multiply meter figures by 100 to change directly to centimeters? __yes__
   b. Can you multiply meter figures by 1000 to change directly into millimeters? __yes__
   c. To change meters to decimeters, multiply by __10__
   d. To change meters to centimeters, multiply by __10__
   e. To change meters to millimeters multiply by __1000__

f. To change centimeters to millimeters, multiply by __10__
g. To change kilometers to meters, multiply by (Be careful.) __1000__

11. When converting from one SI unit to another, you must either multiply or divide. Is there any pattern that will always allow you to decide whether to divide or multiply? Yes, there is.

a. What operation is used in Table 1 to go from millimeters to centimeters? (Millimeters are small in size, centimeters are larger.) __dividing__

b. When changing from small SI units to large units, what mathematical operation (multiplying or dividing) is used? __dividing__

c. Which unit is smaller in size: decimeter or meter? __decimeter__

d. Which unit is smaller in size: centimeter or kilometer? __centimeter__

e. Which unit is smaller in size: meter or kilometer? __meter__

f. When changing from larger SI units to smaller units, what mathematical operation (multiplying or dividing) is used? __multiplying__

g. What operation is used in Table 2 to go from meters to centimeters? __multiplying__

h. Which unit is larger in size: kilometer or millimeter? __kilometer__

i. Which unit is larger in size: decimeter or millimeter? __decimeter__

j. Which unit is larger in size: centimeter or decimeter? __decimeter__

When changing from one unit to another, you must remember:

• If you are changing from a small unit to a larger unit, you must divide. What number to divide by is determined by what new units are being asked for. For example, if changing millimeters to centimeters, divide by 10; if changing millimeters to decimeters, divide by 100 again.

• If you are changing from a large unit to a smaller unit, you must multiply. What number to multiply by is determined by what new units are being asked for. For example, if changing kilometers to meters, multiply by 1000; changing meters to millimeters, multiply by 1000 again; changing kilometers to centimeters, multiply by 100 000.

12. The meter is the main unit for measuring length or distance in the SI system. All changes from one unit to another involve a change of 10, or some multiple of 10. Fill in the blanks.

a. 29 mm = __2.9__ cm
b. 4 dm = __0.4__ m
c. 44 dm = __440__ cm
d. 1205 cm = __120.5__ dm
e. 27 km = __27 000__ m
f. 103 dm = __10.3__ m
g. 0.29 dm = __29__ mm
h. 1202 mm = __120.2__ cm
i. 48 mm = __0.048__ m
j. 7.2 m = __720__ cm

Part B Measuring Volume in SI

1. Examine a graduated cylinder with volume markings of 50 units. Each single line represents a unit of volume called a milliliter (mL). DO NOT confuse this word with millimeter (mm).

2. Fill the cylinder with water to the 25-mL line and place the cylinder on your desk.

3. Compare the level of water in your cylinder with FIGURE 3. On close examination, the water rides up along the edges of the cylinder. The proper reading of volume is judged by the bottom level of water.

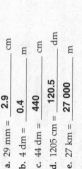

FIGURE 3

26 mL
25 mL
24 mL

---

4. Adjust the volume of water if necessary so that it is exactly 25 mL.

5. Convert your 25-mL volume to centiliter (cL) units. Use the same rule as established for length units. Are you changing from small to large units? If yes, then divide.

Table 3 Volume of Water in Cylinder

Volume	mL	cL	dL	L
	25	2.5	0.25	0.025

Volume	kL	L	dL	cL	mL
	0.032	32	320	3200	32 000

6. Fill in Table 3 for centiliters, deciliters (dL), and liters (L). There are 10 centiliters in a deciliter, and 10 deciliters in a liter.

7. Complete the chart on the right based on the numbers filled in for you. "kL" stands for kiloliter.

8. The liter is the main unit for measuring volume in the SI system. Fill in the blanks.

a. 1.4 L = __1400__ mL
b. 5520 mL = __552__ cL

Questions and Conclusions

1. What SI units studied can be used for measuring length? __millimeter, centimeter, decimeter, meter, kilometer__

2. What SI units studied can be used for measuring volume? __milliliter, centiliter, deciliter, liter, kiloliter__

3. Why is it easier to convert meters to centimeters or millimeters than to convert miles to feet or inches? __One number (10) is used for all SI conversions. No common number works for English system conversions.__

4. Give the symbol for each of the following units.

millimeter = __mm__   kiloliter = __kL__   centimeter = __cm__   liter = __L__

5. What units are represented by each of the following symbols?

dL = __deciliter__   km = __kilometer__   dm = __decimeter__   cL = __centiliter__

6. Circle the larger unit in each of the following pairs.

a. (kiloliter) or liter
b. centimeter or (meter)
c. (decimeter) or millimeter
d. (centimeter) or millimeter
e. millimeter or (kilometer)
f. centiliter or (deciliter)

7. Which mathematical process (multiplying or dividing) is used to change

a. centiliters to liters? __dividing__
b. centiliters to deciliters? __dividing__
c. meters to centimeters? __multiplying__
d. millimeters to meters? __dividing__

Strategy Check

_____ Can you identify and use SI units of length and volume to measure objects?

_____ Did you learn the rules for converting from one SI unit to another?

Chapter 2

LABORATORY MANUAL • **Mixtures and Compounds 3**

Matter is anything that has mass and occupies space. Matter exists in different forms. Three forms of matter are well known to us: elements, mixtures, and compounds. Elements are the basic materials of our world. Elements in a mixture have recognizable boundaries and can be separated by mechanical means. Elements that form a chemical compound can be separated only by a chemical process. Oxygen (O) is an element, which combined with hydrogen forms water, H_2O, a compound. Salt water is a mixture of two compounds, water and salt.

Colors in minerals depend largely on impurities. Organic matter gives a black color; iron, red or yellow; manganese, purple. A good reference book for minerals might be useful.

Strategy

You will separate a mixture into its parts.
You will compare the characteristics of a compound and a mixture.

Materials

granite	sand (coarse)	apron
granite (crushed)	water	goggles
heat source	magnifying glass	
	2 pie pans (disposable)	
	rock salt	

Procedure

1. Use the magnifying glass to observe the sand and granite. Sketch the shapes of the different minerals as found in the granite and the shapes of the sand grains under Sketch A.

2. Sort the crushed granite into separate piles according to color.

3. Sketch the general shape of a piece from each pile of the sorted granite and label it as to color under Sketch B.

4. Mix a spoonful of sand in some water in a pie pan. Sketch what you observed under Sketch C.

5. Examine and sketch the salt crystals under Sketch D. CAUTION: *Do not ingest rock salt. It may contain harmful impurities.*

6. Mix a spoonful of salt in some water in the second pie pan. Sketch what is left in each pan under Sketch E. CAUTION: *Be careful not to get clothes or hair close to the heat source.*

7. Heat both pans until the water is evaporated. Sketch what is left in each pan under Sketch E.

Data and Observations

Sketch A

Granite   Sand

Sketch B

Crushed Granite

— Black, shiny
— White
— Pink
— Black

Sketch C

Sand and Water

Clear   Green

Reddish

Sketch D

Salt Crystals

Salt cubes

Sketch E

Questions and Conclusions

1. Are any of the sand grains similar to any of the granite fragments? __yes__
   If so, describe them. __Most sands contain fragments of quartz, which are present in granite.__

2. How are salt and sand similar? __Both salt and sand contain crystals.__
   How are they different? __Salt will dissolve in water; sand will not.__

3. Is salt water a compound or mixture? __mixture__   Explain. __Salt can be removed by evaporating the water. Salt and water are both compounds but salt water is not composed of elements in a definite ratio.__

4. Is granite a compound or mixture? __mixture__   Explain. __Granite is composed of particles that can be recognized. The granite can be separated into simpler substances by mechanical means.__

5. Name some mechanical processes used to separate mixtures. __evaporation or cooling of solutions; magnetism; sorting by sizes using sieves; filtering of solutions; settling of solutions__

Strategy Check

__You may want to introduce students to distillation as a method of separating mixtures.__

— Can you separate components of a mixture?

— Can you tell the difference between a compound and a mixture?

NAME _____ DATE _____ CLASS _____

Chapter 2

LABORATORY MANUAL • **Constructing Compounds 4**

All elements are made of atoms. Compounds are formed when two or more elements combine to form a different type of matter. A chemical formula is a shortcut chemists take to describe a specific compound. It tells the numbers and types of atoms that make up a single unit of a compound. You probably already know the formula for one common compound—water is H_2O. The formula for water tells us that a molecule of water has two hydrogen atoms and one oxygen atom.

Strategy

You will build models of different compounds.
You will use your models to determine how many atoms of each element are in each molecule.

Materials

modeling clay (red, yellow, and blue)
toothpicks
apron
goggles

Procedure

1. Obtain enough clay to make four balls of each color. Each clay ball represents one atom of an element. Blue balls represent hydrogen atoms, red balls represent oxygen atoms, and yellow balls represent carbon atoms.

2. Using toothpicks to connect your clay atoms (FIGURE 1), construct a model of each of the following compounds. After you construct each model, fill in the blanks for that compound in Table 1 in the Data and Observations section. After you finish making the molecules in parts a and b below, take them apart. Then make the molecule in part c.

  a. H_2O—water (Connect two hydrogen atoms to one oxygen atom.)

  b. CO_2—carbon dioxide (Connect two oxygen atoms to one carbon atom.)

  c. CH_4—methane (Connect four hydrogen atoms to one carbon atom.)

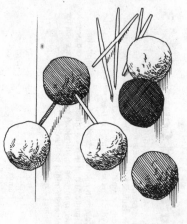

FIGURE 1

Data and Observations

Table 1

Chemical formula	Number of atoms in compound			
	Hydrogen	Carbon	Oxygen	Total
H_2O (water)	2	0	1	3
CO_2 (carbon dioxide)	0	1	2	3
CH_4 (methane)	4	1	0	5

Questions and Conclusions

1. What would the answers in Table 1 be for a molecule of fruit sugar, $C_6H_{12}O_6$?
   <u>hydrogen, 12; carbon, 6; oxygen, 6; total, 24</u>

2. From the formulas given, identify each of the following as either an element or a compound:
   NaCl, Ag, Co, CO, SO_2, AgBr. <u>Ag and Co are elements; the other formulas show more than one</u>
   <u>type of element present, so they are compounds.</u>

3. Each carbon atom can be attached to up to four other atoms. The compound hexane has six carbon atoms joined together in a chain. If only carbon and hydrogen make up the hexane molecule, what is the greatest number of hydrogen atoms that could be in the molecule? Draw a picture of the molecule to help you.
   <u>14—two on each of the four carbon atoms that are not on the ends of the chain and three on</u>
   <u>each of the end carbon atoms</u>

4. Nitrogen in air is in the form of two nitrogen atoms fastened together, N_2. Is nitrogen an element or is it a compound? Explain. <u>Even though there are two atoms present, only one type of atom is</u>
   <u>present, so nitrogen is an element.</u>

Strategy Check

___ Can you make a simple model of a compound based on its molecular formula?

___ Based on a compound's molecular formula, can you figure out how many atoms of each element are in a compound?

___ Do you understand the differences between an element and a compound?

Chapter 3

LABORATORY MANUAL

● Thermal Energy—Radiation 5

Have you ever walked barefoot on pavement on a sunny summer day? The pavement is hot because thermal energy from the sun is transferred to the pavement through radiation. Radiation is the movement of energy in the form of waves. Different materials absorb radiant energy from the sun differently. In today's experiment, you will compare how light-colored materials and dark-colored materials differ in their ability to absorb energy from the sun.

Strategy

You will observe how energy from the sun can increase the temperature of water.
You will determine how color influences the absorption of solar radiation.

Materials

construction paper (black)
construction paper (white)
containers (2 plastic, 500-mL)
graduated cylinder (100-mL)
pencils (colored)

scissors
tape
thermometer (alcohol, Celsius)
timer
water

Procedure

CAUTION: *Use care when handling sharp objects.*

1. Fasten black construction paper on the bottom and sides of one container.

2. Fasten white construction paper on the bottom and sides of the other container.

3. Add 250 mL of room-temperature water to each container.

4. Use a thermometer to find the temperature of the water in each container. Record this data in Table 1.

5. Place the containers side by side in direct sunlight outside or on a sunny windowsill. Be sure both containers receive the same amount of sunshine.

FIGURE 1

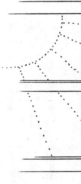
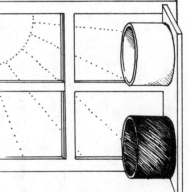

---

6. Measure the temperature of the water in each container at 5-minute intervals for 30 minutes. Record your data in Table 1.

7. Using FIGURE 2, graph the data from the table, using a line graph. Use one colored pencil to show data for the light container and a different one to show data for the dark container. Draw lines to connect the temperature data for each container of water.

Data and Observations

Table 1

Sample Data

Color of Container	Time (min)						
	0	5	10	15	20	25	30
Temp. (°C)—Light	22	23	23	24	26	26	27
Temp. (°C)—Dark	22	24	25	27	29	30	32

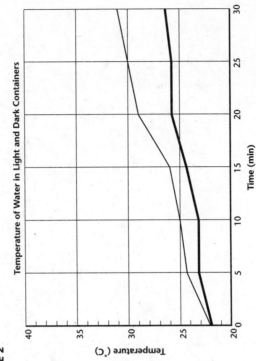

Temperature of Water in Light and Dark Containers

FIGURE 2

175

1. What was the final temperature of the water in the dark container? _____
   Answers will vary, but the temperature should be higher than that in the light container.

2. What was the final temperature of the water in the light container? _____
   Answers will vary, but the temperature should be lower than that in the dark container.

3. How many degrees did the temperature of the dark container increase? _____
   Student answers will vary based on the temperature of the environment and sunlight availability. The amount of increase should be greater than that of the water in the light container.

4. How many degrees did the temperature of the light container increase? _____
   Student answers will vary based on the temperature of the environment and sunlight availability. The amount of increase should be less than that of the water in the dark container.

Questions and Conclusions

1. Did one container of water heat up more quickly? Which one?
   Yes, the water in the dark container heated up more quickly.

2. How do you think color influences the ability of something to absorb energy from the sun?
   Dark colors are better able to absorb solar radiation.

3. Would you get the same results if you placed the containers in the shade? Why or why not?
   No; without sunlight, the dark container would not be able to absorb the solar radiation. Temperatures would stay about the same.

4. If you were stranded in a desert, would you rather be wearing a dark-colored or a light-colored T-shirt? Why?
   Answers will vary, but most students would rather wear a light-colored T-shirt if stranded in the desert because it would not absorb the sun's radiation as quickly as would a dark-colored T-shirt.

Strategy Check

_____ Did you observe the influence of solar radiation on water temperature?

_____ Did you determine how color influences the absorption of solar radiation?

Chapter 4

LABORATORY MANUAL • **States of Matter 6**

Three common states of matter are solid, liquid, and gas. A fourth state of matter, the plasma state, exists only at extremely high temperatures. Differences among the physical states depend on the distance between the atoms or molecules and on the rate of movement of the atoms or molecules. Pressure and temperature control these two factors.

Strategy

You will observe the characteristics of a solid.
You will change a gas to a liquid.
You will compare the characteristics of a solid, a liquid, and a gas.

Materials

beaker (1000-mL)
ice cubes (frozen from 500 mL of water)
ice cube tray
plastic drinking glass (cold or add an ice cube)
water

Procedure

1. Mark the level of the top of the ice cubes while they are still in the tray. Remove the ice cubes and place them in the beaker. Record the characteristics of ice in Table 1.

2. Let the ice cubes melt. Record the characteristics of the resulting water in Table 1.

3. Pour the water back into the tray. Mark the level of the top of the water on the tray. Under "Other characteristics" in Table 1, record whether this level is higher or lower than that of the ice.

4. Place the cold glass in a warm area. After a few minutes record your observations in Table 1.

5. Place an ice cube in the beaker of water. Observe whether or not it floats. Record your observations in Table 1.

Data and Observations

Table 1

Material	State of matter	Takes shape of container		Other characteristics	
		Yes	No	Floats	Yes	No
Ice cubes	Solid		X			X
Water	Liquid	X				
Glass	Observations: Beads of water appear on it.					
Beaker with ice	Observations: Floats				Higher/**Lower** in tray than ice	

Questions and Conclusions

1. What is solid water called? **ice** _____ Liquid water? **water** _____
   Water as a gas? **water vapor** _____

2. Did the ice cube sink or float in water? **float** _____ Explain. **The ice cube is less dense than the water.**

3. Which occupies more volume, an equal amount of water or ice? **ice**
   Explain. **When water freezes, it expands.**

4. Where did the water on the glass come from? **the air** **Water vapor cannot be seen in the air. Water vapor**
   What are the characteristics of water as a gas? **takes the shape of its container. Water vapor fills all available space in its container.**

5. What change caused the water vapor to change to a liquid? **The temperature of the air was lowered by the contact with the cold glass.**

6. If you changed the water to water vapor in a pressure cooker, what volume would the water vapor occupy? **the volume of the pressure cooker**

7. Compare the characteristics of water as a solid, a liquid, and a gas. **Water as a solid resists changes in both shape and volume. Water as a liquid resists changes in volume but not in shape. Water as a gas offers little resistance to changes in shape or volume.**

Strategy Check

___ Can you observe the characteristics of a solid?

___ Can you observe a gas change to a liquid?

___ Can you compare the characteristics of a solid, a liquid, and a gas?

Chapter 4

LABORATORY MANUAL ● Crystal Formation 7

Early in Earth's history, the crust was produced by the cooling of magma. When this molten rock flows into cracks, its temperature is about 1200°C. As the atoms of the different elements that make up the magma cool and slow down, they group themselves into a regular order to form a solid or crystal. This grouping is always the same for a given substance and is referred to as a mineral. When the magma cools to about 500°C, most of the minerals have crystallized out. The remaining minerals are dissolved in water. As the hot solution cools still more and finds its way to the surface where there is less pressure, the water evaporates and the rest of the minerals crystallize out. If the cooling is slow, large crystals result. If the cooling is fast, small crystals result. If the cooling is very fast, and the atoms do not have time to arrange themselves into regular order, an amorphous substance such as opal or glass results.

Strategy

You will observe crystal growth from a melt.
You will see mineral crystals in a sample of granite.
You will discover the effect that cooling rate has on crystal size.
You will discover processes that result in crystal growth.

Materials

beaker tongs
clear small medicine bottle with cap
dilute silver nitrate solution
eyedropper
fine copper wire
goggles
granite samples
hot plate
magnifying glass
microscope (optional)
microscope slides
salol
apron
gloves

Procedure
Part A

1. Using the magnifying glass, look at the sample of granite. The granite was once molten. The minerals that make up the granite can be recognized by their different colors.

Data and Observations

Table 1

2. Fill in the table below by placing an X in the appropriate box.

Mineral (color)	Having a definite shape	Shapeless
a) White or pink	X	
b) Black and shiny	X	
c) Black and dull	X	
d) Clear		X

Questions and Conclusions
Part A

1. The clear material in granite is called quartz. It is nearly the last to crystallize out from a melt (500°C). Why do you suppose quartz is shapeless? **Quartz was last to form so it filled all the spaces that were left, restricting crystal shape.**

2. Were the mineral crystals in granite easy to see with the unaided eye? **yes**

3. What can you say about the cooling rate of granite? **It cooled slowly since it has large crystals.**

Procedure
Part B

1. Place a clean fine copper wire (you may have to clean it with steel wool) about 1 cm long on a clean microscope slide.

2. Put the slide on the stage of a microscope or on a piece of white paper if you are using a hand lens.

3. From the dropper bottle marked silver nitrate solution, put 1 drop of the dilute silver nitrate on the copper wire and immediately watch what happens. **CAUTION:** *Do not spill the silver nitrate or get any of it on your clothes or hands.*

4. Draw a representative sample of the growth and the copper wire in the box below.

Questions and Conclusions
Part B

1. The pattern you have drawn is called a dendritic pattern and is made of silver. Is there a regular pattern to the growth? **Yes, faces are repeated.**

2. Is the pattern repeated? **yes**

3. Are there plane surfaces that might suggest an orderly arrangement of atoms? **yes**

4. Look up the word *crystal* in your textbook. If this activity were to occur in nature, could the silver dendrite be called a crystal? Explain. **Yes, it has all the characteristics of a crystal. Note that the act of making the crystal dendrite in lab disqualifies it as a mineral crystal.**

5. On a very cold day, the water vapor in the air of a warm room contacts the cold windowpane and freezes. The result is a feathery, almost dendritic pattern of ice. Would the dendritic pattern be the result of fast or slow crystallization? What is your evidence? **It would be fast crystallization. This is like the dendrites that formed with the copper wire. The process is rapid.**

Procedure
Part C

1. Place a few crystals of salol into a small glass bottle and screw on the lid.

2. Heat the bottle in a water bath. The salol melts at 43°C, which is a little above body temperature.

3. When the salol has melted, lift the bottle out of the water bath using beaker tongs. Pour some of the liquid salol onto a clean microscope slide.

4. Watch the crystal growth using a magnifying glass or microscope.

Questions and Conclusions
Part C

1. The salol melts at 43°C, but when placed in the closed bottle, it melts at a higher temperature. Why? **This is similar to the conditions that occur when a non-boiling liquid under high pressure reaches the surface from deep in the earth. A release of pressure and then a sudden expansion occurs, which results in the boiling of the fluid.**

2. Where did the crystals begin to form in the "puddle" of salol? **on the outside near the edges of the "puddle" of salol**

3. Where would you expect to find the irregular shaped crystals? **in the middle of the "puddle"**

Strategy Check

___ Can you recognize different crystals in a rock sample?

___ Can you list some natural processes that result in crystal formation?

___ Can you associate crystal size with the rate of cooling?

Chapter 5

LABORATORY MANUAL

● Atoms—Smaller Than You Think! 8

Much matter is composed of atoms, which means that atoms are everywhere. But if atoms are everywhere, why haven't you ever seen a single atom? You aren't able to see atoms because they are so small. But you can use other senses to detect some of the small molecules made from atoms. In this experiment, you will study the small size of single vanilla molecules.

Strategy

You will predict what happens when drops of a liquid are placed in a balloon.
You will observe the small size of molecules.

Materials

rubber balloon
closet or locker
dropper
vanilla extract (2 mL)

Procedure

1. Use a dropper to place 20 to 40 drops of vanilla extract into a rubber balloon (FIGURE 1).

2. Blow up the balloon and tie it tightly at the end.

3. Place the balloon in a small, enclosed area such as a closet or locker for at least 30 minutes.

4. What do you think will happen to the molecules in the vanilla extract in the balloon? Record your prediction in the Data and Observations section.

5. After 30 minutes, open the closet or locker. What did you observe? Record your observation in the Data and Observations section.

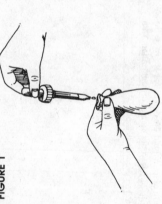

FIGURE 1

Data and Observations

1. What do you predict will happen to the vanilla in the balloon?

Student answers will vary based on their understanding of atoms. Students that already understand how small molecules are will predict that the vanilla molecules will seep out of the balloon.

2. What did you observe when you opened the area that held your balloon?

The area smelled strongly of vanilla.

Questions and Conclusions

1. How do you explain the results of this experiment?

The vanilla molecules are small enough to move through the walls of the balloon.

2. What do your results tell you about the size of the vanilla molecules?

The results indicate that the vanilla molecules are extremely small.

3. What does the fact that helium-filled balloons deflate tell you about the size of helium atoms?

Helium atoms are so small that they pass through the walls of the balloon.

4. Helium gas is made up of single helium atoms. Vanilla molecules have the formula $C_8H_8O_3$. Which do you think will leak more rapidly from equally inflated balloons—helium or vanilla?

The helium atoms are smaller and will leak more quickly from the balloon than will the larger molecules in the vanilla.

Strategy Check

___ Can you observe whether or not atoms and molecules are very small?

___ Can you compare the sizes of different molecules and atoms based on how they behave?

Chapter 5

LABORATORY MANUAL

Isotopes and Atomic Mass 9

A sample of an element, as it occurs in nature, is a mixture of isotopes. All the isotopes of a given element have the same number of protons, but each isotope has a different number of neutrons. Therefore, the atomic masses of elements, as shown on the periodic table, are average atomic masses. In this exercise, you will use a model of isotopes to help you understand the concept of atomic mass.

Strategy

You will model isotopes of two different elements using two colors of candy-coated peanuts and candy-coated chocolate.

You will determine the average mass of the two colors of candy-coated peanuts and candy-coated chocolate.

You will relate your results to the average atomic mass of atoms.

Materials

4 red and 3 green candy-coated peanuts
2 red and 3 green candy-coated chocolates

Procedure

1. Group together four red candy-coated peanuts and two red candy-coated chocolates. The two different kinds of candy represent two isotopes of the same element.

2. Assume that a red peanut has a mass of 2 candy units, and a red chocolate has a mass of 1 candy unit. Calculate the average mass of the red candy as follows:
   a. Multiply the number of red peanuts by the mass in candy units.
   b. Multiply the number of red chocolates by the mass in candy units.
   c. Add the masses and divide by the total number of candies.

3. Repeat steps 2 and 3, but use three green peanuts and three green chocolates. Assume a green peanut has a mass of 4 units, and a green chocolate has a mass of 3 units.

4. Record your calculations in Table 1.

Data and Observations

Table 1

	Peanut	Chocolate	Average
	(candy × candy unit)	(candy × candy unit)	(total mass) / (total candies)
Red	$4 \times 2 = 8$	$2 \times 1 = 2$	$\frac{8+2}{4+2} = 1.7$
Green	$3 \times 4 = 12$	$3 \times 3 = 9$	$\frac{12+9}{3+3} = 3.5$

Questions and Conclusions

1. There were six red and six green candies. Why were their calculated average masses not the same?
Each type of candy was assigned a different mass value.

2. If a sample of element Y contains 100 atoms of Y-12 and 10 atoms of Y-14, calculate the average mass of Y.
$$\frac{1200 + 140}{100 + 10} = 12.18 \text{ units}$$

3. Look at the periodic table and notice that none of the naturally occurring elements have atomic masses that are whole numbers. How does your candy model of atoms help you explain that?
The atomic masses on the periodic table are weighted averages of the isotopes.

4. An element needed for most nuclear reactors is uranium. Its two major isotopes are U-235 and U-238. Look up the mass of uranium on the periodic table. Infer which isotope is the most common.
238; this value is closest to the atomic mass shown on the periodic table.

5. Compare and contrast mass number and atomic mass.
Mass number is the sum of the number of protons and neutrons in an atom of an element. Atomic mass is the average mass of all the isotopes of an element. You get atomic mass from the average of the mass values of all isotopes.

6. Hydrogen has three isotopes. The most common one, protium, has no neutrons. Deuterium, the second isotope, has one neutron. Tritium has two neutrons. Using this information, calculate the mass number of these isotopes.
protium—1; deuterium—2; tritium—3

Strategy Check

_____ Can you explain how candy-coated peanuts and candy-coated chocolate can be a model for isotopes?

_____ Are you able to find the average mass of two different isotopes of the same element?

Chapter 6

LABORATORY MANUAL

Relationships Among Elements 10

The periodic table is a wonderful source of information about all of the elements scientists have discovered. In this activity, you will investigate the relationship among the elements' atomic numbers, radii, and positions in the periodic table.

The radii for elements with atomic numbers from 3–38 are given in Table 1. The radii are so small that a very small metric unit called a picometer is used. A picometer (pm) is one trillionth of a meter.

Strategy

You will plot the atomic radii of elements with atomic numbers 3–38.
You will examine the graph for repeated patterns.

Materials

copy of the periodic table
graph paper
pencil

Table 1

Name and symbol		Atomic number	Atomic radius (picometers)
Aluminum	Al	13	143
Argon	Ar	18	191
Arsenic	As	33	121
Beryllium	Be	4	112
Boron	B	5	85
Bromine	Br	35	117
Calcium	Ca	20	197
Carbon	C	6	77
Chlorine	Cl	17	91
Chromium	Cr	24	128
Cobalt	Co	27	125
Copper	Cu	29	128
Fluorine	F	9	69
Gallium	Ga	31	134
Germanium	Ge	32	123
Iron	Fe	26	126
Krypton	Kr	36	201
Lithium	Li	3	156

Name and symbol		Atomic number	Atomic radius (picometers)
Magnesium	Mg	12	160
Manganese	Mn	25	127
Neon	Ne	10	131
Nickel	Ni	28	124
Nitrogen	N	7	71
Oxygen	O	8	60
Phosphorus	P	15	109
Potassium	K	19	231
Rubidium	Rb	37	248
Scandium	Sc	21	162
Selenium	Se	34	119
Silicon	Si	14	118
Sodium	Na	11	186
Strontium	Sr	38	215
Sulfur	S	16	103
Titanium	Ti	22	147
Vanadium	V	23	134
Zinc	Zn	30	134

Procedure

1. On the graph paper, label the horizontal axis with the numbers 0–38 to represent the atomic numbers of the elements you will be plotting.

2. Label the vertical axis by ten with numbers from 0–280. These numbers represent atomic radii.

3. Plot the atomic radius for each of the elements with atomic numbers 3–38.

Questions and Conclusions

1. Look at the shape of your graph. What patterns do you observe? __The graph peaks, falls into valleys, and rises again with a little peak appearing just before each of the high peaks.__

2. What family is represented by the high peaks in your graph? __alkali metals__

3. What family is represented by the low points in your graph? __halogens__

4. What family is represented by the smaller peaks just before the high peaks in your graph? __noble gases__

5. What do you notice about the radii of the elements at the high peaks as you move from left to right on your graph? Look at your periodic table and find the element that represents each high peak. __The radii increase. Each peak represents__

What does each high peak begin in the periodic table? __The beginning of a new period.__

6. What happens to the radii of the elements between two highest peaks? What does each of these groups of elements represent? __The radii become smaller. Each group of elements represents a period.__

7. How can a graph such as the one you made help to predict the properties of elements that have not been discovered yet?
__A graph of discovered elements predicts the atomic radii of any undiscovered elements that have atomic numbers within the range of the discovered elements. Undiscovered elements would be expected to have properties similar to discovered elements that occupy comparable positions on the graph.__

8. How do the radii of metals in each period compare with the radii of nonmetals in that period? __Metals have larger radii than the nonmetals in the same period.__

Strategy Check

___ Can you plot a graph of the atomic radii of elements?

___ Can you observe repeating patterns in the graph?

NAME _____ DATE _____ CLASS _____

Chapter 6

LABORATORY MANUAL • **Periodicity   11**

A periodic event is one that occurs time after time in a regular, predictable way. If you have a table of repeating events, you can use it to predict what might be true in the future. For example, astronomers are able to predict the appearance of a comet if they know the dates of the comet's appearance in the past. A calendar is a good model for the periodic table of the elements.

Strategy

You will determine missing information on the calendar for a month.
You will make predictions about future and past events based on the calendar.

Procedure 🐾 🖐

1. Label the seven columns of the calendar page in FIGURE 1 with the numbers 1–7. There are seven families, or groups, in this periodic table. They are the days of the week.

2. Label the five rows of the calendar page with the numbers 1–5. There are five periods in this periodic table. Each period is a week.

3. Notice that some information is missing. Fill in the missing information by examining the information in the blocks surrounding the spots where the missing information belongs.

Data and Observations

FIGURE 1

SUN	MON	TUE	WED	THU	FRI	SAT
				1	2	3 Soccer Practice
4	5	6	7	8	9	10
11	12	@	#	15	16	17 Soccer Practice
18	19	20	21	22	23	24
25	26	27	28	29	30 Your Birthday	31

Questions and Conclusions

1. Two of the days in Families 3 and 4 are marked with an @ and a #. What dates should go in these positions? __13 and 14; they are consecutive days that fit between 12 and 15.__

2. Family 5 doesn't have a name. What is the correct name for this family? __Thursday__

3. What dates are included in the third period of the table? __11–17__

4. Assuming that the previous month had 30 days, what day of the week would the 28th of that month have been? __Monday__

A periodic event is one that occurs time after time in a regular, predictable way. If you have a table of repeating events, you can use it to predict what might be true in the future. For example, astronomers are able to predict the appearance of a comet if they know the dates of the comet's appearance in the past. A calendar is a good model for the periodic table of the elements.

Strategy

You will determine missing information on the calendar for a month.
You will make predictions about future and past events based on the calendar.

Procedure 🐾 🖐

1. Label the seven columns of the calendar page in FIGURE 1 with the numbers 1–7. There are seven families, or groups, in this periodic table. They are the days of the week.

2. Label the five rows of the calendar page with the numbers 1–5. There are five periods in this periodic table. Each period is a week.

3. Notice that some information is missing. Fill in the missing information by examining the information in the blocks surrounding the spots where the missing information belongs.

Data and Observations

Questions and Conclusions

1. Two of the days in Families 3 and 4 are marked with an @ and a #. What dates should go in these positions? __13 and 14; they are consecutive days that fit between 12 and 15.__

2. Family 5 doesn't have a name. What is the correct name for this family? __Thursday__

3. What dates are included in the third period of the table? __11–17__

4. Assuming that the previous month had 30 days, what day of the week would the 28th of that month have been? __Monday__

5. What period of this table would it appear in? __period 1__

6. Notice that two dates have been scheduled for regular soccer practice. When would you expect the next two soccer practices to take place? __the first and third Saturdays of next month__

Chapter 7

LABORATORY MANUAL

• Chemical Bonds 12

All substances are made of atoms. The physical and chemical properties of a substance depend on how the atoms that make up the substance are held together by chemical bonds. In this experiment, you will investigate the properties of compounds formed by two types of chemical bonds: covalent bonds and ionic bonds.

In some compounds, called covalent compounds, the atoms are held together by covalent bonds. A covalent bond forms when two atoms share a pair of electrons. In other substances, atoms have either lost or gained electrons to form ions. An ion is an atom that has gained or lost one or more electrons. In these substances, the ions are held together by ionic bonds. These substances are called ionic compounds.

Solutions of ionic compounds can conduct an electric current. Some covalent compounds can also form solutions. However, these solutions do not conduct an electric current. A measure of how well a solution can carry an electric current is called conductivity.

Strategy

You will determine the conductivity of several solutions.
You will classify the compounds that were dissolved in the solutions as ionic compounds or covalent compounds.

Materials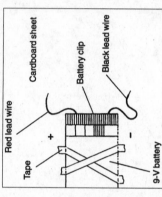

apron
alligator clips (4)
9-V battery and battery clip
cardboard sheet, 10 cm × 10 cm
copper wire, insulated, 20-cm lengths (2)
sucrose solution, 0.1M sucrose
glucose solution, 0.1M glucose
sugar cubes (sucrose)
goggles
LED (light-emitting diode)
microplate, 24-well
paper towels
pipettes, plastic (7)
resistor, 1000-Ω
sodium chloride (rock, crystalline)
sodium chloride solution, 0.1M NaCl
sodium hydroxide solution, 0.1M NaOH
sulfuric acid solution, 0.1M H₂SO₄
tape
water, distilled

To prepare each 0.1M solution, dissolve each in distilled water and dilute each to 1 liter:

34.2 g sucrose
18.0 g glucose
5.9 g NaCl
4.0 g NaOh
5.6 mL H₂SO₄
(Caution: heat involved. Add slowly to 500 mL distilled water, then dilute to 1 liter.)

CAUTION: *Sulfuric acid and sodium hydroxide can cause burns. Avoid contacting them with your skin or clothing. Do not taste, eat, or drink any materials used in the lab.*
Note: The NaOH and H₂SO₄ solutions are very dilute. As long as the teacher prepares the solutions, safety is not a concern. Also, there should not be any vapors.
Testing rock salt can illustrate the difference between conductivity in solution and as a solid. Sugar can be used for contrast.

Procedure

Part A Constructing a Conductivity Tester

1. After putting your apron and goggles on, attach the 9-V battery clip to the 9-V battery. Use tape to attach the battery securely to the cardboard sheet, as shown in FIGURE 1.

2. Attach an alligator clip to one of the lead wires of the 1000-Ω resistor. Connect the alligator clip to the *red* lead wire of the battery clip. Tape the resistor and alligator clip to the cardboard sheet as shown in FIGURE 2. **CAUTION:** *Use care when handling sharp objects.*

3. Attach an alligator clip to the *long* lead wire of the LED. Connect this alligator clip to the second wire of the 1000-Ω resistor. Tape the alligator clip to the cardboard sheet.

4. Attach an alligator clip to the *short* lead wire of the LED. Connect this clip to one end of one of the insulated copper wires. Tape the clip to the cardboard sheet as shown in FIGURE 3.

5. Attach the last alligator clip to one end of the second insulated copper wire. Connect the alligator clip to the *black* lead wire of the battery clip. Tape the alligator clip to the cardboard sheet as shown in FIGURE 4.

6. Check to be certain that the alligator clips, resistor, and battery are securely taped to the cardboard sheet and that the clips are not touching one another.

7. Have your teacher check your conductivity tester.

8. Touch the two ends of the two insulated wires and observe that the LED glows.

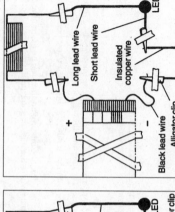

FIGURE 1

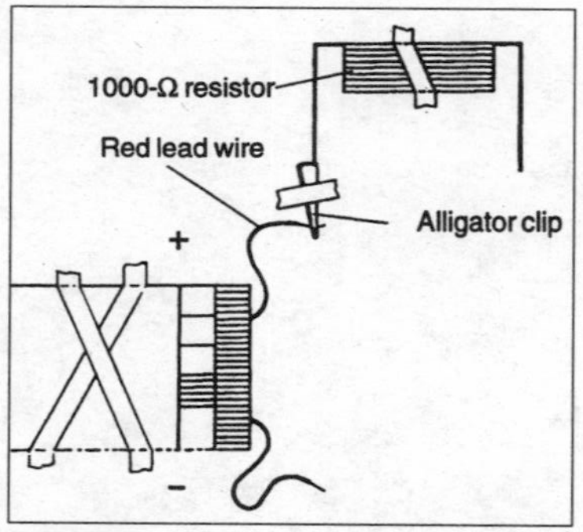

Red lead wire
Tape
+
9-V battery
Cardboard sheet
Battery clip
Black lead wire

FIGURE 2

1000-Ω resistor
Red lead wire
Alligator clip
+
−

FIGURE 3

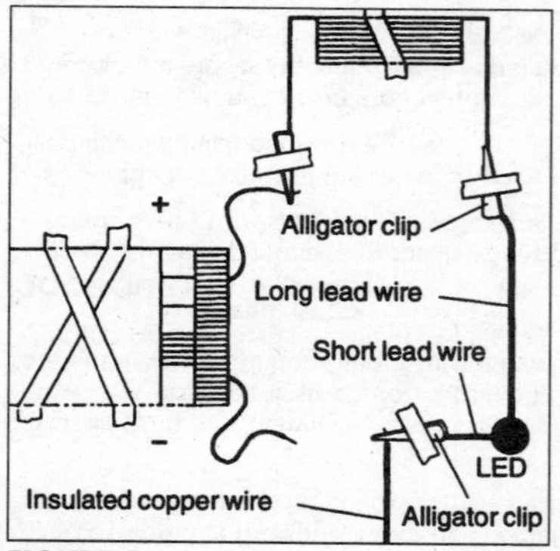

Alligator clip
Long lead wire
Short lead wire
LED
Alligator clip
+
Insulated copper wire
−

FIGURE 4

Long lead wire
Short lead wire
Insulated copper wire
LED
+
Black lead wire
Alligator clip
−

FIGURE 5

A   1   2   3   4   5   6   7   8

$0.1M\ H_2SO_4$ $0.1M\ NaCl$ $0.1M\ NaOH$ $0.1M\ sucrose$ $0.1M\ glucose$ sugar cube   rock salt H_2O

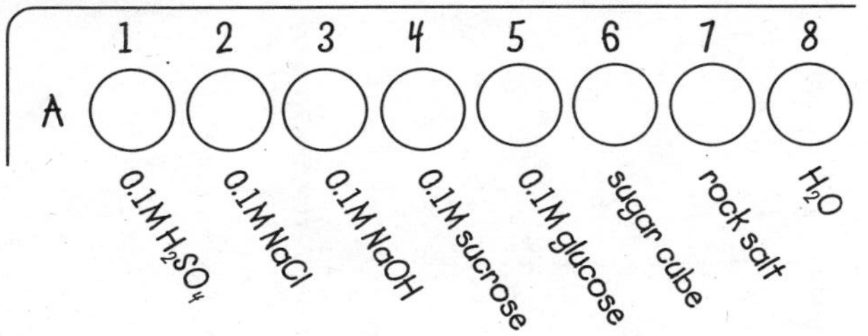

Part B Testing the Conductivity of a Solution

1. Place the microplate on a flat surface. Have the numbered columns of the microplate at the top and the lettered rows at the left. **CAUTION:** *Wash hands immediately after coming in contact with any of the prepared solutions.* **CAUTION:** *Inform your teacher if you come in contact with any chemicals.*

2. Using a clean pipette, add a pipetteful of the sulfuric acid solution to well A1.

3. Using another clean pipette, add a pipetteful of the sodium chloride solution to well A2.

4. Repeat step 3 for each remaining solution or substance. Use a clean pipette for each solution. Add the sodium hydroxide solution to well A3, the sucrose solution to well A4, the glucose solution to well A5, a sugar cube to well A6, and a piece of rock salt to well A7.

5. Using a clean pipette, add a pipetteful of distilled water to well A8.

6. Place the exposed ends of the two insulated copper wires into the solution in well A1, positioning the wires so they are at opposite sides of the well. Be sure that the exposed ends of the wire are completely submerged.

7. Observe the LED. Use the brightness of the LED as an indication of the conductivity of the solution. Rate the conductivity of the solution using the following symbols: + (good conductivity); – (fair conductivity); or 0 (no conductivity). Record your rating in the corresponding well of the microplate shown in FIGURE 6.

8. Remove the wires and dry the ends of the wires with a paper towel.

9. Repeat steps 6, 7, and 8 for each remaining well in the microplate.

Data and Observations Data will vary slightly.

FIGURE 6

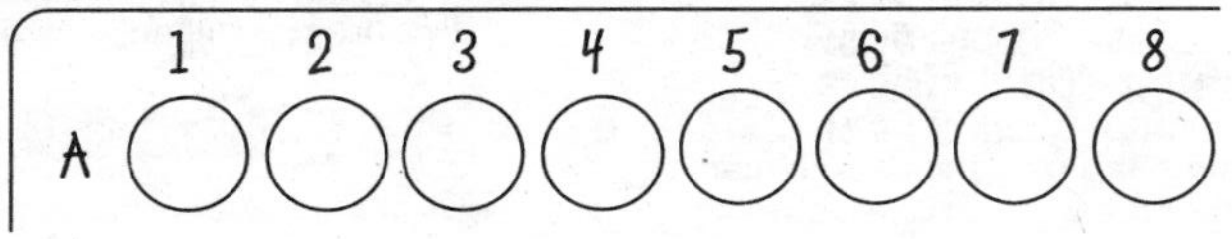

A   1   2   3   4   5   6   7   8

Questions and Conclusions

1. What is the conductivity of distilled water? **The conductivity of distilled water is zero.**

2. Why was the conductivity of the distilled water measured? **The conductivity of the distilled water was measured as a control. Because the conductivity of water is zero, any conductivity by a solution would indicate that the dissolved substances in the solution caused the conductivity.**

3. After studying your results, infer which of the solutions contained an ionic compound. **Students should have observed conductivity in the $0.1M\ NaCl$, $0.1M\ NaOH$, and the $0.1M\ H_2SO_4$ solutions. This observation is evidence of an ionic compound in the solution.**

4. Do your results indicate that any of the solutions contained a covalent compound? **The $0.1M$ glucose and $0.1M$ sucrose solutions should not have shown any conductivity. These solutions contained covalent compounds.**

5. How do the conductivities of solutions of ionic compounds and covalent compounds compare? **Solutions of ionic compounds have good conductivity. Solutions of covalent compounds have no conductivity.**

6. Did the crystal of table salt or the sugar cube conduct electricity? **Students should have observed no conductivity with either substance.**

7. How did the conductivities of the crystal of table salt and the 0.1M NaCl solution compare? **NaCl shows no conductivity in crystalline form, but is a good conductor in solution.**

8. From your results describe one property of an ionic compound. **The results from this experiment indicate that an ionic compound conducts electricity when it is dissolved in water.**

Strategy Check

_____ Can you test the conductivity of a solution?

_____ Can you distinguish between a solution containing an ionic compound and one containing a covalent compound?

Chapter 7

LABORATORY MANUAL • **Chemical Activity 13**

The atoms of most chemical elements can either gain or lose electrons during reactions. Elements whose atoms lose electrons during reactions are classified as metals. Metals are found on the left side of the periodic table of elements. The tendency of an element to react chemically is called activity. The activity of a metal is a measure of how easily the metal atoms lose electrons.

Strategy

You will observe chemical reactions between metals and solutions containing ions of metals.
You will compare the activities of different metals.
You will rank the metals in order of their activities.

Materials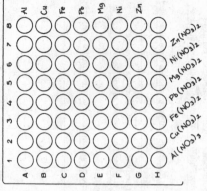

apron
aluminum nitrate solution, 0.1M Al(NO₃)₃
copper nitrate solution, 0.1M Cu(NO₃)₂
goggles
hand lens or magnifier
iron nitrate solution, 0.1M Fe(NO₃)₃
lead nitrate solution, 0.1M Pb(NO₃)₂
magnesium nitrate solution, 0.1M Mg(NO₃)₂
metal strips (8 1-mm × 10-mm strips of each: aluminum, Al; copper, Cu; iron, Fe; lead, Pb; magnesium, Mg; nickel, Ni; and zinc, Zn)
microplate, 96-well
paper, white
paper towels
pipette, plastic microtip
zinc nitrate, 0.1M Zn(NO₃)₂
water, distilled

To prepare each 0.1M solution, dissolve each in distilled water and dilute to 1 liter:

37.5g Al(NO₃)₃·9H₂O
23.3g Cu(NO₃)₂·2½H₂O
40.4g Fe(NO₃)₃·9H₂O
33.1g Pb(NO₃)₂
25.6g Mg(NO₃)₂·6H₂O
29.1g Ni(NO₃)₂·6H₂O
29.8g Zn(NO₃)₂·6H₂O

10-mm lengths of wire of each of the metals may be used

CAUTION: *Many of these solutions are poisonous. Avoid inhaling any vapors from the solutions. These solutions can cause stains. Do not allow them to contact your skin or clothing.*

Procedure

1. Wear an apron and goggles during this experiment.

2. Place the microplate on a piece of white paper on a flat surface. Have the numbered columns of the microplate at the top and lettered rows at the left.

3. Using the microtip pipette, place 15 drops of the aluminum nitrate solution in each of wells A1–H1. Rinse the pipette with distilled water.

4. Place 15 drops of copper nitrate solution in each of wells A2–H2 using the pipette. Rinse the pipette with distilled water.

5. Repeat step 4 for each of the remaining solutions. Add the iron nitrate solution to wells A3–H3, the lead nitrate solution to wells A4–H4, the magnesium nitrate solution to wells A5–H5, the nickel nitrate solution to wells A6–H6, and the zinc nitrate solution to wells A7–H7. Leave the wells in column 8 empty.

6. Carefully clean each metal strip with a paper towel.

7. Place one strip of aluminum in each of wells A1–A8.

8. Place one strip of copper in each of wells B1–B8.

9. Repeat step 8 for the remaining metals. Add the iron strips to wells C1–C8, the lead strips to wells D1–D8, the magnesium strips to wells E1–E8, the nickel strips to wells F1–F8, and the zinc strips to wells G1–G8. Do not put strips in the wells in row H.

10. FIGURE 1 shows the metal and the solution that are in each of wells A1–H8.

11. Wait 10 min.

12. Use a hand lens or magnifier to observe the contents of each well. Look for a change in the color of the solution in each well by comparing it with the color of the solution in well H at the bottom of the column. Look for a change in the texture or color of the metal strip in each well by comparing it with the piece of metal in well 8 at the end of that row. Look for the appearance of deposited materials in the bottom of the well. Each change or appearance of deposits is an indication that a chemical reaction has taken place.

13. If you see an indication of a reaction, draw a positive sign (+) in the corresponding well of the microplate shown in FIGURE 2 in the Data and Observations section. If you see no indication of a reaction, draw a negative sign (−) in the corresponding well of FIGURE 2.

14. Count the number of positive signs in each row of wells in FIGURE 2. Record the value under the corresponding metal in Table 1.

FIGURE 1

	1	2	3	4	5	6	7	8	
A	○	○	○	○	○	○	○	○	Al
B	○	○	○	○	○	○	○	○	Cu
C	○	○	○	○	○	○	○	○	Fe
D	○	○	○	○	○	○	○	○	Pb
E	○	○	○	○	○	○	○	○	Mg
F	○	○	○	○	○	○	○	○	Ni
G	○	○	○	○	○	○	○	○	Zn
H	○	○	○	○	○	○	○	○	
	Al(NO₃)₃	Cu(NO₃)₃	Fe(NO₃)₃	Pb(NO₃)₂	Mg(NO₃)₂	Ni(NO₃)₂	Zn(NO₃)₂		

Data and Observations

Observations will vary.

FIGURE 2

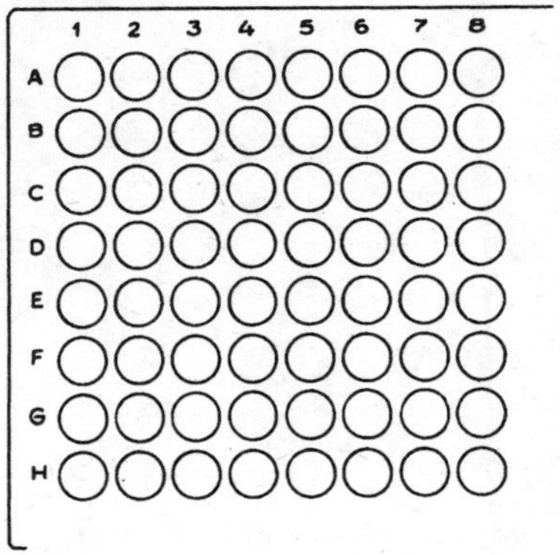

Table 1

Data will vary.

Metal	Al	Cu	Fe	Pb	Mg	Ni	Zn
Number of reactions	5	0	3	1	6	2	4

Questions and Conclusions

1. Why were solutions but not strips of metal placed in wells H1–H7? **These wells are controls with which to compare the color of the solutions in the wells to which metals had been added.**

2. Why were strips of metal but no solutions added to wells A8–H8? **These wells are controls with which to compare the color of the metal strips in the wells to which solutions had been added.**

3. Why did you clean the metal strips with the paper towel? **The metal strips were cleaned to remove any dirt or materials that may have prevented a chemical reaction from taking place.**

4. Using the number of reactions for each metal in Table 1, rank the metals from the most active to the least active. **Mg, Al, Zn, Fe, Ni, Pb, Cu**

5. Solutions of dissolved metal compounds contain metal ions. An ion is an atom that has gained or lost electrons. Ions of metals are positively charged because the metals lose electrons when they react. The activity of the ion of a metal is a measure of how easily an ion gains electrons. Use the results of this experiment to rank the activities of ions of metals in solutions.
   Ions of Cu, Pb, Ni, Fe, Zn, Al, Mg—from the most active to the least.

6. How does the activity of an ion of a metal compare with the activity of the metal? **The more active the metal, the less active the ion, and vice versa.**

Strategy Check

___ Can you identify evidence that a chemical reaction has occurred between a metal and a solution containing metal ions?

___ Can you interpret evidence of chemical reactions between metals and solutions of metal ions and arrange the metals in order according to their activities?

Chapter 8

• Chemical Reactions 14

The changes that occur during a chemical reaction are represented by a chemical equation. An equation uses chemical symbols to represent the substances that change. The reactants, on the left side of the equation, are the substances that react. The products, on the right side of the equation, are the substances that are formed from the reaction.

In the following reaction, two reactants form one product. Water and oxygen are the reactants. The product is hydrogen peroxide.

$$2H_2O + O_2 \rightarrow 2H_2O_2$$

A chemical reaction may have two products from the breakdown of a single reactant. In this example water is the reactant. Hydrogen and oxygen are products.

$$2H_2O \rightarrow 2H_2 + O_2$$

Two reactants can also combine to make two products. In the following reaction, carbon displaces the hydrogen in water and hydrogen and carbon monoxide are released as gases.

$$H_2O + C \rightarrow H_2 + CO$$

Strategy

You will recognize the reactants and products of a chemical reaction.
You will write a word equation for a chemical reaction.
You will write a balanced chemical equation using chemical symbols.

Materials

Part A	Part B	Part C
aluminum foil	baking soda, NaHCO₃	beaker
apron	matches	copper (II) sulfate solution, 0.1M Fe
burner	spoon	common nail, Fe
goggles	test tube	paper towel
matches	test-tube holder	string
steel wool	wood splint	watch or clock
tongs		

To prepare a 0.1M solution, dissolve 25.0 g CuSO₄ • 5H₂O in distilled water, add 3 drops of 18M H₂SO₄, and dilute to 1 liter.

CAUTION: *Copper (II) sulfate solution is poisonous. Handle with care. Wear goggles and an apron.*

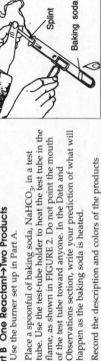

FIGURE 1

FIGURE 2

FIGURE 3

Procedure

Part A Two Reactants→One Product

1. Protect the table with a sheet of aluminum foil. Place the burner in the center of the foil. Light the burner. **CAUTION:** *Stay clear of flames.*

2. Observe the color of the steel wool. Record your observations in the Data and Observations section.

3. Predict changes in the steel wool when it is heated in the flame. Write your prediction in the Data and Observations section.

4. Hold the steel wool (containing iron, Fe) with the tongs over the flame as shown in FIGURE 1. As the steel wool burns, record the changes it goes through.

Part B One Reactant→Two Products

1. Use the burner set up in Part A.

2. Place a spoonful of baking soda, NaHCO₃, in a test tube. Use the test-tube holder to heat the test tube in the flame, as shown in FIGURE 2. Do not point the mouth of the test tube toward anyone. In the Data and Observations section, write your prediction of what will happen as the baking soda is heated.

3. Record the description and colors of the products formed inside the tube as it is heated.

4. Test for the presence of CO₂. Light a wooden splint. Insert the flaming splint into the mouth of the test tube. If the flame of the splint goes out, CO₂ is present. Record your observations of the products of this reaction.

Part C Two Reactants→Two Products

1. Carefully rub the nail with a piece of steel wool until the nail is shiny. Tie a string around the nail. Fill a beaker about half full with the CuSO₄ solution. Record the colors of the nail and the CuSO₄ solution in Table 1. **CAUTION:** *Use care when handling sharp objects. Wash hands immediately after coming in contact with copper (II) sulfate solution.*

2. Dip the nail in the CuSO₄ solution. (See FIGURE 3.) Predict what changes will happen to the appearance of the nail and the solution. After 5 min, pull the nail from the solution and place it on a paper towel. Record the colors of the nail and the solution in Table 1.

3. Put the nail back into the solution and observe further color changes.

Data and Observations

Part A Two Reactants→One Product
Color of steel wool before burning: silver-gray
Prediction of changes in the heated steel wool: Answers will vary.
Color of burned steel wool: dark gray–black

Part B One Reactant→Two Products
Prediction of changes in the heated baking soda: Answers will vary.
Description of deposits inside heated test tube: white solids and clear, colorless liquid
Observations of flaming splint: The flaming splint was extinguished.

Part C Two Reactants→Two Products
Prediction of changes in nail and CuSO₄ solution: Answers will vary.

Table 1

Observation time	Color of nail	Color of CuSO₄ solution
Before reaction	silver	dark blue
After reaction	red	light blue

Questions and Conclusions

1. Identify the two reactants in the heating of steel wool. Iron in the steel wool and oxygen from the air are both reactants.

2. How does the heat from the flame affect the reactants when steel wool is heated? Heat raises the temperature and speeds up the reaction.

3. What evidence suggests that at least two reactants were formed when $NaHCO_3$ was heated? The bubbles are evidence of a gaseous product. The solids remaining in the test tube have changed appearance indicating a new solid was formed.

4. Was the heating of $NaHCO_3$ an endothermic or exothermic reaction? Explain your answer. Energy in the form of heat had to be added before the $NaHCO_3$ changed into new products. The addition of energy suggests an endothermic reaction.

5. From your observations, does the reaction of an iron nail with the copper (II) sulfate yield more than one product? A color change on the surface of the iron nail and a lightening of the bluish color of the copper (II) sulfate suggest that at least two products were formed.

6. Was the addition of the iron nail to the copper (II) sulfate solution an endothermic or exothermic reaction? This reaction took place without adding heat, making it an exothermic reaction.

Strategy Check

____ Can you identify the reactants and products of a chemical reaction?

____ Can you write a word equation for a chemical reaction?

____ Can you write a balanced chemical equation?

Chapter 8

• Reaction Rates and Temperature 15

Not all chemical reactions occur at the same rate. Some chemical reactions are very fast; others are very slow. The same chemical reaction can happen at several different rates depending on the temperature at which the reaction occurs.

In this experiment, you will investigate the effect of temperature on a decomposition reaction. Household bleach is a solution of five percent sodium hypochlorite (NaOCl). This compound decomposes to produce sodium chloride and oxygen gas.

$$2NaOCl \rightarrow 2NaCl + O_2$$

Strategy

You will observe the amount of oxygen produced from the decomposition of household bleach at various temperatures.

You will graph the reaction data.

You will determine the relationship between reaction rate and temperature for this reaction.

Materials 🧤 🔬 🧪 🥽 🔥

apron
beaker (400-mL)
clock with second hand
cobalt nitrate solution, 1M Co(NO₃)₂
goggles
immersion heater or hot plate
microplate (24-well)
pipette, plastic
pipette, plastic microtip
sodium hypochlorite solution, 1M NaOCl
thermometer
washers (4 iron or lead)

CAUTION: *Handle both solutions with care. Solutions can stain clothes and skin. Rinse spills with plenty of water.*

Procedure

Part A—Reaction at Room Temperature

1. Safety goggles and a laboratory apron must be worn throughout this experiment. Look at the equation of the decomposition reaction. In the Data and Observations section, write a prediction of what you might observe during this reaction. Write a hypothesis describing how temperature will affect the reaction rate.

2. Allow 400 mL of tap water to come to room temperature.

3. At the top of Table 1, record the temperature of the water to the nearest 0.5°C.

4. Using the microtip pipette, place 30 drops of 2.5 percent sodium hypochlorite solution in well A1 of the microplate.

5. Rinse the microtip pipette twice with distilled water. Discard the rinse water.

6. Using the rinsed pipette, place 10 drops of cobalt nitrate solution into well C1 of the microplate.

7. Rinse the microtip pipette twice with distilled water. Discard the rinse water.

8. Draw up the sodium hypochlorite solution in well A1 into the bulb of the plastic pipette. Be sure that no solution remains in the stem of the pipette.

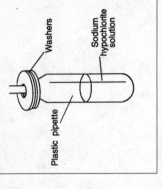

FIGURE 1

9. Place three or four iron or lead washers over the top of the stem of the pipette, as in FIGURE 1.

10. Squeeze and hold the pipette to expel the air from the bulb of the pipette.

11. Bend the stem of the pipette over into the cobalt nitrate solution in well C1, as shown in FIGURE 2. Be prepared to start timing the reaction as soon as you complete the next two steps.

12. Release the pipette bulb and draw the cobalt nitrate solution into the pipette. The two solutions will mix. Record any changes you observe.

13. Quickly submerge the pipette and washer assembly in the beaker of water, as shown in FIGURE 3. Begin timing. If necessary, hold the pipette upright.

14. Count the number of bubbles produced by the reaction as they escape from the stem of the pipette. Every 15 s for 3 min, record in Table 1 the total number of bubbles counted.

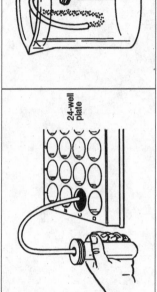

24-well plate

FIGURE 2

Beaker

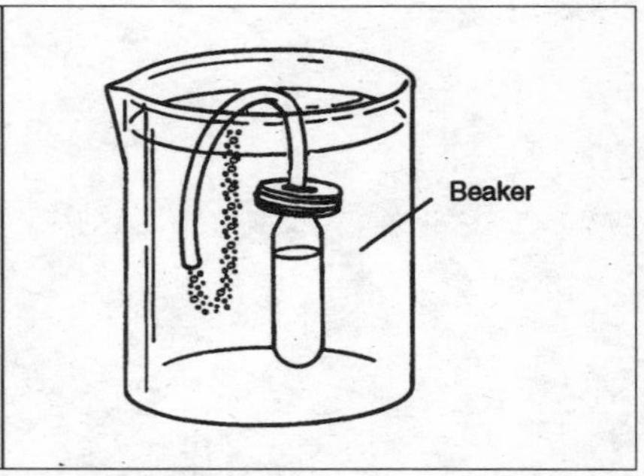

FIGURE 3

15. Use FIGURE 4 to graph the data from Part A. Plot time on the x-axis and the total number of bubbles on the y-axis. Draw a line that best fits the data points.

Part B—Reaction at a Higher Temperature

1. Place the beaker of water in the immersion bath or on the hot plate. Heat the water until its Celsius temperature is 10° higher than that of the room temperature water.

2. Repeat steps 3–14 in Part A, using the water bath at this higher temperature.

3. Plot your data from Part B on the same graph as Part A, but use a different colored pen or pencil.

Part C—Reaction at a Lower Temperature

1. Fill the beaker with tap water. Add ice to lower the Celsius temperature of the water 10° below that of the room temperature water.

2. Repeat steps 3–14 in Part A, using the water bath at this lower temperature.

3. Plot your data from Part C on the same graph as Parts A and B, but use a third color.

Data and Observations

Prediction of observations of reaction: Answers will vary.

Hypothesis relating reaction rate and temperature: Answers will vary.

Table 1   Data will vary.

Time (s)	A. Total number of bubbles (room temperature) ___ °C	B. Total number of bubbles (higher temperature) 35.0 ___ °C	C. Total number of bubbles (lower temperature) 15.0 ___ °C
0	0	0	0
15	0	1	0
30	0	2	0
45	2	4	1
60	4	6	2
75	6	10	4
90	10	12	4
105	14	17	6
120	19	22	9
135	23	26	12
150	26	31	15
165	28	33	20
180	30	37	23

Data will vary. In general, the slope of the line will increase as temperature increases.

FIGURE 4

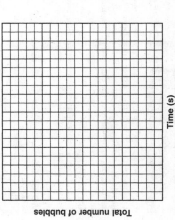

Total number of bubbles

Time (s)

Questions and Conclusions

1. How does raising the temperature affect the shape of the graphs that you plotted in FIGURE 4? **Answers will vary. Students should notice that the slope, or steepness, of the graph increases as the temperature is raised.**

2. Describe the relationship between reaction rate and temperature for the decomposition of sodium hypochlorite. **Answers will vary. Students should conclude that increasing the temperature increases the reaction rate.**

3. Why is it important that there be no sodium hypochlorite solution in the stem of the pipette in step 8 of the procedure? **When the pipette bulb is squeezed to expel air in step 10, any solution in the stem would splatter and be lost.**

4. Soft drinks contain carbonic acid (H_2CO_3). Carbonic acid decomposes to form water and carbon dioxide.

$$H_2CO_3 \rightarrow H_2O + CO_2$$

Two soft drink bottles are opened, and one is placed in a refrigerator while the other is left at room temperature. The carbonic acid in both bottles decomposes, but one bottle goes "flat" faster than the other. Which bottle will go flat first? Explain. **The bottle at room temperature will go flat faster. The decomposition reaction goes at a faster rate at higher temperatures.**

Strategy Check

____ Do you know how to collect data on the amount of oxygen produced by the decomposition of household bleach?

____ Can you determine from a graph of the data how the reaction rate differs when the temperature is changed?

Chapter 9

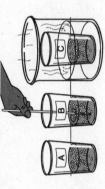

LABORATORY MANUAL ● Solutions 16

If you make a saltwater solution, you can use either table salt or rock salt. As long as the mass of each is the same, the salt with the greater surface area—table salt—will dissolve faster. Other factors affect the rate at which a solute dissolves. For example, temperature and stirring will change the dissolving rate of a solute. In addition, the dissolving rates of gases are affected by changes in pressure.

Strategy
You will explain the effects of particle size, temperature, and stirring on a solid in solution.
You will explain the effects of temperature, stirring, and pressure on a gas in solution.

Materials
beaker (500-mL)
bottle opener
6 cups (transparent plastic)
graduated cylinder (100-mL)
3 paper towels
soda water (bottle)
stirring rod
6 sugar cubes
watch with second hand
water (cold)
tap water (hot) **CAUTION:** *Use care when handling hot liquids.*
apron
goggles
gloves

Procedure
CAUTION: *Do not taste, eat, or drink any materials used in the lab.*

Part A Solid in Solution

1. Label the six plastic cups A through F. Use the graduated cylinder to add 100 mL of cold water to each of cups C, D, E, and F. Add 100 mL of hot water from the tap to each of cups A and B.

2. On three separate paper towels, crush three of the sugar cubes.

3. Add sugar samples to each cup (one at a time) as indicated in Table 1. When adding each sample, observe closely and record the time required for the sugar to dissolve completely. See FIGURE 1. When no sugar particles are visible, record the time in Table 1.

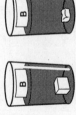

FIGURE 1

Part B Gas in Solution

1. Rinse cups A, B, and C from Part A with water.

2. Observe the unopened bottle of soda water. Open the bottle and observe it again. Compare your observations and record your comparison in Part B of the Data and Observations section.

3. Pour hot water from the tap into the 500-mL beaker until it is about half full.

4. Add 25 mL of soda water to each of the three cups. Stir the soda water in cup B. Place cup C in the beaker of hot water. Leave cup A as your control. Compare the rate of bubbling in each cup. Record your observations in Table 2.

FIGURE 2

Data and Observations
Part A Solid in Solution
Table 1

Cup	Sugar sample	Water conditions	Time	Rating
A	crushed	hot		1
B	cube	hot		4
C	crushed	cold		5
D	cube	cold		6
E	crushed	cold, stirred		2
F	cube	cold, stirred		3

192

Part B Gas in Solution

Observations of unopened and opened bottle: **Bubbles of gas appeared in the opened bottle.**
No (or very few) bubbles seen in the unopened bottle.

Table 2

Cup	Soda conditions	Observations and comparison of bubbling
A	control	little or no bubbling
B	stirred	much bubbling
C	heated	much bubbling

Questions and Conclusions

1. In Table 1 rate the sugar samples from fastest to slowest in dissolving. Give the fastest-dissolving sample a rating of 1. The slowest-dissolving sample should be rated 6.

2. How does particle size affect the rate at which sugar dissolves in water? **Many small particles**
   dissolve faster than one large particle.

3. How does temperature affect the rate at which sugar dissolves in water? **Sugar dissolves in**
   water faster at higher temperatures.

4. How does stirring affect the rate at which sugar dissolves in water? **Stirring increases the rate at**
   which sugar dissolves in water.

5. How did you create a pressure change in the bottle of soda water? What happened as a result
   of this pressure change? **The pressure in the soda water bottle was decreased by opening the**
   bottle. When the bottle was opened, bubbles of CO$_2$ gas escaped from the soda water.

6. What factors cause the rate of bubbling in soda water to increase? **Heating, stirring, and reducing**
   the pressure all increase the bubbling rate of soda water.

7. Carbonated beverages contain dissolved CO$_2$ gas. If you shake the bottle and then open it,
   the beverage may shoot into the air. Explain why this happens. **Shaking the bottle (similar to**
   stirring) causes carbon dioxide to escape from the solution. This released carbon dioxide gas
   increases the pressure on the liquid inside the bottle. When the bottle is opened, there is a
   sudden reduction of the pressure. The dissolved gases quickly come out of solution and expand
   rapidly, forcing the soda out almost explosively.

Strategy Check

___ Can you demonstrate the effect increasing the volume of solvent has on the dissolving rate
    of solids in solution?

___ Can you compare and contrast the effect of temperature on the dissolving rate of solids in
    solution by dissolving sugar in hot tea and iced tea?

Chapter 9

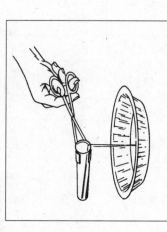

LABORATORY MANUAL   ● **Solubility** **17**

The most familiar kind of solution is a solid dissolved in water. When you make lemonade, a water solution. Usually, no chemical change takes place when a solid is dissolved in a liquid. If the liquid evaporates, the original solid remains chemically unchanged.

The maximum amount of solute that can dissolve in a solvent is called the solubility of the solution. Solubility is often expressed as grams of solute per 100 grams of solvent. The solubility of a substance is not the same for all conditions. For example, temperature changes can affect the solubility of a solid in water.

Strategy

You will determine the solubility of salt.
You will determine the effect of temperature on the solubility of salt.
You will interpret information from a solubility graph.

Materials 👓 🧤 🔥 🥽

apron
balance
2 beakers (250-mL)
graduated cylinder (10-mL)
goggles
hot plate
ice
hot mitt
potassium chloride, KCl (cr)
3 potpie pans (aluminum)
3 test tubes
test-tube holders
test-tube rack
thermometer
water (distilled)

Prepare 5.0 g samples of KCl prior to class. Aluminum potpie pans are used as evaporating dishes.

CAUTION: *Wear safety goggles and a laboratory apron throughout this experiment.*

Procedure

1. Fill one beaker about one-third full of tap water. Heat the water on the hot plate until the temperature reaches 55°C–60°C. Use the thermometer to determine the temperature.

2. Fill the second beaker about one-third full of ice water.

3. Label the three test tubes A, B, and C. Also label the three aluminum pans A, B, and C. Find the mass of each pan and record it in Table 1.

4. Add 5.0 g of KCl to each tube.

5. Using the graduated cylinder, add 5.0 mL of distilled water to each test tube. Hold each tube one-fourth of the way down from the top with your thumb and index finger. Flick the bottom of the tube with the index finger of your other hand. In this way, gently shake each tube for 30 s. Be careful to avoid spilling solution.

6. Place test tube B in the test-tube rack.

7. Place test tube A in the beaker of ice water for about 5 min.

8. Slowly pour the liquid from tube A into pan A, and from tube B into pan B. Do not transfer any of the solid. You will need to pour the liquid slowly.

9. Carefully place tube C in the water on the hot plate. Allow the contents to reach the temperature of the water bath, which will take about 5 min. Use the test-tube holder to remove the tube to the test-tube rack. CAUTION: *The tube will be hot.*

10. Using the test-tube holder, carefully pour the liquid from tube C into pan C. Do not transfer any of the solid. You will need to pour the liquid slowly. See FIGURE 1.

11. Determine the mass of each pan and its liquid. Record the masses in Table 1.

12. Heat the pans on a hot plate using low heat. When all the liquid evaporates, use a pot holder to remove the pans from the heat. CAUTION: *Do not touch the hot pans or the hot plate.* After the pans have cooled, find the mass of each and record this information in Table 1.

FIGURE 1

Data and Observations

Table 1

Data depend on materials used. Sample data are given.

Object	Mass (g)		
	A	B	C
Empty pan	32.4	32.9	33.4
Pan and liquid	38.4	39.2	40.5
Pan after evaporation	33.7	34.5	35.6
Liquid evaporation	4.7	4.7	4.9
Salt after evaporation	1.3	1.6	2.2
Solubility	27.6	34.0	44.9

13. Determine the mass of the liquid evaporated from each pan by subtracting the mass of the pan after evaporation from the mass of the pan and liquid. **Point out to students that for water, 1 mL = 1 g Students should use the proportion,**

14. Determine the mass of the salt left in each pan after evaporation by subtracting the mass of the empty pan from the mass of the pan after evaporation. Record this information in Table 1.

15. Use the masses of the dissolved salts to determine the solubility per 100 g of water. Use a proportion in your calculations. Record the solubility in Table 1.

Questions and Conclusions

1. What type of solid material settled to the bottom of each test tube? **Excess salt and impurities settled to the bottom of each test tube.**

2. What would you expect to happen to the solubility of KCl in each tube if the temperature of the water were increased to 75°C? **The solubility of each would increase.**

3. Look at the solubility graph in FIGURE 2. This graph shows how temperature changes affect the solubility of four common compounds.

    a. How does an increase in temperature affect the solubility of NaCl? **The solubility of NaCl remains almost constant, rising only slightly with increasing temperature.**

    b. How does an increase in temperature affect the solubility of KNO₃? **The solubility of KNO₃ will rise at an increasing rate with increasing temperature.**

FIGURE 2

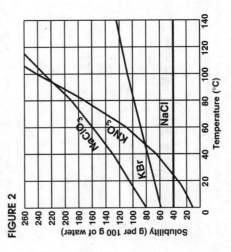

---

4. Refer to FIGURE 2. At what temperature does KNO₃ have the same solubility as KBr? What is the solubility at this temperature? **The two salts have equal solubilities at 49°C. The solubility is about 82g/100g water.**

Strategy Check

___ Can you demonstrate the increased solubility of a solid in a liquid with temperature?

___ Can you compare and contrast the amount of solute in saturated and unsaturated solutions?

Chapter 10

Carbohydrates: Chemistry and Identification 18

Carbohydrates make up a large group of chemical compounds found in cells. Carbohydrates are an energy source or are used in making cell structures. There are three different groups of carbohydrates. They are called monosaccharides, disaccharides, and polysaccharides. *Saccharide* means sugar.

Strategy

You will write simple formulas for several carbohydrates.
You will read structural formulas for several carbohydrates.
You will use models to construct the three main types of carbohydrates.
You will identify the three main types of carbohydrates by using chemical tests.
You will test different food samples to determine what type of carbohydrate they contain.

Materials

beaker (Pyrex)
droppers
glass marking pencil or labels
hot plate
paper models
scissors
test tubes
test-tube holder
apple juice
Benedict's solution
disaccharide solution
honey solution
iodine solution
monosaccharide solution
oat solution
polysaccharide solution
powdered sugar solution
table sugar solution
apron
goggles
gloves

Procedure

CAUTION: *Do not taste, eat, or drink any materials used in the lab.*
CAUTION: *Inform your teacher if you come in contact with any chemicals.*

Part A Carbohydrate Models
Group 1. Monosaccharides (single molecule sugars)
1. A single molecule sugar is called a monosaccharide. The prefix *mono-* means one. Glucose, fructose, and galactose are three monosaccharides. Examine the structural formulas of these three sugars in FIGURE 1. What three chemical elements are present in the three monosaccharides?
carbon, hydrogen, oxygen

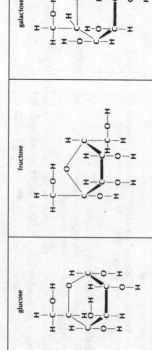

glucose **fructose** **galactose**

FIGURE 1

2. How many atoms of carbon are present in a molecule of
glucose? **6**
fructose? **6**
galactose? **6**

3. Add subscripts to the following to indicate the correct simple formula. Fill in the blanks by counting the total number of carbon, hydrogen, and oxygen atoms in each molecule.
glucose C **6** H **12** O **6**
fructose C **6** H **12** O **6**
galactose C **6** H **12** O **6**

4. Are there two times as many hydrogen atoms as oxygen atoms in a molecule of
glucose? **yes**
fructose? **yes**
galactose? **yes**

5. Are there two times as many hydrogen atoms as oxygen atoms in a molecule of water?
yes

6. Compare the structural formulas of glucose and fructose. Are the two molecules exactly the same shape? **no**

7. Are both glucose and fructose monosaccharides? **yes**

Copy page of paper models that appears at the end of the Teacher's Edition of the Laboratory Manual.
Group 2. Disaccharides (double molecule sugars)
Two monosaccharide sugar molecules can join chemically to form a larger carbohydrate molecule called a double sugar, or disaccharide. The prefix *di-* means two. By chemically joining a glucose with a fructose molecule, a double sugar called sucrose is produced. Use the paper models given to you by your teacher to complete this section.

8. Cut out a model of one glucose and one fructose molecule. CAUTION: *Use care when handling sharp objects. Always be extremely careful with scissors. Cut along solid lines only.* Try to join the two molecules like puzzle pieces.
Do the glucose and fructose fit together easily to form a sucrose molecule? **no**

9. In order to join the molecules, remove an -OH end from one molecule and an -H end from another. Cut along dotted lines. Does removing the -H and -OH ends now allow the molecules to fit together easily? **yes**

10. The -H and -OH ends that were removed can also fit together with each other to form a molecule. This new molecule has a simple formula of ___ **H₂O** ___ and is called ___ **water** ___.

11. Write the simple formula for sucrose by adding together the molecular formulas for glucose and fructose and then subtracting water, H₂O. (Use structural formulas for this step, not the models.)
C₁₂H₂₂O₁₁

Different disaccharide molecules can be made by joining other monosaccharides in different combinations. By chemically joining a glucose molecule with another glucose molecule, a double sugar called maltose is formed.

12. Cut out and attempt to join two new glucose model molecules like puzzle pieces. What must be removed from the glucose model molecules so that they easily fit together?
H end from one molecule and OH end from the other molecule

13. Write the simple formula for maltose. (See question 11.) $C_{12}H_{22}O_{11}$

14. How does the simple formula for sucrose compare to maltose? **They are the same.**

15. Are there two times as many hydrogen atoms as oxygen atoms in a disaccharide? **yes**

16. How many monosaccharide molecules are needed to form one sucrose molecule? **2**

17. How many monosaccharide molecules are needed to form one maltose molecule? **2**

Group 3. Polysaccharides (many molecule sugars)
Just as double sugars were formed from two single sugar molecules, polysaccharides are formed when many single sugars are joined chemically. The prefix *poly-* means many. Starch, glycogen, and cellulose are the three most common polysaccharides. They consist of long chains of glucose molecules joined together.

18. Construct a starch molecule by joining three glucose molecules. This model will represent only a small part of a starch molecule because starch consists of hundreds of glucose molecules. What must be removed from the glucose model molecules in order to have them easily fit together?
H end from one molecule and OH end from another molecule

Part B Identification of Carbohydrates
Chemical Tests on Known Carbohydrates
Benedict's Test
1. Pour water into a 500-mL beaker until it is half full. Bring the water to a boil on a hot plate. CAUTION: *Do not touch hot plate.* The boiling water in FIGURE 2 is called a hot water bath. CAUTION: *Water is very hot. Use care when handling hot liquids.*

2. Number three clean test tubes 1 to 3. Using FIGURE 3 as a guide and a clean dropper for each tube, add the following:
Tube 1—30 drops of monosaccharide solution
Tube 2—30 drops of disaccharide solution
Tube 3—30 drops of polysaccharide solution

3. Add 30 drops of Benedict's solution to each tube. CAUTION: *If you spill Benedict's solution, rinse with water and call your teacher.*

4. Place the three test tubes into the hot water bath for 5 min.

5. Use a test-tube holder to remove the tubes from the hot water bath. CAUTION: *Water and test tubes are very hot. Handle test tubes only with a test-tube holder.*

6. Observe any color changes in the solutions. NOTE: A color change may or may not occur when Benedict's solution is added to a carbohydrate and then heated. A change from blue to green, yellow, orange, or red occurs if a monosaccharide is present. The original blue color will remain after heating if a disaccharide or polysaccharide is present.

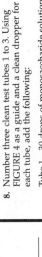

FIGURE 2

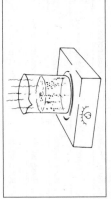

30 drops Benedict's solution in each tube

30 drops monosaccharide solution | 30 drops disaccharide solution | 30 drops polysaccharide solution

BENEDICT'S TEST

FIGURE 3

7. Record the colors of the solutions in the test tubes in column three of Table 1.

8. Number three clean test tubes 1 to 3. Using FIGURE 4 as a guide and a clean dropper for each tube, add the following:
Tube 1—30 drops of monosaccharide solution
Tube 2—30 drops of disaccharide solution
Tube 3—30 drops of polysaccharide solution

9. Add 4 drops of iodine solution to each tube. CAUTION: *Iodine is poisonous. Do not allow iodine to get on your hands. Wash immediately if iodine comes in contact with your skin. Do not inhale iodine fumes.*

10. Mix the contents of each tube by gently swirling.

11. Record in column four of Table 1 the color of the solutions in the three tubes. NOTE: A color change may or may not occur when iodine solution is added to a carbohydrate. A change from its original rust color to deep blue-black occurs if a polysaccharide is present. The original color of the carbohydrate remains if a disaccharide or monosaccharide sugar is present.

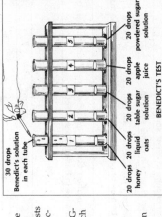

30 drops monosaccharide solution | 30 drops disaccharide solution | 30 drops polysaccharide solution

4 drops iodine solution

IODINE TEST

FIGURE 4

Data and Observations
Table 1

Tube number	Carbohydrate type	Change in color after heating with Benedict's	Change in color after adding iodine
1	Monosaccharide	Green, yellow, orange, or red	Rust, white
2	Disaccharide	Blue	Rust, white
3	Polysaccharide	Blue	Deep blue

Chemical Tests on Unknown Carbohydrates
You have tested known carbohydrates, so you are now ready to test some unknown substances. By comparing results of the Benedict's and iodine tests in Table 1, you should be able to classify monosaccharides, disaccharides, or polysaccharides.

12. Number five clean test tubes 1 to 5. Using FIGURE 5 as a guide and a clean dropper for each tube, add the following:
Tube 1—20 drops of honey
Tube 2—20 drops of liquid oats
Tube 3—20 drops of table sugar solution
Tube 4—20 drops of apple juice
Tube 5—20 drops of powdered sugar solution

13. Add 30 drops of Benedict's solution to each test tube.

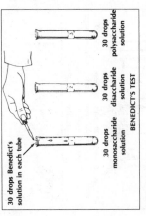

30 drops Benedict's solution in each tube

20 drops honey | 20 drops liquid oats | 20 drops table sugar solution | 20 drops apple juice | 20 drops powdered sugar solution

BENEDICT'S TEST

FIGURE 5

14. Place all five test tubes into a hot water bath for 5 min.

15. Remove the test tubes from the bath with a test-tube holder and note any color changes. Record the color of the solutions in Table 2.

16. Using FIGURE 6 as a guide, prepare five more test tubes containing the same substances just used (honey, oats, and so on). *Do not add Benedict's solution.*

17. Add 4 drops of iodine solution to each tube and mix by swirling.

18. Observe any color changes and record them in Table 2.

19. On the basis of your results, classify each carbohydrate as a monosaccharide, disaccharide, or polysaccharide. Record your answers in Table 2.

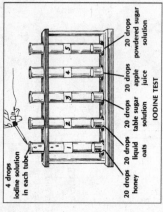

4 drops iodine solution in each tube

20 drops honey 20 drops liquid oats 20 drops table sugar solution 20 drops apple juice 20 drops powdered sugar solution

IODINE TEST

FIGURE 6

Table 2

Carbohydrate	Benedict's color	Iodine color	Carbohydrate type
Honey	Green, yellow, orange, or red	Rust, white	Monosaccharide
Oats	Blue	Blue	Polysaccharide
Table sugar	Blue	Rust, white	Disaccharide
Apple	Green, yellow, orange, or red	Rust, white	Monosaccharide
Powdered sugar	Blue	Rust, white	Disaccharide

Questions and Conclusions

1. Name the three categories of carbohydrates studied in this investigation. **monosaccharides, disaccharides, polysaccharides**

2. What three elements are present in all carbohydrates? **carbon, oxygen, and hydrogen**

3. Give two examples each of sugars that are
   a. monosaccharides. **glucose, fructose, or galactose**
   b. disaccharides. **maltose, sucrose**
   c. polysaccharides. **starch, glycogen, or cellulose**

4. a. How many times larger is the number of hydrogen atoms than oxygen atoms in all carbohydrates? **2 times larger**
   b. In water? **2 times larger**

5. *Mono-* means one, *di-* means two, and *poly-* means many. Why are these terms used in describing the three types of sugars? **One molecule forms a monosaccharide; two monosaccharides form a disaccharide; many monosaccharides form a polysaccharide.**

6. How can you tell by using Benedict's and iodine solutions if a sugar is a
   a. monosaccharide? **Monosaccharides cause color change in Benedict's solution.**
   b. disaccharide? **Disaccharides cause no color change in either solution.**
   c. polysaccharide? **Polysaccharides cause color change in iodine solution.**

7. A certain sugar has no change in color when tested with Benedict's solution. Can you tell what type of saccharide it is? Explain. **No. It might be a di- or polysaccharide. Results of the iodine test are needed.**

8. A certain sugar has a color change in Benedict's solution. Can you tell what type of saccharide it is? Explain. **Yes. Monosaccharides cause color change in Benedict's solution.**

9. Give an example of a food that is a
   a. monosaccharide. **honey**
   b. disaccharide. **table sugar**
   c. polysaccharide. **oats**

Strategy Check

_____ Can you write simple formulas for some carbohydrates?

_____ Can you read and understand structural formulas for carbohydrates?

_____ Can you make models of the three main types of carbohydrates?

_____ Can you identify monosaccharides, disaccharides, and polysaccharides by means of chemical tests?

_____ Can you test food samples to determine whether they contain carbohydrates and what kind they contain?

Chapter 10

● Proteins: Chemistry and Identification 19

Living things are made up of many different molecules. One important group of chemical molecules is proteins. Proteins make up the bulk of all solid material within your body and the bodies of other animals. Your muscle, skin, hair, and inside organs are largely protein. Proteins are essential for body growth and repair. They also make up some hormones that are involved in the chemical control of the body.

Strategy

You will recognize simple formulas for amino acids.
You will use models of different amino acids to construct a protein molecule.
You will use chemical tests to determine if a protein is present in a substance.

Materials

dropper
glass-marking pencil or labels
paper models
scissors
test tubes
test-tube rack (or tin can)
absorbent cotton
cream cheese
dog hair (white)
egg white (hard-boiled)
fingernail clippings
nitric acid
apron
goggles
gloves

Procedure

Part A—Models of Protein: Amino Acids, Building Blocks of Protein

Proteins are complex molecules made up of smaller molecules called amino acids. There are about 20 different amino acids found in nature. The element nitrogen (N) is present in all amino acids.

1. Examine the structural formulas of the four representative amino acids shown in FIGURE 1, and name the four elements present in these amino acids.

 __carbon, hydrogen, oxygen, nitrogen__

2. What is the simple formula for the amino acid

 a. glycine? __C 2 H 5 O 2 N 1__

 b. alanine? __C 3 H 7 O 2 N 1__

 c. valine? __C 5 H11 O 2 N 1__

 d. threonine? __C 4 H 9 O 3 N 1__

FIGURE 1

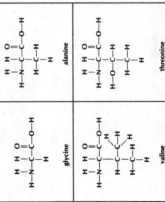

3. How do the simple formulas for all of the amino acids differ?

 __in the number of each molecule present__

4. Note the upper right corner of each amino acid. These ends have a special arrangement of carbon, oxygen, and hydrogen atoms. This end arrangement is called a carboxyl group and looks like this:

Circle the carboxyl group on each structural formula in FIGURE 1.

5. Note the upper left hand corner of each amino acid. These ends have a special arrangement of nitrogen and hydrogen atoms. The end arrangement is called an amino group and looks like this:

Use dashed lines to circle the amino groups on the structural formulas in FIGURE 1.

In the previous lab, you studied carbohydrates.

 a. Do carbohydrates have carboxyl groups? __no__

 b. Do carbohydrates have amino groups? __no__

6. How does the number of hydrogen atoms compare with the number of oxygen atoms in each amino acid? __There are more hydrogen than oxygen atoms.__

7. Amino acids are not protein molecules. They are only the "building blocks" of protein. Several amino acids must be joined in a chain to form a protein molecule. You can show how amino acids join by using models. Use the paper models given to you by your teacher to complete this section.

8. Cut out the four amino acid models. CAUTION: *Always be extremely careful with scissors. Cut along the solid lines only.* Attempt to join the amino acids. Can the amino acid models easily join to form a protein molecule? __no__

9. Join the molecules by removing as many —OH groups and —H groups as needed from the amino acids. All four amino acids can be joined in this manner to form a protein. Join them in the order valine—threonine—alanine—glycine. **Use an enlarged copy of FIGURE 1 for students to cut.**

10. Join the left over —OH and —H ends.

11. What chemical substance is formed with the —OHs and —Hs joined? __water__

12. How many molecules of water are formed when four amino acids are joined? __three__

13. What chemical compound is formed when the four amino acids are joined? __protein__

14. Describe the difference between an amino acid molecule and a protein molecule.

 __Several amino acids combine to form one protein molecule.__

15. There are thousands of different proteins in living organisms. Use your models to construct two proteins different from the one you already made. Identify the proteins as *a* or *b* and list the order in which you connected the amino acids. __Answers will vary.__

Part B—Identification of Proteins

1. Number five clean test tubes 1 to 5. Place them in a test-tube rack. Using FIGURE 2 as a guide, add the following substances to each test tube:

 tube 1—fingernail clippings tube 4—dog hair, white
 tube 2—egg white, hard-boiled tube 5—cream cheese
 tube 3—absorbent cotton

2. Add 5 drops of nitric acid to each test tube.
 CAUTION: *Nitric acid is harmful to skin and clothing. Rinse with water if spillage occurs. Call your teacher.*

199

3. A substance containing protein will turn yellow when nitric acid is added to it. No color change to yellow indicates that the substance being tested has no protein. Wait several minutes. Then record the color of the items placed in each tube in Table 1.

4. On the basis of the nitric acid test, indicate in the last column of Table 1 if the substances tested contain protein.

FIGURE 2

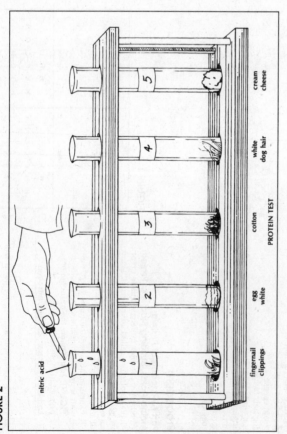

nitric acid

fingernail clippings   egg white   cotton   white dog hair   cream cheese

PROTEIN TEST

Data and Observations

Table 1

Substance	Color change due to nitric acid	Substance tested is a protein (answer yes or no)
Fingernail	yellow	yes
Egg white	yellow	yes
Cotton	no change	no
Dog hair	yellow	yes
Cream cheese	yellow	yes

Questions and Conclusions

1. Name four amino acids. __glycine, alanine, valine, threonine__

2. a. How many amino acids are there? __20__

   b. How are amino acids used by living things? __They make up molecules of protein.__

3. List several of your body parts that are protein. __muscle, hair, skin, inside organs such as liver, stomach__

4. Name the four chemical elements present in the amino acids studied. __carbon, hydrogen, nitrogen, oxygen__

5. Name the two special end groups present in amino acids. __carboxyl groups, amino groups__

6. What element is present in protein that is not present in carbohydrates? __nitrogen__

7. Explain how a protein molecule is formed in a living organism. __Several amino acids join to form a protein and water.__

8. Explain how one protein differs from another protein. __number of amino acids, type of amino acids, shape of molecule__

9. Describe how you can tell if a substance is a protein by using nitric acid. __A protein turns yellow when nitric acid is added to it.__

10. a. List those substances you tested that were protein. __fingernail, egg white, dog hair, cream cheese__

    b. List those substances you tested that were not protein. __cotton__

11. Using what you have learned about proteins, decide which of the following substances are protein. Place a check mark on the line next to each substance that is a protein.

   a. hamburger _____ X   e. liver _____ X

   b. chicken _____ X   f. human hair _____ X

   c. peanut oil _____   g. stomach _____ X

   d. maple syrup _____   h. 207 amino acids joined _____ X

Strategy Check

_____ Can you identify an amino acid from its formula?

_____ Can you construct a protein molecule using models of amino acids?

_____ Can you explain a test used to determine whether a substance contains a protein?

Chapter 11

• **Speed and Acceleration   20**

Speed is the distance an object travels divided by the time interval. Speed can be expressed as kilometers per hour (km/h), meters per second (m/s), and so on. In most cases, moving objects do not travel at a constant speed. The speed of an object usually increases and decreases as the object moves. Therefore, the average speed is used to describe the motion. Average speed is a ratio between the total distance and the total time that the object traveled.

$$average\ speed = \frac{total\ distance}{total\ time}$$

In straight line motion in one direction, *acceleration* is the rate at which an object's speed changes. You can express acceleration as meters per second each second (m/s²). This unit represents the change in speed in meters per second each second. If a car has an average speed of 80 km/h on a hilly road, it probably changes speed many times. If the car is traveling at a constant speed of 80 km/h on a straight and level road, it is not changing speed. The acceleration of the car is zero.

Strategy
You will determine the average speed of a small toy car.
You will study the forces that affect the motion of the car.

Materials
books (stack about 20 cm tall)
meterstick
pen or pencil
ramp (wood about 50 cm long)
stopwatch or watch with a second hand
tape (masking)
toy car or ball

Procedure
1. Clear a runway (preferably uncarpeted) about 6 m long.   **A school hallway is fine.**

2. At one end of the runway, set up a launching ramp. Put one end of the wood ramp on the stack of books and the other end on the floor. (See FIGURE 1 on page 58.) You will launch the toy car on its test runs from the top of the ramp.

3. Place a masking tape marker where the ramp touches the floor. Label this marker 0.0 m. Place similar markers at 1.0 m, 2.0 m, 3.0 m, 4.0 m, 5.0 m, and 6.0 m distances from the bottom of the ramp.

FIGURE 1

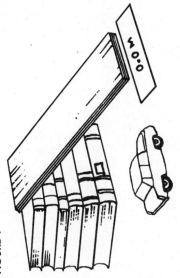

0.0 m

4. Practice launching the toy car down the ramp several times. Observe the car's motion and path. Add or remove books from the ramp so that the car travels a distance of 5.0 m. Remember that the 5.0-m distance begins at the bottom of the ramp.

5. Measure the time that the car takes to travel the 5.0 m. Record the time in Table 1. Measure and record the times of three more trials.

Data and Observations

Table 1

Trial	Times (s)	Speed (m/s)
1	4.0	1.25
2	5.0	1.00
3	5.0	1.00
4	4.0	1.25
Average	4.5	1.11

FIGURE 2

Speed (m/s) vs Trial (1, 2, 3, 4, Average)

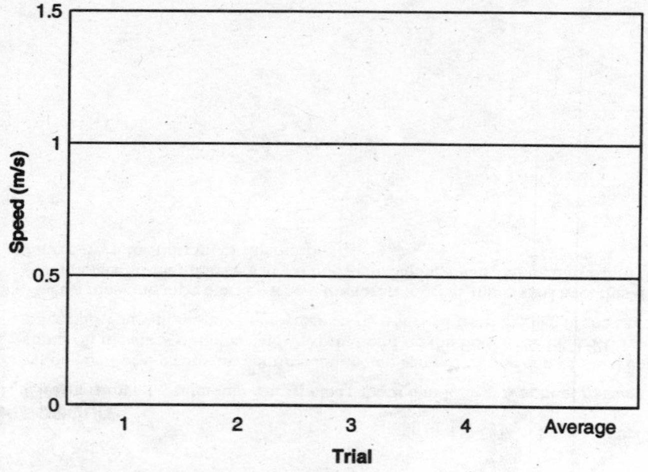

Questions and Conclusions

1. Calculate the speed for each of the four trials by dividing the distance by time. Record the results in Table 1.

2. Calculate the average time for the four trials. Record the results in Table 1.

3. Calculate the average speed of the toy car by dividing the distance by the average time. Record the results in Table 1.

4. Plot the speed of the toy car on the bar graph in FIGURE 2.

5. Describe the motion of the car as it moved across the floor. **The car slowed.**

6. What caused the car to slow down and stop? **friction between the wheels of the car and the floor**

7. Did the toy car travel at a constant speed? How do you know this? **No. The car started at zero, reached a maximum speed at the bottom of the ramp, then slowed to zero again.**

---

8. How could you change this experiment to make the car accelerate at a faster rate? **The slope of the ramp or the surface over which the car moved could be changed.**

9. Consider the 5.0 m that the car traveled. What conditions are necessary for the car to have no acceleration? **The car would have frictionless wheels and move on a nearly frictionless surface, such as ice.**

Strategy Check

___ Why must all the cars start at the same point on the ramp?

___ Why do you measure the 5.0 m starting from the bottom of the ramp rather than the top?

202

Chapter 11

LABORATORY MANUAL ● Projectile Motion 21

The path followed by a projectile is called a trajectory. FIGURE 1 shows the shape of a toy rocket's trajectory. Because the force of gravity is the only force acting on it after the fuel is spent, the toy rocket has an acceleration of 9.8 m/s² downward. However, the *motion of the projectile is upward and then downward.*

FIGURE 2 shows the velocity vector for a toy rocket at different moments along its trajectory. The rocket's velocity upward begins to decrease after the force exerted by the engine is less than the force of gravity. And then, for an instant at the highest point of its trajectory, its velocity upward is zero because it stops moving upward. The rocket then begins to fall, and its velocity begins to increase downward.

FIGURE 1

FIGURE 2

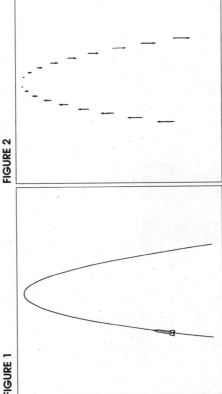

As you can see, the shape of the upward trajectory of the rocket is a mirror image of the shape of its downward trajectory.

Strategy
You will measure the flight times of a projectile.
You will analyze the flight times of a projectile.

Materials
goggles
3 stopwatches
toy water rocket and launcher
water (bucket)

Assign three students as timers for each toy rocket flight—one to record the rocket's time up, one to record the rocket's total flight time, and one to record the rocket's time down.

Toy water rockets are available at most toy shops and hobby shops.

Procedure
1. Wear goggles during this experiment.
2. Fill the water rocket to the level line shown on the rocket's body. Always fill the rocket to the same level during each flight in the experiment.
3. Attach the pump/launcher to the rocket as shown in the manufacturer's directions.
4. Pump the pump/launcher 10 times. **CAUTION:** *Do not exceed 20 pumps or the maximum number suggested by the manufacturer, whichever is lower. Be sure to hold the rocket and pump/launcher so that the rocket is not directed toward yourself or another person.*
5. At a given signal to the timers, launch the rocket. Your teacher will have timers measure specific parts of the flight using stopwatches. Record the values measured by the timers as Total time, Time up, and Time down in Table 1.
6. Repeat steps 2–6 twice.
7. Repeat steps 2–6 three more times, increasing the number of pumps to 15 for each launch. **CAUTION:** *Do not exceed the maximum number of pumps suggested by the manufacturer.*
8. Calculate the average of the total times, the average of the times up, and the average of the times down for the two sets of launches. Record these values in Table 2.
9. Make a bar graph of the data in Table 2 in FIGURE 3 in the Data and Observations section.

Data and Observations

Table 1   Sample data. Data will depend upon type of toy rocket used.

Number of pumps	Total time (s)	Time up (s)	Time down (s)
10	4.04	2.06	2.20
10	4.12	2.24	2.02
10	3.98	1.94	2.16
15	4.76	2.46	2.44
15	4.60	2.32	2.34
15	4.54	2.50	2.42

Table 2   Data will vary.

Number of pumps	Average total time (s)	Average time up (s)	Average time down (s)
10	4.05	2.08	2.13
15	4.63	2.43	2.40

Questions and Conclusions

1. How well did your predictions agree with the measured times?
   Answers will vary.

2. Do your results support the statement that the time for a projectile to reach its highest point is equal to the time for the projectile to fall back to Earth? Explain.
   Answers will vary. Students should recognize that average time up and time down were almost equal to each other for each of the two sets of launches.

3. Why was the number of pumps used to launch the rocket kept the same during each set of launches?
   The number of pumps was kept constant so that conditions remained the same for all launches in a set. By keeping the number constant during each set of launches, averages of the three time measurements could be calculated.

4. Why would you expect the flight times to be greater for the launches that were done using 15 pumps than those that were done with 10 pumps?
   The 15 pumps produced greater air pressure inside the rocket. When the rocket was launched, the increased air pressure caused a greater vertical velocity and the rocket went higher.

Strategy Check

____ How does the angle at which the rocket is launched affect its motion?

FIGURE 3

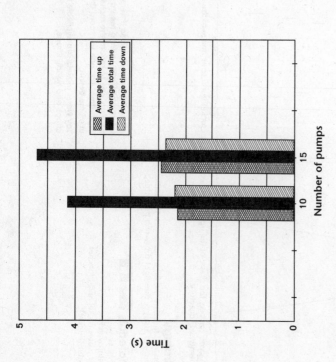

Chapter 12
LABORATORY MANUAL

Static and Sliding Friction 22

When two objects are in contact, the molecules on their surfaces rub against one another. These surfaces are not smooth; small lumps and grooves exist. When one object slides over the other, the surfaces catch and stick as these lumps and grooves nestle together. The force that results between materials due to the irregularities in their surfaces is called friction. Many factors affect the force of friction, including the nature and conditions of surfaces and how hard the surfaces are pressed together.

For a block sliding on a level horizontal surface, the weight of the block pushes the two surfaces together. The coefficient of friction, symbolized by the Greek letter μ, is the ratio of friction force to the force pushing the objects together. This relationship holds true on a flat horizontal surface when the force that presses the surfaces together is the weight acting on the top object.

When an object is at rest, static friction holds the object in place. This type of friction must be overcome to move the object. When one object is already sliding over another, sliding friction occurs. The force needed to sustain the constant motion of the object must equal the sliding friction force.

Strategy
You will calculate coefficients of static and sliding friction.
You will compare static friction to sliding friction.
You will describe the effect of weight on the force of friction.
You will determine the effect of surface area on friction.

Materials
eye hook
set of masses
spring scale calibrated in newtons
2" × 4" wood block

Procedure
1. Screw the eye hook into the end of the block. Weigh the wood block and eye hook using the spring scale. Record the weight in Table 1.

2. Lay the wood block on a flat surface as shown in FIGURE 1.

3. Find the force required to move the block from rest. Pull on the spring scale and notice the highest reading that occurs before the block moves. That is the static friction.

4. Find the force required to keep the block moving at a constant velocity. As you pull on the spring scale, the reading will not be exact because the friction value will vary. Make the best judgment you can for the value of sliding friction. Record this information in Table 1.

5. Repeat steps 3 and 4 with different weights added on top of the friction block. Be sure to record the new weight of the block and its added weight.

FIGURE 1

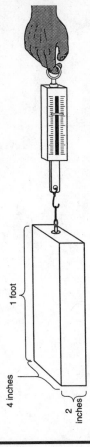

4 inches
1 foot
2 inches

6. Repeat steps 3 and 4 without masses added and with the block resting on a side with a different area.

7. Calculate the coefficient of static friction for each of the trials using the equation below.

$$\mu_{static} = \frac{\text{static friction force}}{\text{weight}}$$

8. Calculate the coefficient of sliding friction for each of the trials using the equation below.

$$\mu_{sliding} = \frac{\text{sliding friction force}}{\text{weight}}$$

9. Graph the relationship between the weight of the block and each force of friction in FIGURE 2. Use a single graph to compare the data for sliding and static friction.

Data and Observations

Table 1

Friction Coefficients

Force of static friction	Force of sliding friction	Weight of block	μstatic	μsliding	Area of side
0.9 N	0.6 N	3.0 N	0.30	0.20	105 cm²
1.3 N	0.8 N	4.0 N	0.33	0.20	105 cm²
1.5 N	1.1 N	5.0 N	0.30	0.22	105 cm²
1.9 N	1.2 N	6.0 N	0.32	0.20	105 cm²
0.9 N	0.6 N	3.0 N	0.30	0.20	270 cm²

FIGURE 2

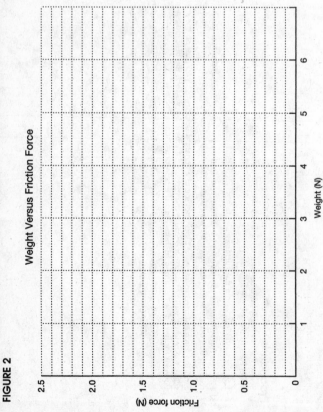

Weight Versus Friction Force

Questions and Conclusions

1. How did the addition of more weight affect the friction? **More weight on the block caused there to be more friction.**

2. How did the change in surface area of the contact between the block and the table affect the friction? **A change in surface area had no effect on the friction.**

3. How did the force of friction relate to the weight of the block? **As the weight of the block increased, both the static-friction force and the sliding-friction force increased.**

4. How do static friction and sliding friction relate to each other? **Static friction is always greater than sliding friction.**

5. What could be a source of error in this experiment? **Answers may vary. One major source of error could be the fact that getting exact readings from the spring scale was difficult. Some guessing was involved.**

6. What happened to the coefficients of friction as the weight increased? **The coefficients remained constant.**

7. What happened to the coefficients of friction as the surface area of the contact increased? **The coefficients remained constant.**

8. Does the coefficient of sliding friction depend on the weight of the block? Explain. **No. The coefficient of sliding friction does not depend on the weight of the block. As the weight increases, the friction force increases in direct proportion. The ratio of the friction force to weight does not change.**

9. Coefficients of friction are rarely listed with a precision greater than one digit past the decimal. Why is greater precision not used? **Variety among surfaces of the same material prevents greater precision.**

10. Does the area of contact between objects make a difference in the friction forces? Explain how you know. **No. The narrow and wide parts of the block produced identical results.**

11. If you are buying new tires for a car, would you prefer a high or a low coefficient of friction? Explain. **A high coefficient of friction would be best. High coefficients result in high friction forces for specific weights. High friction in tires allows them to hold onto the road well.**

Strategy Check

Why is it important that you pull straight forward on the spring attached to the wood block, rather than at an angle?

Chapter 12

• Newton's Second Law 23

Newton's second law of motion deals with acceleration, which is how fast something speeds up or slows down. Acceleration depends on the mass of an object and the force pulling or pushing it. One way to write Newton's second law is *force = mass × acceleration*. Another way to think of Newton's second law is that if the same force acts on two objects, the object with the greater mass will accelerate more slowly.

Strategy

You will time the acceleration of a small toy car.
You will observe the effects of increasing mass on acceleration.

Materials

balance
large table
meterstick
modeling clay (about 300 g)
small toy car with free-spinning wheels
stopwatch
string or thread
tape

Teacher note: Small metal toy cars are available at most toy stores for about a dollar. You can ask your students to bring cars from home. Wind-up cars won't work; cars must have free-spinning wheels.

Procedure

1. Cut a piece of string or thread 110 cm long. Tie a small loop in one end of the string.

2. Make a small ball of clay with a mass of about 2.5 g. Attach this ball of clay to the string by folding the clay around the loop. The loop will prevent the clay ball from falling off the string.

3. Divide the remaining clay into 40-g pieces.

4. Use your balance to measure the mass of the toy car. Write the mass of the car in the Data and Observations section.

5. Use a meterstick to find a spot on the table 1 m from the edge. Mark it with a small piece of tape. This spot will be the starting point for the toy car during the experiment.

6. Put the front of the toy car at the starting point. Hold the piece of string on the table so that the clay ball is about 3 cm over the edge. Tape the other end of the string to the front of the toy car. Trim any excess string so that it does not interfere with the car's wheels. Check that your setup is similar to that shown in FIGURE 1.

FIGURE 1

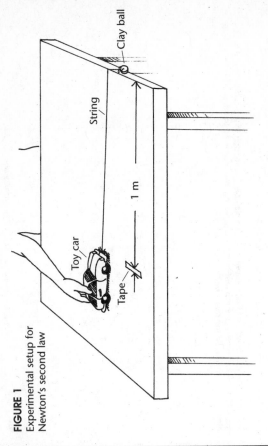

FIGURE 1
Experimental setup for
Newton's second law

7. Pick someone in your group to be the timer, someone to be the recorder, someone to hold the toy car in place and release it, and someone to catch it as it falls off the table.

8. Release the car. Use a stopwatch to measure the time it takes for the car to reach the table edge.

9. Write the travel time in Table 1.

10. Repeat steps 8 and 9 two more times. Use the data to calculate the average travel time for the car.

11. Add one 40-g piece of clay to the top of the car. Be careful that the clay does not interfere with the car's ability to roll freely.

12. Time three trips of the car. Record the travel times, calculate the average time, and record the average time in Table 1.

13. Repeat steps 11 and 12 until you have timed the car carrying 160 g of clay.

Data and Observations

Mass of car = __33.8__ g

Table 1

Sample data

Mass (g)		Travel Time (s)			
Total clay on top of car	Total car and clay	Time 1 (T1)	Time 2 (T2)	Time 3 (T3)	Average time (T1 + T2 + T3) ÷ 3
0	33.8	2.50	2.67	2.53	2.57
40	73.8	4.01	4.11	4.26	4.13
80	113.6	5.12	5.01	5.21	5.11
120	153.8	6.08	6.13	6.24	6.15
160	193.8	7.59	7.45	7.73	7.59

FIGURE 2

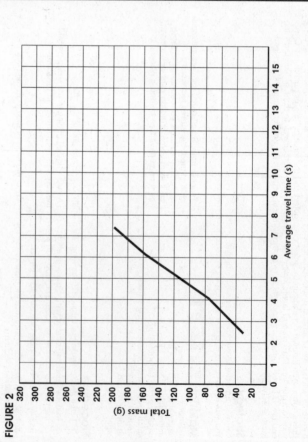

Questions and Conclusions

1. Make a graph of total mass versus time on the graph in FIGURE 2.

2. Explain how your data supports Newton's second law of motion.
   Newton's second law states that $F = m \times a$. The force (weight of the clay ball) is the same each time. Given the same force, a more massive object will accelerate more slowly. This slower acceleration was observed as mass was added to the car.

3. Why is it important to average three travel times for each one of the total masses?
   Even though the mass is the same, travel times can be slightly different. By averaging three travel times, you can be more certain that your number is close to the actual time.

4. What were some possible sources of error in this lab? In other words, what things might have caused differences in travel time for the same mass?
   Student responses will vary. Possible sources of error are reaction time in releasing the car and starting the stopwatch, reaction time in stopping the stopwatch when the car reaches the edge, faulty release of the car by either pushing it with fingers or having it stick, and friction between the table and the string.

5. Use your graph to predict how much mass would be necessary to cause a travel time of 15 s. Test your prediction. What happened?
   Student responses will vary. To make the prediction, students should extend the graph line until it intersects the line for 15 s. Students should be able to explain how they arrived at their predictions.

Strategy Check

____ Can you find the average of several numbers?

____ Can you measure distance and time?

____ Can you relate force, mass, and acceleration?

Teacher note: It is important that the weight of the clay ball be enough to move the car but not so great that the car accelerates too fast for accurate timing. You may need to adjust the mass of the clay ball depending on the mass of the cars you use.

Chapter 13

LABORATORY MANUAL

● The Bicycle 24

You have learned about many simple machines that are used in compound machines. The bicycle is a familiar compound machine that uses a wheel and axle.

James Starley designed and manufactured one of the first successful bicycles in 1868. He developed his design so that once it was moving, only a small amount of force would be required to keep the vehicle and driver in motion on level ground.

A multigear bicycle can either multiply its speed or increase the force on the wheels. However, it can never do both at the same time. The bicycle's gears increase or decrease the force pushing the pedals. This results in slower or faster wheel speed. The mechanical advantage of a bicycle is the number of times the force applied by the rider's legs is multiplied. The speed advantage is the number of times the bicycle multiplies the speed for a given effort force. For example, if the bicycle multiplies the force of your legs by a factor of two, the speed is reduced by one-half.

Strategy

You will determine the mechanical advantage and the speed advantage of a multigear bicycle.
You will explain the relationship between mechanical advantage and speed advantage.
You will describe the distance traveled by a bicycle depending on the gear combination used.

Materials

1 foot-long block of wood
meterstick
multigear bicycle

Be sure that every student does not bring in his or her bicycle. However, make sure there is a variety to be used by the class.

Procedure

1. Place a block of wood under the bottom bracket of the bicycle's frame so the rear wheel is lifted off the ground. Have your lab partner steady the bicycle by holding the handle bars and the seat as shown in FIGURE 1.

2. **CAUTION:** *Avoid placing your hand or any object near the rear wheel, chain, or gears.* Rotate the forward pedals with one of your hands to make the rear wheel turn. Shift the gears and observe the speed of the rear wheel as you shift through each gear. Be sure to continue rotating the pedal as you switch gears. Switching gears without moving the pedal may result in the chain jumping off the gears. Record your observations in the Data and Observations section.

3. Remove the bicycle from the block of wood and lay it on its side. Count the number of teeth in each gear of both the front section and rear section. Record the data in Table 1.

4. Measure the diameter of the bicycle's rear wheel to the nearest centimeter. Record this in Table 1.

5. Set the bicycle upright. Place the gears in the lowest gear combination, with the chain on the smallest sprocket of the front gears and the largest sprocket of the back gears.

FIGURE 1

Block of wood

FIGURE 2

Rear gears

Front gears

6. Measure how many centimeters the bicycle travels as the pedal makes one complete revolution. Mark the starting and ending points using the front edge of the front tire and measure the distance between these two points. Record this distance in the Experimental column in Table 1.

7. Repeat steps 5 and 6 for each of the other gear combinations. Record your observations in the data table.

8. Calculate the mechanical advantage (M.A.) for each gear combination using the equation below. Record your answers in Table 1.

$$M.A. = \frac{\text{number of teeth on rear gear}}{\text{number of teeth on front gear}}$$

9. Calculate the speed advantage (S.A.) for each gear combination using the equation below. Record your answers in Table 1.

$$S.A. = \frac{\text{number of teeth on front gear}}{\text{number of teeth on rear gear}}$$

10. Find the theoretical distance the bicycle should travel as the pedal makes one revolution for each gear combination using the equation below. Record your answers in the table. ($\pi = 3.14$)

$$\text{Distance} = S.A. \times \text{rear wheel diameter} \times \pi$$

11. Calculate the experimental error between the theoretical and the experimental distance traveled using the equation below. Record your answers in the table.

$$\text{Percent error} = \frac{\text{theoretical} - \text{experimental}}{\text{theoretical}} \times 100$$

12. Graph the mechanical advantage versus the speed advantage.

Data and Observations

Effect shifting gears has on the rear wheel speed: **If the pedals are rotated at a constant speed, the wheel speed should increase as the gears are shifted from low to high.**

Bicycle's rear wheel diameter: **Answers will vary. Example: 68.9 cm**

_____

_____

209

Table 1

Bicycle Data

Front teeth	Rear teeth	M.A.	S.A.	Experimental distance (cm)	Theoretical distance (cm)	Percent error
42	34	0.81	1.24	260	268	3.0%
42	29	0.69	1.45	300	313	4.1%
42	24	0.57	1.75	360	378	4.7%
42	19	0.45	2.21	480	478	0.4%
42	14	0.33	3.00	650	649	0.2%
52	34	0.65	1.53	350	331	5.7%
52	29	0.56	1.79	370	387	4.4%
52	24	0.46	2.17	480	469	2.3%
52	19	0.37	2.74	600	593	10.2%
52	14	0.27	3.71	840	803	4.6%

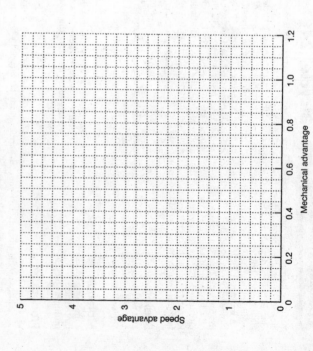

Questions and Conclusions

1. Why is a high mechanical advantage important to bicycle riders? A large mechanical advantage allows the riders to climb hills easily.

2. Why is a high speed advantage important to bicycle riders? A greater speed advantage allows riders to travel farther and faster with a minimal number of pedal revolutions.

3. What simple machines are involved in a bicycle? The wheels and gears involve wheels and axles. The gears also use pulleys. The gearshifts and the pedals are levers.

4. What is the mathematical relationship between mechanical advantage and speed advantage? Inversely proportional; as mechanical advantage increases, speed advantage decreases.

5. Which gear combination produced the greatest mechanical advantage in the bicycle you tested? The combination with the fewest number of teeth in front and the most number of teeth in back produced the greatest M.A.

6. Which gear combination produced the greatest speed advantage in the bicycle you tested? The combination with the most number of teeth in front and the fewest number of teeth in back produced the greatest S.A.

7. Under what conditions is it good to increase friction on a bicycle? When going up a large hill or riding across a slick surface, the friction between the ground and the tires is essential for balance and continued forward motion. When going around a corner, friction keeps the wheels from sliding out from under the bicycle.

8. When is it good to reduce friction on a bicycle? When moving fast down the road, there should not be too much friction on the chain, the wheels and axles, and the gears.

Strategy Check

_____ Can you determine how many gear combinations are possible?

Chapter 13

LABORATORY MANUAL

● Work and Power 25

Work is energy transferred through motion. When a force acts on an object and moves that object a certain distance, work is done on that object. Therefore, work (W) is defined by the following equation.

$$W = F \times d$$

In this equation, F represents a force acting on the object and d represents the distance through which the object moves as that force acts on it. In the metric system, force is measured in newtons (N), and distance is measured in meters (m). If a force of 1 newton acts on an object and the object moves 1 meter while the force is acting on it, the value of $F \times d$ equals 1 newton-meter (N-m). That amount of work is equal to 1 joule (J) of energy being transferred.

Power (P) is the rate at which work is done. It can be determined by the following equation.

$$P = W/t$$

In this equation, W represents the work done and t represents the amount of time required to do the work. In the metric system, the unit of power is the watt (W). If 1 joule of work is done in 1 second, W/t has a value of 1 J/s, which is equal to 1 watt.

Strategy

You will determine the amount of work required to lift an object.
You will determine the power used while lifting the object.

Materials 🌡️ ✂️ 🔧

dowel (wood, about 50 cm long)
mass (1-kg)
meterstick
scissors
spring scale (metric)
stopwatch
string
tape (masking)
wire tie (plastic-coated)

Procedure

1. Weigh the 1-kg mass using the metric spring scale. Record this value in the Data and Observations section.

2. Cut a 1.3-m length of string. Tightly tie one end of the string to the center of the wood dowel. Secure the knot with a piece of masking tape to prevent the string from slipping.

3. Make a small loop at the other end of the string and knot it. Attach the 1-kg mass to the loop with a plastic-coated wire tie.

4. Measure a 1-m distance along the string from the dowel using the meterstick. Mark this distance on the string with a small strip of masking tape.

FIGURE 1

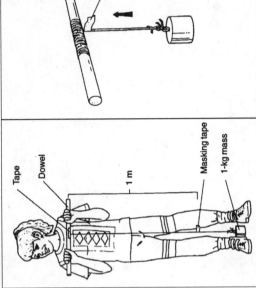

Tape
Dowel
1 m
Masking tape
1-kg mass

FIGURE 2

Tape

5. Hold the dowel at both ends as shown in FIGURE 1.

6. Raise the 1-kg mass by winding up the string on the dowel as shown in FIGURE 2. Keep the winding motion steady so that the string winds up and the mass rises at a constant speed. Practice raising the mass in this manner several times.

7. You are now ready to have your lab partner measure the time it takes for you to raise the mass a distance of 1 m.

8. Suspend the 1-kg mass from the dowel as before. At a signal from your lab partner, begin to raise the mass at a constant speed by winding the string on the dowel. Have your lab partner use a stopwatch to measure the time required for the piece of masking tape on the string to reach the dowel. Record this value under Student 1 in Table 1.

9. Reverse roles with your lab partner and allow him or her to repeat steps 6–8. Record the time value under Student 2 in Table 1.

10. The size of the force that was needed to raise the 1-kg mass is equal to the weight of 1 kg. The distance that the 1-kg mass was raised is the distance between the dowel and the piece of masking tape, which is 1 m. Record the values for the force and distance under Student 1 and Student 2 in Table 1.

11. Calculate the work you did to raise the 1-kg mass and record this value under Student 1 in Table 2.

12. Calculate the power you developed lifting the 1-kg mass. Record the value under Student 1 in Table 2.

13. Complete Table 2 using your lab partner's data from Table 1.

Data and Observations

Weight of 1-kg mass:

<u>9.8 N Data will vary.</u>

Table 1

Data will vary.

Measurement	Student 1	Student 2
Time	5.0	6.0
Force (N)	9.8	9.8
Distance	1.0	1.0

Table 2

Data will vary.

Calculation	Student 1	Student 2
Work (J)	9.8	9.8
Power (W)	2.0	1.6

Questions and Conclusions

1. Compare the amounts of work that you and your lab partner did.
   The work was the same.

2. Why would you expect both amounts of work to be the same?
   They should be the same because the values of the force acting on the 1-kg mass and the
   distance the mass moved each time were the same.

3. Compare the amounts of power developed by you and your lab partner.
   Answers will vary. Students should recognize that the student who raised the 1-kg mass in the
   shorter period of time developed more power.

4. Why would you expect the amounts of power to differ?
   Answers will vary. Students should recognize that each student lifted the mass at a different
   rate, and therefore, the time to lift the mass will differ for each student.

5. How do the amounts of work and power depend on the speed at which the 1-kg mass is lifted?
   The amount of work is independent of the speed at which the 1-kg mass is lifted. The amount of
   power is directly related to the speed.

Strategy Check

____ Can you determine the amount of work required to lift an object?

____ Can you determine the power used while lifting an object?

Chapter 14

LABORATORY MANUAL • **Velocity of a Wave   26**

Energy can move as waves through material such as ropes, springs, air, and water. Waves that need a material to pass through are called mechanical waves. Sounds and ripples in flags are examples of mechanical waves. Other energy, such as light, can be transmitted as waves through empty space as well as matter.

The high part of a transverse wave is the crest. The low part of a transverse wave is the trough. The amplitude of the wave is the distance the crest rises above or the trough falls below the wave's center line.

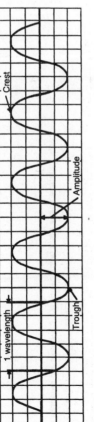

FIGURE 1

The wavelength is the distance between two similar points on successive waves. The number of wavelengths that pass a point in 1 s is the frequency of the wave. Frequency is measured in a unit called the hertz (Hz). A wave with a frequency of 1 Hz indicates that one wavelength is passing a point each second. The frequency can be found using the following equation:

$$frequency = \frac{number\ of\ wavelengths}{1\ s}$$

The velocity of a wave depends upon the material through which the wave passes. The velocity of a wave is equal to the product of its wavelength and its frequency. A wave's velocity is expressed in the same units as any measurement of velocity—meters per second (m/s).

$$velocity = wavelength \times frequency$$

Students may find it difficult to get satisfactory photographs. You may wish to forgo the photography and simply have students sketch the waves.

Strategy

You will identify the crest, trough, and amplitude of a wave.
You will determine the wavelength and frequency of a wave.
You will calculate the velocity of a wave.

Materials 🥽📞

camera (instant developing)
goggles
apron
meterstick
yarn (20 colored pieces)
rope (about 5 m long) **clothesline or other rope**
or
toy spring

Procedure

CAUTION: *Wear safety goggles throughout the experiment.*

Part A Frequency of a Wave

1. Tie the pieces of yarn to the rope at 0.5-m intervals. Use the meterstick to measure the distances.

2. Tie one end of the rope to an immovable object, such as a door knob. Pull the rope so it does not sag.

3. Make waves in the rope by moving the free end up and down. Continue to move the rope at a steady rate. Observe the crests, troughs, and amplitude of the waves. (See FIGURE 2.)

4. Continue making waves by moving the rope at a constant rate. Observe a particular piece of yarn. Count the number of waves that you produce during a period of 30 s. Record this value in Table 1 as wave motion A.

5. Slow the rate at which you are moving the rope. Predict what will happen to the frequency. Count the number of waves produced in 30 s while maintaining this constant slower rate. Record this value in Table 1 as wave motion B.

6. Repeat the procedure in step 4, moving the rope at a faster rate. Maintain this constant rate for 30 s. Record the number of waves in Table 1 as wave motion C.

7. Calculate the frequency of each of the three waves produced in Part A. Use the equation for the frequency given in the introduction. Record the values of the frequencies in Table 1.

You may wish to increase the time to 60 s. Remind students that a yarn marker moves from a crest to a trough to a crest as one wave passes that point.

FIGURE 2

Part B Speed of a Wave

1. Use the same rope setup from Part A. Have a classmate move the rope with a constant motion. Record the number of waves produced in 30 s in Table 2 as wave motion A. Photograph the entire length of the moving rope using the instant developing camera. Rest the camera on a table to keep it still.

2. Have your classmate increase the motion of the rope and take another photograph. Predict what will happen to the wavelength. Again count the number of waves produced in 30 s and record these values in Table 2 as wave motion B.

3. Observe the developed photographs. For each photograph, use the yarn markers to determine the length of one wavelength. Record the values in Table 2. You may tape the photographs below.

4. Calculate the frequencies of the two waves produced in Part B. Record these values in Table 2.

5. Calculate the velocities of the two waves using the values of the wavelengths and frequencies in Table 2. Use the equation for velocity of a wave given in the introduction. Record these values of the velocities in Table 2.

Data and Observations
Part A Frequency of a Wave

Table 1 Data depend on such factors as the type of rope used, its diameter, and its tautness.

Wave motion	Number of waves in 30 s	Frequency (Hz)
A	41	1.4
B	21	0.97
C	54	1.8

Part B Velocity of a Wave

Table 2 Data depend on such factors as the type of rope used, its diameter, its tautness.

It is important that students maintain the same frequency during each 30 s period.

Wave motion	Number of waves in 30 s	Frequency (Hz)	Wavelength (m)	Velocity (m/s)
A	35	1.2	2.7	3.2
B	50	1.8	1.7	3.1

Attach the wave photographs here.

If students are sketching the waves, have them attach sketches here.

Questions and Conclusions

1. As you increased the motion of the rope, what happened to the frequency of the waves? **The frequency of the waves increased.**

2. As the frequency of the waves increased, what happened to the wavelength? **The wavelength decreased.**

3. As the frequency of the waves increased, what happened to the velocity of the wave? **The velocity remained constant.**

4. Do your data indicate that the velocity of a wave is dependent on or independent of its frequency? Explain. _____ **The data indicate that the velocity of a wave moving in a material is independent of its frequency. The velocity of the wave remained constant even though its frequency increased.**

Strategy Check

___ Can you observe transverse waves in a lake or pond?

___ Can you compare and contrast the frequencies of high-pitched and low-pitched sounds?

Chapter 14

• Wave Reflection, Refraction, and Diffraction 27

Waves enable you to see this page and to hear voices and music. Waves carry energy from one place to another without carrying matter. Waves often bounce off objects, called reflection, change direction when they travel from one medium to another, called refraction, and spread around barriers, called diffraction.

Strategy

You will construct a simple wave tank.
You will observe and study how waves reflect, refract, and diffract.

Materials 🧤 🥽

steel barrier (1 m × 4 cm × 1 cm)
paraffin blocks, 2 (10 cm × 6 cm × 1 cm)
paraffin block (4 cm × 4 cm × 1 cm)

wood block (15 cm × 3 cm × 7 cm) to use as wave generator
wood frame (1 m × 1 m × 10 cm) with plastic sheet for lining of wave tank

Procedure

1. Fill the wave tank with water to a depth of 3 cm.

2. Hold the wooden block in the water so that it is just touching the bottom near one end of the wave tank and is parallel with the ledge of the tank. Lift the block out of the water. This entire motion should take about 1 s. Repeat the motion until you can produce uniform waves.

3. Once you are satisfied that you can produce uniform waves, set up the other simulations as illustrated in the diagrams. Each simulation will take at least 5 min. During that period of time, observe the waves and their behavior.

4. After you have finished the simulations, answer the following questions.

Questions and Conclusions

Simulation A

1. Describe the behavior of waves before and after they reflect from the steel barrier. _____
Before—travel parallel to block that produced them. After—waves travel parallel to steel barrier.

2. Change the angle of the barrier and repeat Simulation A. What happens to the direction of the reflected waves? _____
The reflected waves will travel parallel to the barrier.

Simulation B

3. When the waves passed over the glass plate, they entered shallower water. What happened to their speed? _____
They went slower.

4. The change in speed simulates what happens when a wave passes from one medium into another in which its speed is less. How was the direction of the wave affected? _____
The waves over the glass plate traveled parallel to the edge of the plate.

5. The change in direction of a wave when it passes from one medium into another is called refraction, and the line drawn perpendicular to the edge of the plate is called the normal. Did the water waves bend away from the normal or toward the normal when they passed over the plate? _____
The waves bent toward the normal.

Simulation C

6. Describe what happened to the waves after they passed the small paraffin block. _____
The waves curved around the block.

7. The bending of the waves around a barrier is called diffraction. How would diffraction affect a boat docked just inside the entrance to a harbor on a seacoast? _____
The boat would be pushed toward the shore.

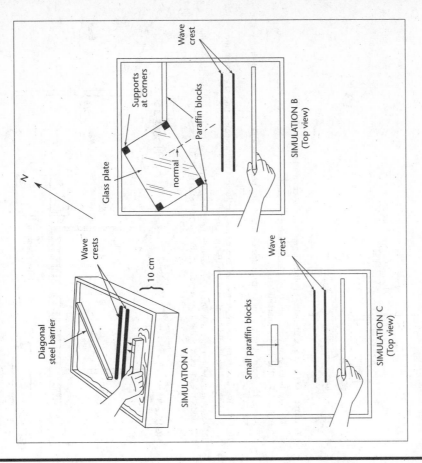

SIMULATION A

Diagonal steel barrier

Wave crests

} 10 cm

SIMULATION B
(Top view)

Glass plate

normal

Supports at corners

Paraffin blocks

Wave crest

SIMULATION C
(Top view)

Small paraffin blocks

Wave crest

N

Strategy Check

Can you observe how refraction occurs when you use a magnifying glass to examine a small object?

Can you describe how diffraction enables you to hear someone talking in another room?

Chapter 15

LABORATORY MANUAL

● Light Intensity 28

Have you ever noticed how the brightness of the light from a flashlight changes as you move closer or farther away from it? Likewise, have you ever noticed how the strength of the signals from a radio station fades on a car radio as you move away from the transmitting tower? Both light and radio signals are similar forms of energy. These two examples seem to suggest that the intensity of energy and distance are related. What is the relationship between light intensity and distance? Is there also a relationship between light intensity and direction?

In this experiment you will use a photo resistor. A photo resistor is a device that changes its resistance according to the intensity of the light hitting it. The resistance of a photo resistor is directly related to the intensity of the light striking it. The resistance of a photo resistor is measured in a unit called an ohm (Ω). Photo resistors are often used in burglar alarm systems. A beam of light shines on the photo resistor. If anyone or anything passes through the beam, the intensity of the light striking the photo resistor is changed. This causes the resistance of the photo resistor to change also. Because the photo resistor is in a circuit, the current in the circuit changes, which causes an alarm to sound.

Strategy

You will measure the effect of distance and direction on light intensity.
You will interpret graphs relating light intensity, distance, and direction.

Materials 🖐️ 🧤 🔬 🥽 📏

25-W lightbulb and lamp socket
meterstick
multimeter or ohmmeter
pencil
pencils (colored)

photo resistor
ring stand
tape (black)
utility clamp

Photo resistors are available from scientific equipment supply houses and electronics stores.

Procedure

1. In the Data and Observations section, write hypotheses explaining the relationships between light intensity and distance and between light intensity and direction.

2. Mount the photo resistor on a pencil with tape (see FIGURE 1).

3. Lay the meterstick on a flat, hard surface. Place small pieces of black tape at 10-cm intervals along the meterstick.

4. Set the lightbulb and socket on a smooth, flat surface.

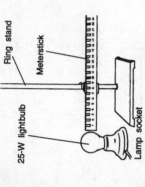

FIGURE 1

Pencil

Photo resistor

Tape

---

5. Clamp the meterstick to the ring stand with the utility clamp. Arrange the meterstick so that the lightbulb is at the 0-cm marker (see FIGURE 2).

6. Attach the wires of the photo resistor to the multimeter or ohmmeter. If using a multimeter, set the meter to measure resistance and attach the wires to the appropriate terminals. Darken the room before any measurements are taken.

FIGURE 2

Ring stand

Meterstick

25-W lightbulb

Lamp socket

7. Turn off the bulb and place the photo resistor at the 100-cm marker (see FIGURE 3).

8. Turn the bulb on and measure the resistance using the multimeter or ohmmeter. Record the value in Table 1 in the column marked *East*.

9. Move the photo resistor to the 90-cm marker. Measure the resistance and record the value in the same column of the table.

10. Continue advancing the photo resistor to each marker. Record the meter reading at each position. The last reading should be taken at the 10-cm marker.

11. Assume that the meterstick was oriented with the 100-cm marker pointing to the east. Repeat the procedure for each of the three remaining directions shown in FIGURE 4.

FIGURE 3

FIGURE 4

Multimeter or ohmmeter

Photo resistor

North

West

South

East

Data and Observations

Hypothesis relating light intensity and distance: **Intensity will decrease with increase in distance.**

Hypothesis relating light intensity and direction: **Intensity will be the same in all directions.**

Table 1

Distance (cm)	Resistance (Ω)			
	East	West	North	South
100	1.4			
90	1.7	Data for the other directions should be similar.		
80	2.2			
70	2.9			
60	3.9			
40	8.8			
30	15.5			
20	35.0			
10	140.0			

Graphs will vary. Students should plot the data in reverse order from the order in which readings were taken; that is, the data should be plotted from 0.10 m to 1.00 m (from the bottom of Table 1 to the top). Readings are taken with decreasing distance to show students the dramatic increase in resistance, and therefore in light intensity, as the distance decreases.

FIGURE 5

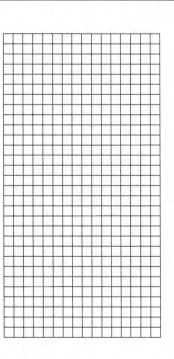

Have the more mathematically able students plot the resistance and the *square* of the distance on a piece of graph paper. Have them verify that the resistance (and, therefore, light intensity) varies inversely as the square of the distance. That is, $R_1 d_1^2 = R_2 d_2^2$. Intensity at twice the distance will be 1/4 the intensity of the first point.

---

1. Use FIGURE 5 to graph your data. Place the distance values on the *x* axis and the resistance values on the *y* axis. Label the *x* axis *Distance from light source (cm)* and the *y* axis *Resistance (Ω)*.

2. Graph the data for each of the other three directions on the same graph. Use a different colored pencil for each direction.

Questions and Conclusions

1. Look at your graph. Describe how the resistance and distance are related. **The graph indicates that the resistance of the photo resistor decreases as distance from the light increases.**

2. How are light intensity and distance related? **Light intensity decreases as the distance from its source increases.**

3. What does the graph indicate about the relationship between intensity of light and direction? **The four sets of data overlap on the graph. This indicates that the intensity of the light is the same in all directions from the light.**

4. Why was it necessary to darken the room before doing this experiment? **Other lights in the room would affect the photo resistor. With the room darkened, only the light from the lightbulb will affect the photo resistor.**

5. Do the results of this experiment support your original hypotheses? **Most students will probably be able to respond positively for both hypotheses.**

6. Light from the sun travels to Earth from a distance of almost 150 million kilometers. If Earth were farther away from the sun, what effects would be felt on Earth's surface? What effects would be felt if Earth were closer to the sun? **If Earth were farther from the sun, the intensity of the sun's energy striking Earth would be less and its surface would be cooler. If the sun were closer, the intensity of the solar energy striking Earth would be greater and its surface would be warmer.**

Strategy Check

_____ Can you measure the effect of distance and direction on light intensity?

_____ Can you interpret graphs relating light intensity, distance, and direction?

Chapter 15

◀ LABORATORY MANUAL

● Investigating Invisible Waves 29

Electromagnetic radiation that has a range of frequencies from 430 trillion to 760 trillion hertz is known as the visible spectrum. Electromagnetic radiation that has frequencies less than 430 trillion hertz or greater than 760 trillion hertz is the invisible spectrum. In this experiment, you will investigate the behavior of some types of electromagnetic radiation in the invisible spectrum. These include radio and infrared waves and ultraviolet light.

Strategy

You will compare the speed of sound in air to the speed of light.

You will examine the behavior of infrared waves used to operate an electronic device from a remote control unit.

You will study fluorescence that results when some materials are exposed to ultraviolet light.

You will determine how certain substances that are added to laundry products are able to whiten and brighten clothes.

Materials 🧤 🔌 ☎

drum
fluorescent materials such as crayons or paints
light (bright, with switch)
rope (100-m)
stopwatch that can measure 0.01 s
television or another electronic device that is operated by an infrared remote control device
thermometer
ultraviolet light
walkie-talkies (pair)

Procedure

Part A Speed of Light and Speed of Sound

1. This part of the activity is done with a partner outdoors. Select an open area such as a field.

2. Use the rope to measure a distance of 100 m in a straight line.

3. First partner—stand at one end of the measured distance with the drum and one walkie-talkie.

4. Second partner—stand at the other end of the measured distance with the stopwatch and the other walkie-talkie.

5. First partner—create a loud, short noise by striking the drum.

6. Second partner—use the stopwatch to time the interval between when you hear the drum on the walkie-talkie and when you hear the drum through the air. Record this time in Table 1 in the Data and Observations section. Carry out a total of three trials.

FIGURE 1

7. Switch places and repeat the experiment. This will eliminate any effect of wind in one direction. After three trials record your results in Table 2 in the Data and Observations section.

8. Determine the functioning range of the walkie-talkies by seeing how far apart they can be and still transmit. See what types of obstacles, such as buildings or trees, will block the radio transmission. Record your observations.

9. First partner—stand at one end of the functioning range with the bright light and a walkie-talkie. Signal on the walkie-talkie when you turn on the light.

10. Second partner—time the difference between when you hear the signal and when you see the light. Record the time and distance in the Data and Observations section.

Part B Infrared Remote Control

1. Set up the TV or other electronic device you are using in a long room. Determine the maximum distance at which the infrared remote control device will still operate the electronic device. Record that distance in the Data and Observations section.

2. Hold the remote control device about 5 m from the electronic device. Have someone stand between the remote control device and the electronic device. See if the remote control device will operate the electronic device. Record your observations in the Data and Observations section.

3. Determine if the remote control device can operate the electronic device at angles other than pointing straight at the device. Try "bouncing" the infrared beam off a wall, the floor, or the ceiling. See if the beam will bounce off a person or some other object and still operate the electronic device. Record your observations.

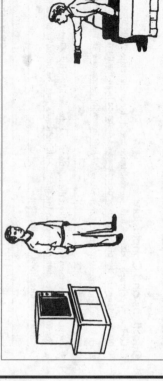

FIGURE 2

Part C Ultraviolet Waves and Fluorescence

1. When some substances absorb ultraviolet light, they can emit light waves that have a lower energy and frequency than the absorbed light. This is called fluorescence.

2. Test the fluorescent substances under the ultraviolet lamp (sometimes called a "black light") to see if they glow. This glow is called fluorescence. Record your results in the Data and Observations section.

3. Use the ultraviolet lamp to test various powdered laundry products that advertise that they whiten and brighten clothes. Shine the ultraviolet lamp on the boxes that these laundry products come from. Record your observations in the Data and Observations section.

Data and Observations

Part A

Table 1 With the Wind

Distance (m)	Time (s)	Speed (m/s)
100	0.29	341
100	0.31	323
100	0.28	357

Table 2 Against the Wind

Distance (m)	Time (s)	Speed (m/s)
100	0.30	333
100	0.32	313
100	0.31	323

Range of walkie-talkies from step 8: __450 m__

Observations of obstacles from step 8: __Buildings and trees did not affect the reception at 100–200 m.__

Speed of light data from step 10: __The light was seen and the sound was heard at exactly the same instant.__

Part B

Observations from step 1: __Maximum distance for remote control device was 13 m.__

Observations from step 2: __The remote control device would not operate the electronic device when someone blocked the path.__

Observations from step 3: __The remote control device operates the electronic device when the beam is reflected off a smooth surface.__

Part C

Observations from step 2: __The fluorescent substance glows brightly.__

Observations from step 3: __The powder glows bright white. The boxes glow.__

Questions and Conclusions

1. Why is there a difference between the time it takes you to hear the drum on the walkie-talkie and the time it takes you to hear it through the air? __The speed of sound through air is much slower than the speed of the radio wave, which travels at the speed of light.__

2. How can you explain the results from step 8 of Part A, when you tested to see if buildings or trees affected the walkie-talkie reception? __Radio waves are able to pass through buildings and trees.__

3. How can you explain the results from step 10 of Part A, when you tried to time the speed of light? __Light travels so fast that it is nearly impossible to determine it. Also, the light wave travels at the same speed as the radio wave.__

4. How can you explain the results of step 2 of Part B, when someone blocked the infrared wave? __The infrared wave does not pass through dense objects.__

5. How can you explain the results of step 3 of Part B, when you tried to operate the infrared remote control at angles other than pointing straight at the device? __The infrared wave can be reflected.__

6. What type of substance is added to laundry detergents to make clothes whiter and brighter? __Fluorescent substances are added so that when the UV from the sun hits the clothes, the clothes fluoresce and look brighter and whiter.__

Strategy Check

____ Can you compare the speed of sound in air to the speed of light?

____ Can you examine the behavior of infrared waves?

____ Can you observe the fluorescence that results when some materials are exposed to ultraviolet light?

____ Can you determine how certain substances whiten and brighten clothes?

Chapter 16

• Conductivity of Various Metals 30

Some materials are excellent conductors of electricity, while other materials do not conduct electricity at all. For example, metals are generally good conductors of electricity, whereas materials like wood and rubber do not conduct electricity. That is why electricians generally wear rubber gloves to protect their hands from electric shock. You will investigate how well various materials conduct electricity.

Strategy

You will determine how well different materials conduct electricity.
You will observe the behavior of a diode.

Materials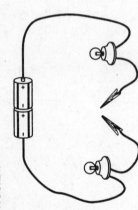

testable materials
aluminum foil
brass screw
copper pipe
diode
glass rod
graphite (pencil lead)
nail
paper clip
plastic pen cap
rubber eraser
wooden stick

circuit parts
2 alligator clips
4 20-cm lengths of insulated copper wire
2 lightbulbs
2 lightbulb holders
2 1.5-volt batteries
wire strippers

Procedure

CAUTION: *Be careful working with sharp objects.*

1. Set up a test circuit as shown in FIGURE 1 and described below.

2. With wire strippers, carefully scrape off 1 cm of insulation at the end of each wire.

3. Attach two wires to each of the lightbulb holders.

4. Attach one wire from each of the lightbulb holders to one exposed terminal of the batteries.

5. Leave the other wire from each lightbulb holder unattached. Attach an alligator clip to the free ends of the wires.

6. Put a lightbulb in each lightbulb holder.

FIGURE 1

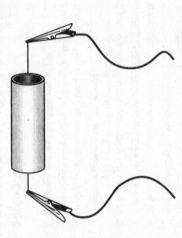

7. Before testing each material, predict whether it will allow the lightbulbs to light. Record your prediction in Table 1.

8. Test each material by attaching the alligator clips to each end as shown in FIGURE 2. Record your observations in Table 1.

9. Reverse the direction of current in each material by switching the alligator clips. Record your observations in Table 1.

10. After testing all the materials, dismantle the circuit and place the components where instructed by your teacher.

FIGURE 2

Data and Observations

Table 1

Conductivity of Various Materials

Material	Prediction before connecting	Observations when initially connected	Observations when connected in reverse
Aluminum foil	Predictions	bulbs light	bulbs light
Brass screw	will vary.	bulbs light	bulbs light
Copper pipe		bulbs light	bulbs light
Glass rod		no change	no change
Graphite		bulbs light	bulbs light
Nail		bulbs light	bulbs light
Paper clip		bulbs light	bulbs light
Plastic pen cap		no change	no change
Rubber eraser		no change	no change
Wooden stick		no change	no change
Diode	bulbs light on either initial or reversed connection		

Questions and Conclusions

1. From the data in Table 1, prepare a list of the materials that are conductors of electricity. **The list should include aluminum foil, brass screw, copper pipe, graphite, nail, paper clip, and sometimes a diode.**

2. From the data in Table 1, prepare a list of materials that are not conductors. **The list should include glass rod, plastic pen cap, rubber eraser, wooden stick, and sometimes a diode.**

3. Did any of the materials appear in both lists? **The diode appeared in both lists.**

4. How can you tell when there is a current in the circuit? **The bulbs light due to current in the circuit.**

5. Were all of the metal materials good conductors of electricity? **Students should have observed that all metal materials conducted well.**

6. Of the materials that conducted electricity, were there any nonmetals? **Graphite is a nonmetal.**

7. Which materials would make good insulators? **Plastics, glass, wood, and rubber make good insulators.**

8. How could a diode be used in a circuit? **A diode could be used to ensure that a current runs in one direction only.**

Strategy Check

___ Can you determine how well different materials conduct electricity?

___ Can you observe the behavior of a diode?

221

Chapter 16

LABORATORY MANUAL ● **Batteries 31**

A wet-cell battery converts chemical energy into electrical energy. Chemical reactions taking place at each of the battery terminals cause electrons to pile up at the negative terminal. Voltage is a measure of the force that causes electrons to flow from the negative terminal to the positive terminal through a conductor. The flow of charges through a conductor is current.

The amounts of voltage and current produced by a battery depend on the nature and the concentration of the chemicals in the battery. For example, a car battery produces more current and voltage than a flashlight battery does. A car battery also contains chemicals that differ in nature and concentration from the chemicals in a flashlight battery.

Strategy

You will build wet-cell batteries.
You will measure the voltage of the batteries.

Materials

2 alligator clips	graduated cylinder (100-mL)
aluminum foil, heavy gauge	0.1 *M* hydrochloric acid
aluminum strip	paper towels
apron	vinegar
beaker (250-mL)	voltmeter
copper strip	gloves
glass rod	water
goggles	2 wires

FIGURE 1

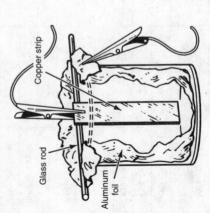

Copper strip

Glass rod

Aluminum foil

Procedure

1. Line the inside of a 250-mL beaker with aluminum foil. The foil should hang over the outside edges of the beaker as shown in FIGURE 1.

2. Place a glass rod across the mouth of the beaker.

3. Using an alligator clip, hang a copper strip from the glass rod into the beaker. The copper strip should hang near one side of the beaker, but the copper strip should NOT touch the aluminum foil. Attach a wire to the alligator clip. Then attach the other end of the wire to the positive (+) terminal of the voltmeter.

4. Attach a wire to the alligator clip. Then attach the other end of the wire to the positive (+) terminal of the voltmeter.

5. Attach a second alligator clip to the aluminum foil hanging over the edge of the beaker. This second alligator clip should be attached across from the copper strip as shown in FIGURE 1.

6. Attach a wire to the second alligator clip and connect the other end of this wire to the negative (−) terminal of the voltmeter as shown in FIGURE 2.

FIGURE 2

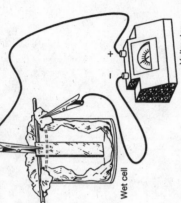

Wet cell

Voltmeter

7. Observe the wet cell and record any changes in Table 1. Observe the voltage on the voltmeter and record it in Table 1.

8. Carefully add 75 mL of 0.1 M HCl to the foil-lined beaker. **CAUTION:** *HCl can cause burns. Rinse any acid spills immediately with water.*

9. After adding HCl, observe the wet cell and notice any changes to the system. Record your observations in Table 1.

10. Observe the voltage on the voltmeter and record the reading in Table 1.

11. Disconnect the wires. Under your teacher's supervision, carefully empty the acid from the beaker. Thoroughly rinse the beaker and copper strip with water and dry them with paper towels. Discard the aluminum foil.

12. Repeat steps 1 through 10 using vinegar instead of HCl. Be sure to always use new aluminum foil.

13. Repeat steps 1 through 10 using an aluminum strip instead of the copper strip. Be sure to use fresh hydrochloric acid and fresh aluminum foil.

Data and Observations

Table 1

Battery conditions	Changes to system	Voltage reading
Without liquid	no changes	0 volts
HCl, copper, aluminum	some bubbling	Answers will vary.
Vinegar, copper, aluminum	some bubbling	Answers will vary.
HCl, aluminum, aluminum	no changes	0 volts

Questions and Conclusions

1. From the data in Table 1, determine which battery conditions produced the largest voltage.
   The battery conditions with the copper strip, aluminum foil, and hydrochloric acid should
   produce the highest voltage.

2. Which liquid—HCl or vinegar—produced a higher voltage? Explain.
   HCl produced the higher voltage because it is a stronger acid.

3. How do you know that a chemical reaction took place in the battery after the vinegar was added?
   Bubbles were observed, and a voltage was produced.

4. What metals were used to produce the batteries? How did they affect the results?
   Copper and aluminum together produced the best batteries.

5. How did the effect of hydrochloric acid on the copper strip differ from its effect on the aluminum foil?
   Students should observe little change in the appearance of the copper strip, but the aluminum
   foil should show definite evidence of corrosion.

Strategy Check

____ Can you build a wet-cell battery?

____ Can you measure the voltages produced by different wet-cell batteries?

Chapter 17

LABORATORY MANUAL ● **Star Colors 32**

In 1665, Isaac Newton demonstrated that sunlight was composed of many colors. Today the spectra of a star is one of the most important tools scientists use to determine the star's surface temperature and composition. The Draper system of spectral classification is used in this activity.

The number of stars visible at any one time from one place may vary greatly. Usually the number does not exceed one or two thousand.

Strategy

You will define the term *star*.
You will observe and record star colors.
You will classify stars based on their color.

Materials 🔭 📓

binoculars or telescope (optional)
graph paper

Table 1—Star Classification Chart

Star spectral type	Color	Surface temperature (K)
M	red	2000–4000
K	red to orange	3500–5000
G	yellow	5000–6000
F	yellow-white	6000–7500
A	white	9000
B	bluish-white	11 000–25 000
O	bluish-white	60 000

Procedure

1. On a clear, bright night observe the stars with your eyes or with the binoculars or telescope.

2. Use some landmarks and divide the sky into four sections. Label the landmarks in the diagram under Data and Observations.

3. Observe and record the color of each star in each section. Record your observations on your diagram under Data and Observations.

4. Compile your data showing the star color, class, and number of stars in each section in a table. Set up your table on one end of your graph paper.

5. Draw a bar graph showing the star classes and the number of stars in each class under the table on the graph paper.

Data and Observations

Diagram night sky here.

Questions and Conclusions

1. What property did you use to classify a celestial body as a star? **apparent brightness, color; All stars "twinkle" and seem to occupy fixed positions in the sky. Students may suggest other properties that they used.**

2. Which star class is the most abundant? **Answers will vary. Most stars fit into one of the seven basic spectral types given at the beginning of this activity.**

3. Which star class does our sun belong to? **G**

4. What is the surface temperature of our sun? **5000–6000 K**

5. The temperature of stars is given in Kelvins. Changing from the Celsius scale to the Kelvin scale is very easy: $K = °C + 273°$. What is the temperature of the sun in Celsius degrees? **4727–5727°C**

Strategy Check

___ Can you define the term *star?*

___ Can you observe and record the colors of the stars?

___ Can you classify stars based on their color?

Chapter 17

• Star Positions 33

When you watch the stars on a clear night, do you get the impression that you are in an upside-down bowl? The ancient Greeks believed that the stars were fixed to a clear bowl that slowly rotated around Earth. Although today we know that Earth rotates, the celestial sphere is still a good model to use to locate stars and other celestial bodies.

Strategy

You will construct a model of the north celestial hemisphere.
You will plot the stars on the celestial sphere.

Materials

globe (mounted)
hemisphere (clear plastic or terrarium top)
pen (felt-tip)
string to go around celestial equator

Procedure

1. The celestial sphere appears to move around a line that is an extension of Earth's axis. The north and south celestial poles are the points where Earth's geographic axis intersects the celestial sphere (see FIGURE 1). Label the north celestial pole with a dot on the inside of the hemisphere.

2. The celestial equator is the intersection of a plane that passes through Earth's equator and the celestial sphere. Place the clear hemisphere over the globe so that the north pole and the north celestial pole are in line. Mark the celestial equator on the hemisphere. The celestial equator is 90° from the celestial poles (see FIGURE 1).

3. Planes comparable to latitude on Earth are called *declination* on the celestial sphere. Positions north of the celestial equator are called *plus declination* and measured in degrees. Positions south of the celestial equator are called *minus declination*, also measured in degrees.

4. The celestial circle that corresponds to the prime meridian of longitude on Earth is called *right ascension*. Right ascension is measured from the point where the sun crosses the celestial equator about March 21 (the vernal equinox).

5. Right ascension is measured in hours, minutes, and seconds. On the equator, 15 degrees of arc equals 1 hour. Take a length of string and measure the distance around the celestial equator in centimeters. Record. Divide this distance by 24. Measure and mark these spaces around the celestial equator. Each mark represents 1 hour. Start at the prime meridian and move eastward around the celestial equator (see FIGURE 1).

6. Now you have a grid system similar to latitude and longitude.

7. Map the locations of the stars in Table 1 on the celestial sphere.

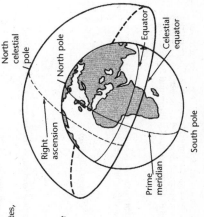

North celestial pole

North pole

Right ascension

Prime meridian

South pole

Celestial equator

Equator

FIGURE 1

Table 1

Common name	Scientific name	R.A. hr	R.A. min	Dec. (°)
Vega	Lyrae	18	35	38
Arcturus	Boötes	14	13	19
Altair	Aquilae	19	48	8
Betelgeuse	Orionis	05	52	7
Aldebaran	Tauri	04	33	16
Deneb	Cygni	20	40	45
Regulus	Leonis	10	06	12
Castor	Geminorum	07	31	32

Data and Observations

Celestial equator = _____ cm   **Answers will vary depending on the size of the hemisphere used.**

Questions and Conclusions

1. How is right ascension like longitude?   **Right ascension lines pass through the celestial poles.**
How is it different?   **Right ascension is measured in hours, minutes, and seconds.**

2. Compare declination to latitude.   **Both are measured in degrees. Declination gives the location of a star above or below the celestial equator.**

3. What does the vernal equinox on the celestial sphere correspond to on geographic maps?   **the prime meridian**

4. Why are different stars visible during the year?   **Different stars are visible because as Earth revolves around the sun, different portions of the sky become visible to us.**

5. Why can't you see a star with a minus declination from the northern hemisphere?   **These stars are below the horizon.**

Strategy Check

____ Can you construct a model of the north celestial hemisphere?

____ Can you locate stars on the celestial sphere?

Chapter 18

LABORATORY MANUAL ● Earth's Spin 34

The speed at which Earth turns on its axis can be described in two ways. The velocity of rotation refers to the rate at which Earth turns on its axis. Velocity of rotation refers to Earth as a whole. For any point on Earth's surface, the speed of Earth's rotation can be described as its instantaneous linear velocity. This velocity is the speed of the point as it follows a circular path around Earth.

Strategy

You will determine the instantaneous linear velocity of some points on Earth.
You will compare the linear velocities of points at different locations on Earth.

Materials

globe (mounted on axis) stopwatch tape (adhesive)
meterstick string

Procedure
Part A

1. Place small pieces of adhesive tape on the Prime Meridian, at the equator, at 30° N latitude, at 60° N latitude, and at the north pole.

2. Line up the tape with the metal circle above the globe; see FIGURE 1.

3. With your finger on the globe, move it west to east for one second; see FIGURE 2.

4. For each location marked by tape, measure the distance from the Prime Meridian to the metal circle. Use the string and the meterstick to get accurate distances. Record the distances in Table 1.

5. Realign the metal circle with the pieces of tape. Move the globe west to east for 2 s. Record the distances from the tapes to the metal circle in Table 1.

6. Repeat step 5, moving the globe for 3 s. Record your results in Table 1.

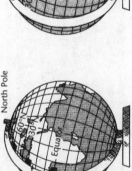

FIGURE 1

FIGURE 2

Part B

Calculate the speed of each point for each trial. Record in Table 2. Use the formula:

$$velocity\ (cm/s) = \frac{distance\ (cm)}{time\ (s)}$$

Data and Observations Answers will vary depending on the accuracy of the student.

Table 1

Latitude	Distance moved (cm)		
	1 s	2 s	3 s
Equator			
30° N			
60° N			
North Pole			

Table 2 You may wish to have students show their velocity calculations.

Latitude	Velocity (cm/s)		
	Trial 1	Trial 2	Trial 3
Equator			
30° N			
60° N			
North Pole			

Questions and Conclusions

1. Which point moved the farthest distance in all three trials? the point on the equator

2. Which point moved the least distance in all three trials? the point at 60° N

3. Which point did not move at all in the three trials? the point on the North Pole

4. On what does the linear velocity of a point depend? the latitude or the distance north or south of the equator

5. How does the linear velocity change as you move from the equator to the poles? The linear velocity decreases from the equator to the poles.

Strategy Check

___ Can you determine instantaneous linear velocity?

___ Can you see that the linear velocity is not the same for all points on Earth?

Chapter 18

LABORATORY MANUAL ● **Earth's Shape 35**

You've probably seen photographs of Earth taken by satellites in space. Such photographs clearly show Earth's round shape. Early astronomers didn't have spacecraft to help them study Earth. They had to rely on observation and measurement. In this activity, you'll explore some methods used by early astronomers to determine Earth's true shape.

Strategy

You will demonstrate evidence of Earth's shape.
You will describe the type of shadow cast by Earth during a lunar eclipse.

Materials

basketball
small piece of cardboard
flashlight
textbook
scissors

Procedure

1. Cut out a triangular piece of cardboard so that each side measures approximately 6 cm.

2. Hold a basketball at eye level about 33 cm from your eye. Have your partner slowly move the cardboard up and over the basketball from the opposite side.

3. In the space below, sketch the cardboard as it appears when the top of the cardboard first comes in sight over the basketball. Make another sketch of the cardboard as it appears when fully visible above the basketball.

4. Darken the room. Use a flashlight to cast a shadow of a textbook against the wall. Do the same for the basketball. In the space below, draw the shadows of the textbook and the basketball.

Data and Observations

Cardboard drawings

Shadow drawings

Questions and Conclusions

1. Compare and contrast your three drawings of the cardboard.
Students should note that only the tip of the cardboard is visible in the first drawing. In the second drawing, half of the cardboard triangle is visible. In the last drawing, the complete triangle is visible.

2. How were your different views of the cardboard similar to the view of a ship on the horizon approaching shore?
As a ship approaches from across the ocean, the top of the ship comes into view first, followed by the remainder of the ship.

3. How did the cardboard activity demonstrate evidence of Earth's shape?
The tip of the cardboard comes into view first because the cardboard is moving over a curved surface—the basketball. Similarly, the top of the ship at sea comes into view first because the ship is moving over a curved surface—Earth.

4. Compare and contrast your drawings of the shadows cast by the basketball and the textbook.
Students should note that the shadow cast by the textbook was rectangular while the shadow cast by the basketball was round.

5. During a lunar eclipse, Earth casts a shadow on the moon. What type of shadow would Earth cast if it were flat? What type of shadow does Earth cast on the moon during a lunar eclipse?
If Earth were flat, its shadow would look like a flat "bar" on the moon during a lunar eclipse. Instead, Earth casts a curved shadow on the moon.

6. How do the shadows you observed demonstrate evidence of Earth's shape?
The basketball, a round object, casts a curved shadow. The textbook, a flat object, casts a sharp-edged shadow. Thus, Earth's curved shadow on the moon during a lunar eclipse is evidence of Earth's round shape.

7. Can you think of any other evidence that demonstrates Earth's round shape? Describe this evidence.
Answers will vary. Students may mention photographs of Earth from space or their own observations of other objects in space, such as the sun and moon. Accept all reasonable answers.

Strategy Check

___ Can you demonstrate evidence of Earth's shape?

___ Can you describe the type of shadow cast by Earth during a lunar eclipse?

227

Chapter 19

LABORATORY MANUAL

● Venus—The Greenhouse Effect 36

Because Venus is closer to the sun, it receives almost twice the amount of solar radiation received by Earth. Venus reflects more radiation to space than Earth because of its clouds. We might expect Venus, therefore, to have surface temperatures similar to Earth. However, the *Pioneer* Venus vehicles have measured surface temperatures of 460°C. Some scientists explain this high temperature as the "greenhouse effect." When the solar energy strikes the surface of Venus, the energy is absorbed and changed into heat energy. This heat energy is reflected back to the atmosphere where it is trapped.

A good reference for this activity is "The Riddle of the Twins," by Jonathan Eberhart, *Sci Quest*, Vol. 53, No. 1, pp. 10–16.

Strategy

You will build a model to show the greenhouse effect.
You will compare this model to Earth.
You will form a hypothesis about temperatures on Venus using data collected from this model and from the *Pioneer* spacecraft.

Materials

cardboard (stiff)
graph paper
heat lamp (mounted)
pencils (colored)
plastic storage box and lid, clear
soil
thermometer
watch

Procedure

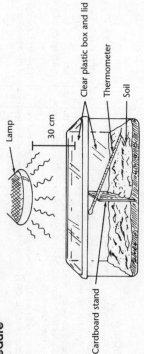

FIGURE 1

1. Place about 3 cm of soil in the bottom of the clear plastic box.

2. Thoroughly moisten the soil with water.

3. Cut the piece of cardboard so that it makes a divider for the box. The cardboard should not quite reach the top of the box. Insert the divider into the box.

4. Lean the thermometer against the divider with the bulb end up (see FIGURE 1). Put the lid on the box.

5. Position the box and lamp in an area of the room where no direct sunlight reaches. **CAUTION:** *Use care when handling heat lamp.*

6. Place the heat lamp about 30 cm above the box and direct the light so it shines on the thermometer bulb.

---

7. Turn off the lamp and allow the thermometer to return to room temperature. Record room temperature in Table 1.

8. Turn on the lamp and measure the temperature every minute for 20 min. Record the temperatures in Table 1.

9. Turn off the lamp and allow the thermometer to return to room temperature. Remoisten the soil and repeat step 8 with the lid off the box. Record your data in Table 1.

Data and Observations

Table 1

Time (min)	Temperature (°C) Lid off	Temperature (°C) Lid on
1		
2		
3		
4		
5		
6		
7		
8		
9		
10		
11		
12		
13		
14		
15		
16		
17		
18		
19		
20		

Graph the data using two different colors. Plot Temperature on the vertical axis and Time on the horizontal axis.

Questions and Conclusions

1. Did the temperature increase the most with the lid on or off? __on__
Why? __The lid reflected the heat back into the box; no heat could escape into the air.__

2. Draw a diagram of Earth showing its atmosphere and what occurs to solar radiation in the atmosphere. List the components of Earth's atmosphere on your diagram. Write a brief explanation of the greenhouse effect on Earth. __The shortwave radiation from the sun is absorbed by Earth's__ __surface. The surface then reradiates longwave radiation that is absorbed by the atmosphere__ __(carbon dioxide and water vapor). This process heats the atmosphere near the surface.__
_____
_____
_____

3. Compare the activity to the greenhouse effect on Earth. How are they similar? How are they different? __The lid prevents the longwave radiation from escaping by reflecting it back into the__ __box. The atmosphere prevents the longwave radiation from escaping by absorbing some of the__ __energy. Some energy leaks back to space.__
_____

4. Venus's atmosphere is composed mainly of carbon dioxide, carbon monoxide, water, nitrogen, and sulfuric acid. Venus's atmosphere is 100 times as dense as Earth's atmosphere. From the surface of Venus up to 20 km, there appears to be a clear region of atmosphere. A thick layer of clouds extends from about 50 km to 80 km above the surface of Venus. These clouds are composed of drops of sulfuric acid. Above and below these clouds are other thinner layers of haze. Venus's ionosphere extends from 100 km to 200 km above the surface. Like the ionosphere of Earth, it has layers. The temperature in the ionosphere of Venus is cooler than the temperature in Earth's ionosphere.

   Draw a diagram of Venus showing its atmosphere and what happens to solar radiation in the atmosphere. List the components of Venus's atmosphere on your diagram. Write a brief explanation of the greenhouse effect on Venus. __Sunlight striking Venus's surface is absorbed and reradiated as__ __longwave radiation. The radiation is trapped close to the surface of Venus.__
_____
_____
_____

5. Compare the greenhouse effect on Earth and Venus. Can you think of a reason why the surface of Venus is so much hotter than the surface of Earth? __Carbon dioxide present in both atmospheres__ __absorbs the reradiated energy from the surface. The atmosphere of Venus is more dense,__ __however, and more heat is retained by the large amounts of carbon dioxide.__

Strategy Check

___ Can you build a model to show the greenhouse effect?

___ Can you compare this model to Earth?

Chapter 19

LABORATORY MANUAL

• Jupiter and Its Moons 37

Jupiter and its moons are similar to a model of the solar system. Four of the moons are called the Galilean moons since Galileo first observed them in 1610. The moons are called Io, Ganymede, Callisto, and Europa.

Strategy
Consult an astronomical atlas to select the best viewing time for Jupiter. October is usually a good month.

You will build an astronomical telescope.
You will observe the Galilean moons of Jupiter.
You will place the four moons in order outward from Jupiter.

Materials 🔌🗜🔩

2 cardboard mailing tubes, 9-cm and 18-cm (9-cm one should be slightly smaller in diameter than the 18-cm one)
2 convex lenses
  eyepiece, short focal length
  objective, long focal length
tape (masking)
Star and Sky, Astronomy, or *Sky and Telescope,* current issue

Procedure
1. Tape the objective lens to one end of the larger, longer tube.
2. Tape the eyepiece lens to one end of the smaller, shorter tube.
3. Slide the small tube inside the large tube.
4. View a book through the telescope. Move the small tube back and forth to focus. Record your observations under Data and Observations.
5. Look up the position of Jupiter in a current issue of one of the magazines.
6. After dark, take the telescope outside and locate Jupiter. Observe and sketch the four visible moons. Sketch the moons in Table 1.
7. Repeat this observation every clear night for two weeks. Record all data in Table 1.

Data and Observations
Observations of book using the telescope: _The book is upside down when viewed_
through the telescope. The book should appear closer to the observer than it actually is.
_____

Table 1

Date/Time	Moon	Sketch

Questions and Conclusions

1. Why is the book upside down when you view it through the telescope? _The objective lens inverts_
   the image.

2. List the four Galilean moons of Jupiter in order outward from Jupiter. _Io, Europa, Ganymede,_
   Callisto

3. Write a brief description of each moon. Use magazines such as *Newsweek, Time, Science, Scientific American,* or *Astronomy* as sources for your material. _Io—volcanic eruptions and extensive lava_
   flows; Europa—yellow in color, rocky surface with fractures; Ganymede—largest moon of
   Jupiter, mixture of rock and ice; Callisto—series of concentric rings on the surface

Strategy Check

____ Can you build an astronomical telescope?

____ Can you place Jupiter's moons in order outward from the planet?

Chapter 20

LABORATORY MANUAL

● Star Trails 38

As Earth rotates on its axis, the stars appear to move also. The north star, Polaris, is a fixed reference point because it is almost directly above the north pole of Earth's axis of rotation. The pole position does not appear to move.

Strategy

You will photograph Polaris in a time exposure.
You will determine how many degrees Earth has rotated during the time exposure.

Materials

camera with time exposure   paper (tracing)
compass (drawing)   protractor
film (black and white)   tripod or support for camera

Procedure

1. Load the camera and mount it on the tripod.

2. On a clear, moonless night, set up the camera outside. Aim the camera so that Polaris is in the center of the viewing field.

3. Set the focus on infinity and open the shutter for a time exposure. Record the time and the landmark that is right under Polaris in Table 1.

4. Three hours later, close the shutter. Record the landmark that is under Polaris in Table 1. Have the film developed. Explain to the developer what you photographed, and ask for special care in the developing.

5. Trace several of the arcs on your developed print on the tracing paper. Be sure to include the arc traced by Polaris. Label the end points.

6. Use the compass to determine the center of the circle of which the arc of Polaris is a part. CAU-TION: *Use care when handling sharp objects.* Mark the center of the circle with a dot.

7. Draw a line from the center of the circle made by Polaris to the ends of five star curves you traced. Measure the angles between each pair of lines with a protractor. Record each angle in Table 2.

Data and Observations

Table 1

Landmark	
Start	
Finish	

Table 2

Star pairs	Angle (°)
Polaris and Star 1	
Polaris and Star 2	
Polaris and Star 3	
Polaris and Star 4	
Polaris and Star 5	

Questions and Conclusions

1. Did the landmarks change? **yes** _____ In what direction do the stars appear to move? **westward or counterclockwise**

2. What does your print show? **The print will show a point in the center with arcs of light surrounding it.**

3. What is the central point in the picture? **Polaris is the center.** Explain. **The stars have traced arcs of light around Polaris as Earth rotated on its axis.**

4. How far did the stars appear to move per hour in degrees? **15°**

5. How long does it take Earth to make one complete rotation based on your average arc? **24 hours**

6. How long could you have left the shutter open? **until sunrise** _____ Explain. **The light from the sun would be too bright for us to see the starlight and it would overexpose the film.**

7. Do the stars actually move as the print seems to prove? **no** _____ Explain. **The stars appear to move because Earth is rotating on its axis. The speed of apparent star motion is slow because of the great distances to the stars.**

8. If the shutter had been left open for 4 hours, how many degrees would Earth have rotated? **4 hours = 60° (4 × 15° = 60°)**

Strategy Check

_____ Can you photograph Polaris?

_____ Can you determine how far Earth rotates during a time exposure?

Chapter 20

• Spectral Analysis 39

The photograph of the spectrum of a star, sorted by color across a plate, will reveal spectral lines upon close examination. The lines are produced by elements in a star at high temperature. These lines represent the chemical composition of the star. Each element has its own "fingerprint." To analyze the spectra of stars, scientists collected spectra of all the known elements. If we compare the spectral lines of an unknown star with the spectral lines of elements, we can determine the chemical composition of the star. More recently, we have discovered not only the composition of the stars but also their temperatures, their rotational rate, and their relative motion with regard to Earth.

Strategy

You will construct a simple spectral analyzer.
You will determine the composition of a star using the spectral analyzer.
You will determine other characteristics of a star by comparing the spectral lines with a standard.

Materials

scissors

Procedure

1. Turn to the third page of this lab. Cut out the pull tab card; the spectroscope fingerprints card; and Stars B, C, and D along the dashed lines.

2. Make five slits along the dashed lines A, B, C, D, and E on the fingerprints card.

3. From left to right, insert "Pull Tab Out" up through slit E, down through slit D, up through slit C, down through slit B, and up through slit A.

4. Keeping the sodium doublets aligned, compare the lines of each known element with the lines of Star A. If lines match, then that element is present in Star A. Record your findings in Table 1.

5. Star B, Star C, and Star D are provided for further study and comparison. Each can be placed over Star A.

Data and Observations

Table 1

Star	Chemical composition	Other characteristics
A	iron, calcium, sodium, hydrogen, helium	
B	iron, sodium, hydrogen	the standard
C	iron, sodium, hydrogen	Answers will vary.
D	iron, sodium, hydrogen, mercury	Answers will vary.

Questions and Conclusions

1. When we say that the neon colored lights look beautiful at night, what color comes to mind? **Red, as there** red _____ What color is suggested by the "fingerprints" of neon? **are a lot of lines in the red wavelengths.**

2. Did any of the stars have the same chemical composition? Look at the table. **Students should say B, C, and D. It should be noted that Star D has the same composition, but the spectral lines are slightly shifted to the red wavelengths.**

3. Sometimes scientists see spectral lines that do not fit the usual pattern. The lines might be shifted from their usual positions. This may suggest that the star is moving either toward the observer (shift toward the blue) or moving away from the observer (shift toward the red). Look at the spectral lines for Star B and Star D. Star B is the standard for comparison. How is Star D different? What is a possible explanation for the difference? **Star D's spectral lines are shifted toward the red part of the spectrum. The star is moving away from the observer. You might review the Doppler effect with students.**

4. If the scientist sees the spectral lines wider than usual, he or she relates this spectral broadening to either rotational speed (the broader the faster), temperature (the broader the hotter), or pressure (the broader the greater pressure). Look at the spectral lines for Star B and Star C. Star B is the standard. How is Star C different? What could be a possible explanation? **Star C's spectral lines are wider than Star B's. This could be caused by any one of the reasons given in the paragraph above.**

5. Complete Table 1 by filling in the Other characteristics column.

Strategy Check

____ Can you construct a simple spectral analyzer?

____ Can you determine the composition of a star using the spectral analyzer?

____ Can you determine other characteristics of a star by comparing the spectral lines with a standard?

NAME _____   DATE _____   CLASS _____

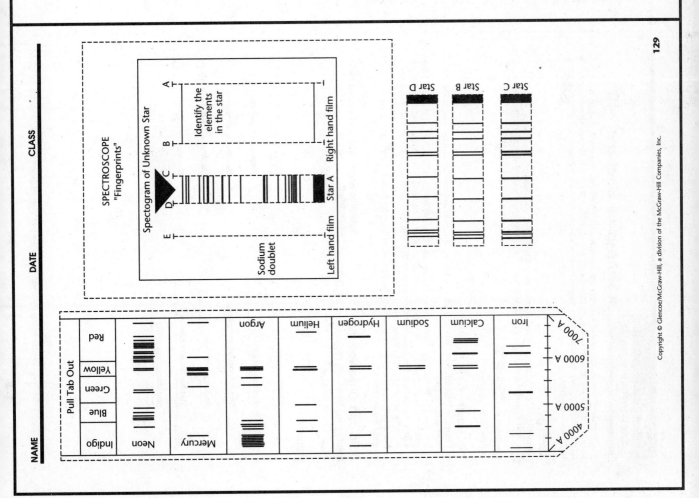

SPECTROSCOPE
"Fingerprints"

Spectogram of Unknown Star

E   F   D   C   B   A

Sodium doublet

Left hand film   Star A   Right hand film

Identify the elements in the star

Star D

Star B

Star C

Pull Tab Out

	Indigo	Blue	Green	Yellow	Red
Neon					
Mercury					
Argon					
Helium					
Hydrogen					
Sodium					
Calcium					
Iron					

4000 Å   5000 Å   6000 Å   7000 Å

Chapter 21

LABORATORY MANUAL

● Shapes of Bacteria 40

Thousands of different types of bacteria are known and have been observed, and there are possibly many more that have not yet been observed. How can a scientist tell those organisms apart when they are so small? One way is by their characteristic shapes, or patterns of joining together in groups.

Strategy

You will identify bacteria by using their shape and other characteristics as clues.

You will discover a process of elimination or "key" that will be used to help in the identification.

Materials 🕮 🛡️

key on the next page

Procedure

1. Examine FIGURE 1 in Data and Observations, which shows bacteria magnified 2000 times their natural size.

2. Use the key to identify each type of bacterium (singular for bacteria). Start at the top, following the directions. The key will allow you to identify each bacterium by name. Each bacterium has a first name that describes its shape in scientific language, and a last name that may also describe some special characteristic. The key also lists in parentheses the disease caused by the bacterium or type of food in which the bacterium may be found. Label each bacterium in Data and Observations.

Data and Observations

Identify and label each bacterium in FIGURE 1.

Scientific names should be italicized or underlined.

FIGURE 1

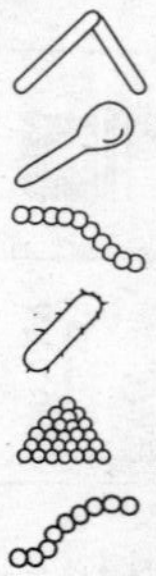

Bacillus lactis

Bacillus tetani

Streptococcus pyogenes

Bacillus typhosa

Staphlococcus aureus

Streptococcus lactis

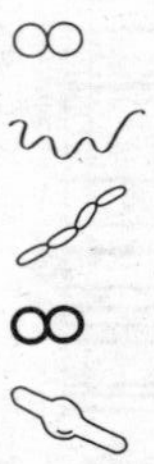

Diplococcus meningitidis

Treponema pallidum

Bacillus anthracis

Deplococcus pneumoniae

Bacillus botulinum

KEY

If the general shape of a bacterium is round, go to I, skip II and III.
If the general shape of a bacterium is rod (long and straight), go to II, skip I and III.
If the general shape of a bacterium is spiral, go to III, skip II and I.

Section I

If in pairs, go to a or a′ only.
If in chains, go to b or b′ only.
If in clumps, go to c only.

a—without a heavy cover-*Diplococcus meningitidis* (spinal meningitis)
a′—with a heavy cover (capsule)-*Diplococcus pneumoniae* (Pneumonia)
b—large in size-*Streptococcus pyogenes* (Tonsillitis)
b′—small in size-*Streptococcus lactis*-(Buttermilk)
c—*Staphylococcus aureus* (Boils)

Section II

If in chains, go to d only.
If in pairs, go to e only.
If single, go to f or f′ or f″.

d—*Bacillus anthracis* (Anthrax)
e—*Bacillus lactis* (Sauerkraut)
f—with hairs (flagella)-*Bacillus typhosa* (Typhoid fever)
f′—with a bulge (spore) in the middle-*Bacillus botulinum* (Botulism poisoning)
f″—with a bulge at the end-*Bacillus tetani* (Tetanus)

Section III

Treponema palladium (Syphilis)

Questions and Conclusions

1. What part of the word is the same for all bacteria found in Section I? **coccus**

This word refers to the shape of a bacterium. The shape is **round or sphere.**

2. The word "diplo-" when placed in front of a bacterium name must mean **two.**

3. The word "strepto-" when placed in front of a bacterium name must mean **in chains.**

4. The word "staphylo-" when placed in front of a bacterium name must mean **in clumps.**

5. What word is the same for all bacteria found in Section II? **bacillus**

This word refers to the shape of a bacterium. The shape is **rod or rectangular.**

6. Some bacteria produce chemicals that provide food with a certain taste. Name two such foods.

sauerkraut and buttermilk

Strategy Check

Have students prepare a key of common objects in the classroom, such as chalk, pencils, and so on.

____ Can you use the key to identify bacteria by their shape and other characteristics?

____ Can you understand how the use of scientific names helps to describe certain features of bacteria?

Chapter 21

● Bacterial Growth 41

Bacteria are supposed to be everywhere. But have you ever seen them? If a bacterium (singular of *bacteria*) has good growing conditions, this single cell will grow and quickly multiply. If enough cells get together, you may be able to see the colony (group of bacterial cells) that forms.

Strategy

You will prepare a growth chamber for bacteria.
You will test an object to see if bacteria are present on it.
You will determine whether or not bacteria were present on the object tested upon examination of your growth chambers.

A pressure cooker or autoclave is needed to sterilize the growth chambers.

Materials

aluminum foil   ruler
paper cups   scissors
potato (raw)

tape (adhesive or masking)
wax paper

If available, glass petri dishes and nutrient agar may be substituted for the paper cup, foil, and potato.

Procedure

Part A—Preparing Growth Chambers

1. Prepare two growth chambers. For each chamber, cut out a circle of aluminum foil 12 cm in diameter and a circle of wax paper 8 cm in diameter. Cut off the top 3 cm of a paper cup (see FIGURE 1). CAUTION: *Always be careful when using scissors.*

2. Mold the foil around the top of the paper cup to form a dish.

3. Cut a slice of potato and put it in your foil dish.

4. Cover the foil dish with the circle of wax paper, crimping the edges of the aluminum foil and wax paper together. Do not close the dish completely; leave one side open (see FIGURE 2B). Close the opening with tape and print your name on the tape (see FIGURE 2C). Your teacher will sterilize your growth chambers before you add bacteria to the potato.

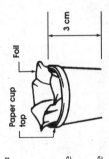

Paper cup top   Foil

FIGURE 1

Seal must be airtight   Tightly crimped

2A   Potato slice

2B   Open

2C   Tape   Name

FIGURE 2
Sterilize the growth chambers for 10 min at 67.5 newtons (15 pounds) pressure.

Part B—Adding Bacteria to the Potato

1. Set one of your growth chambers aside. This chamber is your control. Label it C, for control.

2. Open the taped end of the second growth chamber. Using your fingertips, touch the potato in this chamber.

3. Reseal the second chamber with tape after touching the potato. Set this chamber aside with the first growth chamber.

Part C—Examining the Potatoes for Bacteria

1. Open both growth chambers after two days. Examine the potatoes for bacterial growth. Small white, cream, or yellow dots are colonies of bacteria resulting from one bacterium that has multiplied and grown very rapidly to form millions of bacteria cells. CAUTION: *Do not touch the potato surface with your hands.*

2. Count the number of bacteria colonies on the surface of the treated (touched) potato. Compare the number of colonies on the untreated (control) potato with the number of colonies on the treated potato. If separate colonies cannot be counted, compare the surface of the untreated potato with the surface of the treated potato.

3. CAUTION: *Give all growth chambers and potato pieces to your teacher for disposal.*

Always wash your hands after handling living tissues. Dispose of the growth chambers by sealing in a plastic bag and placing in the garbage container.

Data and Observations

1. Record your observations in Table 1.

Table 1 Student data will vary.

Untreated potato	bacteria colonies barely visible or no colonies
Treated potato	many bacteria colonies

Questions and Conclusions

1. How do you explain finding more bacteria on the treated potato than on the untreated potato? _____

The untreated potato was not exposed to bacteria and increase in number. What supplied the food to the

2. Bacteria requires food in order to live and increase in number. What supplied the food to the bacteria?   The potato supplied food and water to the bacteria.

3. Why isn't everything on Earth covered with bacteria colonies if they are so easy to grow? _____

Proper conditions for rapid growth are not always present.

Strategy Check

___ Did you prepare a growth chamber for bacteria?

___ Did you test an object and find out if bacteria are present on it?

Chapter 22

LABORATORY MANUAL • Molds 42

Molds are fungi that need food for energy. They contain no chlorophyll, so they cannot make their own food. Will molds grow on almost any surface that provides them with food? Will they grow only on surfaces that provide certain conditions?

Strategy

You will build an apparatus to test for mold growth.
You will test the conditions in which mold will grow by using different foods, different light conditions, and different amounts of moisture.
You will observe and record the conditions in which molds grow.

Materials 🧤 🚫 ♻️ 🧪 ✋

8 baby food jars (with lids)   potato flakes (dried) **available in grocery stores**
cotton swab   paper towels
graduated cylinder (10-mL)   spoon
labels   water
mold source
Grocery stores usually throw out moldy produce daily. Ask them to supply you with some.

Procedure

1. Your teacher will assign a group with which you will work. Your group will prepare eight jars for testing mold growth.
2. Put a spoonful of dry potatoes in each of four baby food jars. Put a crumpled paper towel in each of the other four jars.
3. Observe and record in Data and Observations the appearance of mold your teacher supplies to you.
4. Rub a cotton swab over the surface of the mold and then rub it over the surface of the towels in the four jars. Rub the swab over the surface of the mold again. Then rub it over the surface of the potato flakes in the other four jars. CAUTION: *Give all swabs to your teacher for proper disposal. Always wash your hands after handling microbes.*
5. Put 5 mL of water into each of two potato jars and two paper towel jars.
6. Seal all of the jars with lids. Label the jars with your name and the date. Also write the growth conditions for the jar on each label: dry-dark, dry-light, wet-dark, wet-light.
7. Place one dry potato jar in the light and the other dry potato jar in the dark. Your teacher will tell you the best places to put your jars. Place one wet potato jar in the light and the other in the dark. Do the same for the wet and dry paper towel jars.
8. Observe the jars every day for one week. Record your daily observations in Table 1 in Data and Observations. CAUTION: *Give all jars to your teacher for proper disposal.* **Place swabs and jars into a plastic bag, seal, and dispose of in the garbage.**

Data and Observations

1. Record the appearance of the mold provided by your teacher.
   Answers will vary.

2. Record your daily observations in Table 1.

Table 1

Conditions	Day 1	Day 2	Day 3	Day 4	Day 5	Day 6	Day 7
Potato-dry-light	no	no	no	no	no	no	no
Potato-dry-dark	no	no	no	no	no	no	no
Potato-wet-light	no	no	no	no	yes	yes	yes
Potato-wet-dark	no	no	yes	yes	yes	yes	yes
Towel-dry-light	no	no	no	no	no	no	no
Towel-dry-dark	no	no	no	no	no	no	no
Towel-wet-light	no	no	no	no	no	no	no
Towel-wet-dark	no	no	no	no	no	no	no

3. If mold is observed growing in any jar after several days, describe its appearance here.
   Answers will vary. The mold will be similar to the mold provided at the beginning of the activity.

Questions and Conclusions

1. Is the new mold growing in the jar similar to the original mold? **yes**
   Give evidence of this. **Their appearance is similar.**

2. Does mold require food in order to grow? **yes**
   Give evidence of this. **Mold grows on potatoes but not on paper towels.**

3. Does mold require water to grow if food is supplied? **yes**
   Give evidence of this. **Mold grows on wet potatoes but not on dry ones.**

4. Does mold grow better in light or dark conditions if food and moisture are supplied? **dark**
   Give evidence of this. **Mold appears first in the wet potato jar placed in the dark.**

Strategy Check

___ Can you build an apparatus for testing mold growth?

___ Can you test mold growth in different conditions?

___ Can you determine from your results if mold needs food to grow?

___ Can you determine from your results if mold needs water to grow?

___ Can you determine from your results if mold grows better under light or dark conditions?

Prepare jars again as directed in the activity. Add some commercial mold retardant (such as Lysol®) to some of the jars. Find out how well the products work.

Chapter 22

LABORATORY MANUAL • **Yeasts 43**

Yeast are fungi that need food for life. When yeast use food for energy, they give off carbon dioxide as a waste product. The production of carbon dioxide is evidence that yeast are converting food to energy. You can demonstrate that yeast produce carbon dioxide.

Strategy

You will build an apparatus to show that yeast produce carbon dioxide.
You will provide some yeast with food and some yeast with no food.
You will observe yeast producing carbon dioxide gas.

Materials 🥽🧤

beaker (large) or **large milk**
pancake syrup **cartons**
2 dropper/rubber stopper
(one hole) assemblies
2 test tubes

graduated cylinder
watch or clock
water
yeast (cake type)
Dry yeast can also be used.

Have students work in pairs or groups of four.

Procedure

1. Work with a partner. Fill two test tubes 1/4 full of water. Push a 1-cm cube of yeast into each tube.

2. Add 5 mL of pancake syrup to one of the test tubes. Do not add syrup to the other test tube. Put your finger over the mouth of the test tube and mix the contents by shaking the tube slightly.

3. Obtain two dropper/rubber stopper assemblies from your teacher. Then push a stopper into the mouth of each test tube as shown in FIGURE 1. NOTE: Make sure the bottom end of the dropper is *not* below the level of the liquid in the tube. If it is below that level, pour some of the liquid out. This is very important.

4. Fill a large beaker nearly full with warm, but not hot, water. Submerge both tubes in the beaker. NOTE: The tops of the stoppers in each of the tubes must be just below the surface of the water in the beaker. If the tube floats, add a plug of clay to the outside.

5. Wait 4 min, then begin to count the number of bubbles that come from the top of each tube. You can watch one tube while your partner watches the other.

6. Count the number of bubbles rising from the tubes for 2 min. Record this number in Table 1. Continue to count and record the number of bubbles that rise during each of ten 2-min intervals. **The first bubbles to appear should not be counted. If no bubbles appear, the tip of the dropper may be clogged. Clear it and try again. A tight seal of the stopper in the test tube is extremely important.**

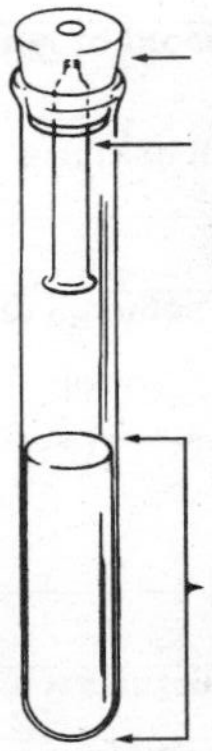

Review the procedure for inserting a glass tube in a rubber stopper. Assemble the apparatus before class. Put soapy water or glycerol on the outside of the droppers. Carefully insert the tip of a dropper into each one-hole stopper as shown in FIGURE 1. Be sure to wrap the glass tubing and stopper in cloth toweling.

One-hole stopper
Dropper with rubber top removed

Yeast and water or yeast, water, and syrup

FIGURE 1

Data and Observations

1. Record your observations in Table 1.

Table 1
Student answers will vary.

	Tube	
	Water and yeast	Water, yeast, and syrup
First 2 minutes	2	54
Second 2 minutes	3	55
Third 2 minutes	3	54
Fourth 2 minutes	3	49
Fifth 2 minutes	2	48
Sixth 2 minutes	4	46
Seventh 2 minutes	4	44
Eighth 2 minutes	3	42
Ninth 2 minutes	5	39
Tenth 2 minutes	5	37

The tube containing only water and yeast may show no reaction at all.

Questions and Conclusions

1. In which tube were more bubbles of carbon dioxide given off?
the tube with water, yeast, and syrup

2. In which tube was little or no carbon dioxide gas given off?
the tube with water and yeast

3. What does the tube that makes the most carbon dioxide have in it that the other tube does not have?
a food supply—syrup (sugar)

What do yeast do with this substance?
use it as a food source

4. Does the experiment tell you what specific type of food is best for yeast? **no**
Explain. **Only syrup was used. No comparison was made.**

5. Why were the tubes placed in warm water?
Yeast does not convert food to energy at low temperatures.

6. Design an experiment that tests how different temperatures of water in the beaker change the speed of carbon dioxide production by yeast cells.

   Set up beakers containing water of different temperatures (ice water, water at room temperature, warm water, etc.). Place tubes with the same amounts of yeast, water, food, and (syrup) into each beaker. Record the number of bubbles that come from each tube for 20 min. The tube with the most bubbles indicates the optimum water temperature for carbon dioxide production. (Answers will vary.)

7. Which tube is the control?

   the tube with water and yeast

8. Does the activity prove that the gas being given off by yeast is carbon dioxide? Explain.

   No, the gas would have to be tested. However, when an organism changes food to energy, carbon dioxide is the gas given off.

9. Does the activity prove that it is actually the yeast and not the syrup that is giving off carbon dioxide? Explain.

   No. You would have to set up a test tube with only syrup and water to prove it.

Strategy Check

_____ Did you build an apparatus to show that yeast produce carbon dioxide?

_____ Do you know that gas bubbles given off means that food is being used by yeast?

_____ Do you know that the more gas given off, the more food the yeast is using?

_____ From your results, can you determine if food is needed by yeast?

You may want students actually to perform the activity they design in answer to Question 6.

Chapter 23

LABORATORY MANUAL

• Root Structure and Functions 44

Roots hold a plant in the ground. They also absorb, store, and transport water and minerals. They have small threadlike side roots with root hairs that absorb water and minerals from the soil.

Strategy

You will examine a dissected carrot root.
You will label a diagram of a root and list the function of each part.

Materials 🧪 🔬

carrot sliced crosswise
carrot sliced lengthwise
hand lens

Some carrots may not show root hairs. In this case, germinate some radish seeds on moist paper towels in covered dishes. In a few days the roots will develop a "furry" appearance due to the growth of root hairs. Students can then examine them with hand lenses or microscopes.

Procedure

1. Your teacher will prepare a crosswise slice of a carrot for you.
2. Hold the slice up to the light. Compare what you see with FIGURE 1 under Data and Observations.
3. Examine the lengthwise slice of the carrot. Use the hand lens. Look at both the inner and outer parts.
4. The outside layer of the root is the epidermis. Lateral roots grow from the epidermal cells and root hairs grow from them. Label the epidermis, lateral roots, and root hairs if all of these structures are present.
5. Inside the epidermis, you will find several layers of large, loosely packed cells that store food. This is the cortex. Food stored in the cortex can be used by other cells of the plant. Label the cortex.
6. Inside the cortex are tubelike xylem cells that carry water and minerals in the plant. Label the xylem cells.
7. Other tubelike cells inside the xylem carry food in the plant. These cells are called phloem cells. Label the phloem cells.

Students will probably not be able to distinguish easily between xylem and phloem cells. Xylem cells are more woody and more central than phoelm cells.

Data and Observations

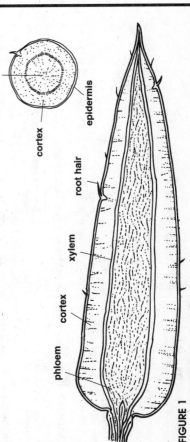

FIGURE 1

xylem and phloem

cortex

epidermis

root hair

xylem

cortex

phloem

Questions and Conclusions

1. What type of root is the carrot?

   a taproot

2. What is the function of the root hairs?

   Root hairs absorb water and minerals from the soil.

3. How many different kinds of cells did you see in the carrot slice?

   four

4. What is the name and function of the outer ring of cells?

   The epidermis protects the root.

5. What is the green part at the top end of the carrot?

   the stem

6. What is the name and function of the thicker layer of cells next to the epidermis?

   This layer is the cortex. Its cells store food for the plant.

7. What cells are found in the inner core?

   xylem and phloem

8. What is the function of these cells?

   The xylem cells transport water and minerals. The phloem cells transport food.

9. Why do you think taproots are used as food more often than fibrous roots?

   Taproots contain a thick cortex with stored food. The amount of stored food is larger than in fibrous roots.

10. List some other food plants that have a taproot.

    radish, beet, turnip, parsnip, rutabaga

Strategy Check

___ Can you examine a carrot root?

___ Can you identify the locations of each part of a root?

Chapter 23

LABORATORY MANUAL

● Parts of a Fruit 45

Some of the plants that we call vegetables are actually fruits. Fruits are formed inside flowers that have been pollinated and fertilized. After fertilization takes place, the petals fall off and the ovary begins to develop into the fruit.

Strategy Review parts of the flower.

You will study the structure of typical fleshy and dry fruits.

You will examine several fruits and classify the fruits as fleshy or dry.

Materials 🧤✂️ Only the teacher should slice the fruits.

acorn	bean in a pod	peanut	olive	sunflower seed
apple	corn	pear	pea in a pod	tomato
avocado	okra	plum	peach	

Other dry fruits: **milkweed, mimosa, locust, cotton, poppy, dandelion, maple, ash, elm, hazelnut, wheat, barley**

Procedure

1. Read the following paragraphs and study the diagrams.

The peach is a fleshy fruit. A fleshy fruit consists of a single ripened ovary with a soft fleshy ovary wall when ripe. Three kinds of fleshy fruits are the drupe, pome, and berry. The peach is a drupe. The exocarp is the covering of skin. The mesocarp is fleshy. The endocarp is hard and encloses the seed.

The apple is a pome. The stem is the stalk by which the flower was attached. At the other end are the remains of the sepals, petals, and a ring of dried stamens. The thin skin is the epidermis. The fleshy part inside the skin developed from the receptacle, or flower stalk. The papery core is the ovary wall. Within the ovary are the seeds.

The grape is a berry. The entire ovary is soft.

Dry fruits have an ovary wall that is dry and brittle when ripe. They are classified as dehiscent or indehiscent. A dehiscent fruit splits along a definite seam when ripe. The bean has a dehiscent fruit called a legume. It splits along two seams. Fruits that do not split along a definite seam when ripe are indehiscent. Grains are indehiscent.

2. Examine each of the fruits listed in Table 1 and determine if they are fleshy or dry. Determine the type of fruit (drupe, pome, or berry and dehiscent). Record your answers in the table.

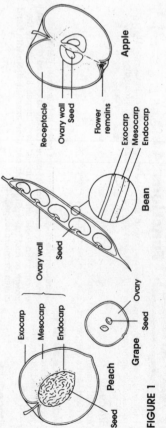

FIGURE 1

Data and Observations

Table 1

Fruit	Fleshy or Dry	Type
Plum	fleshy	drupe
Tomato	fleshy	berry
Apple	fleshy	pome
Peach	fleshy	drupe
Peanut	dry	dehiscent (legume)
Acorn	dry	indehiscent (nut)
Okra	dry	dehiscent (capsule)
Olive	fleshy	drupe
Pear	fleshy	pome
Pea	dry	dehiscent (legume)
Avocado	fleshy	drupe
Sunflower	dry	indehiscent (achene)
Corn	dry	indehiscent (grain)

Questions and Conclusions

1. What part of a flower becomes the fruit? **ovary**
2. What part of a flower becomes the seed? **ovule**
3. What are some fruits that we call vegetables? **cucumber, squash, beans, peas**
4. What are some seeds that people eat? **beans, corn, peas, peanuts, other nuts, wheat, barley, oats**
5. From what part of the flower does a peach develop? **ovary wall**
6. From what part of the flower does a grape develop? **whole ovary**

Strategy Check

_____ Did you study the structure of fleshy and dry fruits?

_____ Did you examine several fruits and classify them as fleshy or dry?

Chapter 24

LABORATORY MANUAL

● Earthworm Anatomy 46

The earthworm is an invertebrate that has a segmented body and specialized body parts. Oxygen from the air moves into its body through its moist skin. Carbon dioxide moves out of its body through the skin. The earthworm has a series of enlarged tubes that act as hearts. The tubes pump blood through the blood vessels of an earthworm's body. The segmented body plan makes an earthworm's anatomy easy to study.

Strategy

You will observe the external parts of an earthworm.
You will dissect an earthworm.
You will identify the internal organs and organ systems of an earthworm.

Materials

dissecting needle
dissecting pan
dissecting pins
earthworm (preserved) **CAUTION:** *Wash hands thoroughly after handling worm.*
hand lens
dissecting scissors

Procedure

Part A External Structure

1. Place a preserved earthworm lengthwise on a paper towel in the dissecting pan with the darker side up. This is the dorsal or top side.
2. Examine the external structure and identify the parts shown in FIGURE 1.
3. Run your fingers lightly along the top, bottom, and sides of the earthworm. The bristles that you feel are setae. Examine the setae with a hand lens. Estimate the number of setae on each segment.
4. Locate the mouth. The part that hangs over the mouth is called the prostonium.
5. Find the thickened band circling the body. This is the clitellum. It forms a cocoon for depositing the eggs during reproduction.
6. Locate the anus (see FIGURE 1).

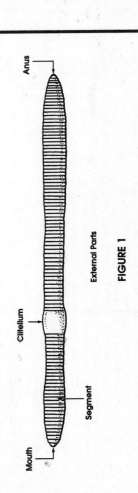

Mouth

Clitellum

Anus

Segment

External Parts

FIGURE 1

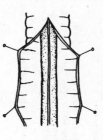

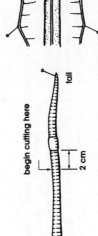

Prostonium

Mouth cavity

Pharynx

Brain

Esophagus

Seminal vesicles

Crop

Nephridium

Dorsal blood vessel

Ventral nerve cord

Ventral blood vessel

Clitellum

Intestine

Gizzard

Aortic arches

Seminal receptacles

FIGURE 2

Part B Internal Structure

Read the instructions carefully and study FIGURES 1 and 2 before you begin to cut. Identify structures to be cut before you begin. **CAUTION:** *Always be careful with all sharp objects.*

1. With the dorsal side up, pin both ends of the worm to the wax in the dissecting pan.
2. With scissors, begin about 2 cm in front of the clitellum and cut forward through the body wall just to the left of the dorsal blood vessel. Use care to cut through only the body wall (see FIGURE 3).
3. Separate the edges of the cut. Observe the space between the body wall and the intestine. This is the body cavity or coelom.

begin cutting here

tail

2 cm

head

FIGURE 3

4. Observe the partitions between the segments from the body wall to the intestines. Use a dissecting needle to break these partitions. Then pin down the sides of the body wall.
5. Observe the tubelike digestive system. Identify the pharynx in segments 4 and 5. It is used to swallow food.
6. Follow the esophagus to segment 15.
7. Locate the large thin-walled crop. Food is stored in the crop until it is digested.
8. Locate the gizzard just behind the crop. Food is broken down by a grinding action here. The intestine extends from the gizzard to the anus. Digestion of food occurs in the intestine.
9. Each earthworm has both male and female reproductive organs. Alongside the esophagus in segments 9 and 10 are two pairs of seminal receptacles. The seminal receptacles receive sperm from another worm. In front of the receptacles in segments 10, 11, and 12 are seminal vesicles where sperm is stored.
10. Use a hand lens to find the small ovaries where eggs are produced. They are located under the seminal vesicles.
Students may have difficulty finding the ovaries.

241

11. Locate the dorsal blood vessel. It carries blood forward to the heart. Carefully remove the white seminal vesicles from the left side of the body. Find the aortic arches, which branch from the dorsal blood vessel and pass around the esophagus. They join the ventral blood vessel below the esophagus. These aortic arches contract and function as hearts. The ventral blood vessel carries blood toward the skin and intestine.

12. Use a hand lens to observe the small white tubes along each side of the digestive tract. These tubes are excretory organs called nephridia. They are found in all segments except the first three and the last. They remove the waste from the body cavity.

13. Find the double nerve ganglion, or brain, of the earthworm near segment 2. The brain connects with the ventral nerve cord, which extends the length of the body. The nerve cord is a white line on the ventral body wall.

14. CAUTION: Give all dissected materials to your teacher for disposal. *Always wash your hands after a dissection procedure.*

Data and Observations

1. Record the organs found in each system in Table 1.

Table 1

Systems and Organs of an Earthworm

System	Organs
Digestive	pharynx, crop, gizzard, intestine
Reproductive	clitellum, seminal vesicles, seminal receptacles, ovaries
Circulatory	aortic arches, dorsal and ventral blood vessels
Excretory	nephridia
Nervous	brain, ventral nerves

Questions and Conclusions

1. How many setae were located on each segment? **four pairs**

2. What is the function of the setae? **aid in movement**

3. Describe the function of the following organs.

a. pharynx **to swallow food**

b. crop **to store food**

c. gizzard **to grind food**

d. aortic arches **to function as hearts (pump blood)**

e. dorsal blood vessel **to carry blood forward to aortic arches**

f. ventral blood vessel **to carry blood toward skin and intestine**

g. clitellum **to form a cocoon for depositing eggs**

h. nephridia **to remove wastes**

i. seminal vesicles **to store sperm**

j. intestine **to digest food**

k. ganglia **to function as brain**

4. Why is it said that the earthworm has a "closed" circulatory system? **"Blood" is carried in a system of tubes.**

Strategy Check

_____ Can you dissect an earthworm?

_____ Can you identify the external and internal parts of the earthworm?

To observe the pulse of blood as it moves through the dorsal blood vessel, obtain living earthworms. The pulse can easily be observed through the somewhat transparent skin. Place the worms in cold water (10°C) for a brief time and record their pulse per minute. Transfer the worms to warm water (20°C) and again record their pulse per minute. Cold temperatures should slow the worms' pulse rate, and warm temperatures should speed up the pulse rates. Discuss pulse rate as a function of temperature in relation to cold- and warm-blooded animals.

● Grasshopper Anatomy 47

A grasshopper is well adapted to its way of life. Its features are representative of the insect group. A grasshopper is large enough that its features can be seen easily.

Strategy

You will observe and identify the specialized body parts of the grasshopper.
You will examine and identify the internal structure of the grasshopper.

Materials

dissecting needle   grasshopper (preserved)   scissors
dissecting pan   hand lens
forceps

Have students use a hand lens to observe the simple eyes.

Procedure

Part A—External Structure

1. Place the grasshopper in the dissecting pan. Locate the head, thorax, and abdomen. (See FIGURE 1.) Use your hand lens to observe the grasshopper carefully. As you observe, record your data in Data and Observations.

2. Observe the parts of the head. The grasshopper has two compound eyes and three simple eyes. The sensory parts located on the head are the antennae.

3. Identify the mouth parts. (Refer to FIGURE 2.) With your forceps remove the parts. The labrum is the hinged upper lip that is used to hold food. The mandibles are crushing jaws. The maxillae are used to chew and taste food. The labium is the broad fat lower lip used to hold food while it is being chewed.

4. Locate the eardrums or tympana, small drum-shaped structures on either side of the thorax.

5. All insects have six legs. In the grasshopper, the front pair is used for walking, climbing, and holding food. The middle legs are used for walking and climbing. The hind legs are large and enable the grasshopper to jump.

6. Locate the two pairs of wings.

7. Use the hand lens to look at the tiny openings along the abdomen. These are breathing pores called spiracles through which oxygen enters and carbon dioxide leaves.

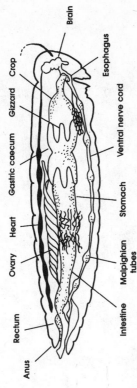

FIGURE 1

FIGURE 2

---

8. A female grasshopper has a much longer abdomen than a male. It ends in a four-pointed tip called an ovipositor through which eggs are laid.

Part B—Internal Structure

1. Remove the three left legs. Insert the point of your scissors under the top surface of the last segment of the abdomen. Make a cut to the left of the mid-dorsal line. Be careful not to cut the organs underneath. In front of the thorax, cut down the left side to the bottom of the grasshopper. Cut down between the next to the last and last abdominal segments. (See FIGURE 3.)
CAUTION: *Always be careful when using scissors.*

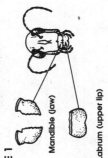

FIGURE 3

2. Use your forceps to pull down the left side. Locate the large dorsal blood vessel.

3. Use your scissors to cut the muscles close to the exoskeleton. Locate the finely-branched trachea leading to the spiracles.

4. Cut through the exoskeleton over the top of the head between the left antenna and left eye to the mouth. Remove the exoskeleton on the left side of the head. Find the dorsal ganglion or brain.

5. Cut away the tissue to show the digestive system. Refer to FIGURE 3 and identify the mouth, esophagus, crop, gizzard, and stomach. Note that the gizzard and stomach are separated by a narrow place. The digestive glands that secrete enzymes into the stomach are attached here.

6. Another narrow place separates the stomach from the intestine. Tubules that collect wastes from the blood are located here.

7. Observe the colon, which enlarges to form the rectum. Wastes collect here before passing out the anus.

8. In the female, the ovary is located above the intestines. In the male, a series of whitish tubes, the testes, are located above the intestine.

Data and Observations

1. What are the three sections of a grasshopper's body? _____

   head, thorax, abdomen

2. Record your observations of grasshopper body parts in Table 1. Complete the table by listing the function of each part.

Table 1   Structure of the Grasshopper

Body part	How many?	Function
Eyes	5—3 simple, 2 compound	seeing
Antennae	2	sensing
Labrum	1	holding food
Mandibles	2	chewing food
Maxillae	2	chewing and tasting food
Labium	1	holding food
Eardrums	2	hearing
Legs	6—3 pairs	walking, climbing, jumping
Wings	4	flying
Spiracles	many	respiration
Ovipositor (if female)	1	laying eggs
Digestive glands	many	secreting enzymes into stomach
Tubules	many	collecting wastes from the blood
Rectum	1	wastes collect here

Questions and Conclusions

1. How is a grasshopper's mouth adapted for plant eating? The mouth is designed so that the grasshopper can hold and chew plants.

2. What is the difference between a grasshopper's skeleton and yours? Grasshoppers have an exoskeleton made up of chitin. Humans have an endoskeleton made of bone and cartilage.

3. How is a grasshopper's digestive system different from yours? The grasshopper has a crop and a gizzard for grinding food. A human has teeth.

4. How do a grasshopper's legs help it to survive? The grasshopper's legs are adapted to jumping, which helps it escape predators.

---

5. To which phylum does the grasshopper belong? **Arthropoda**

6. List three characteristics common to all animals in the phylum. **Jointed legs, exoskeleton, body divided into sections**

7. To which class does the grasshopper belong? **Insecta**

8. List three characteristics of this class. **three body sections, one pair of antennae, three pairs of legs, wings (most insects)**

Strategy Check

____ Did you observe specialized parts of the grasshopper?

____ Can you identify the internal and external parts of the grasshopper?

Chapter 25

LABORATORY MANUAL • **Whale Insulation 48**

Mammals are endotherms that have adaptations, such as hair, that conserve and maintain body temperature. Whales are mammals that are nearly hairless, yet they live in cold seawater. How do whales maintain body temperature? Whales have a layer of fat called blubber beneath their skin. Blubber helps insulate the whale so it can survive in cold water.

Strategy

You will measure and compare the rate of cooling of insulated and uninsulated test tubes.
You will relate the results to the effectiveness of blubber as a means to maintain body temperature in whales.

Materials

Use gloves when working with ice or heated materials to protect your hands.

test tubes (3)
solid food shortening
plastic sandwich bags
plastic spoons
beakers (600-mL)
ice water
heat source
thermometers
rubber bands
watch with a second hand
apron
goggles
gloves

If shortening is not available, students could use butter or margarine, or they could substitute pieces of Styrofoam or other insulating materials.

Procedure

CAUTION: *Do not taste, eat, or drink any materials used in the lab.*

1. Place a beaker on a hot plate, filled with approximately 400 mL of water. CAUTION: *Do not touch hot plate.* Heat the water to 80°C. CAUTION: *Use care when handling hot liquids.*

2. Place one test tube into a plastic bag. Seal the top of the bag around the test tube using a rubber band.

3. Place a spoonful of shortening into a second plastic bag. Place a second test tube into this plastic bag. Spread the shortening over the test tube by moving it with your fingers on the outside of the plastic bag. Seal the top of the plastic bag with a rubber band.

4. Place several spoonfuls of shortening into a third plastic bag. Place a third test tube into this plastic bag. Spread this thick layer of shortening around the test tube and secure the top of the plastic bag.

5. Fill three beakers with ice water.

6. Fill all three test tubes three-quarters full with the heated water and take the temperature of each. Record this temperature in Table 1 under Data and Observations.

7. Place one test tube into each of the three beakers filled with ice water.

8. Measure and record the temperatures of each test tube every 5 minutes for 30 minutes.

9. Graph your results using a line graph with the temperature on the y-axis and time on the x-axis. Use a different color for each test tube.

153

Data and Observations

Table 1

Temperature (in °C)	Test tube in plastic bag alone	Test tube in plastic bag and thin layer of shortening	Test tube in plastic bag and heavy layer of shortening
0			
5			
10			
15			
20			
25			
30			

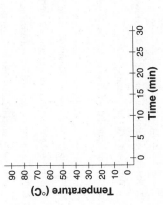

The graph will show a faster rate of cooling for the uninsulated test tube. Students should observe that it takes about twice as long for the insulated test tube to lose heat and take on the temperature of the ice bath as it does for the uninsulated test tube.

FIGURE 1

Questions and Conclusions

1. How did the temperature change in each of the test tubes? **Test tubes with insulation lost heat more slowly than the test tube without insulation.**

2. How did the rate of cooling of the uninsulated test tube compare to the others? Explain. **The rate of cooling of the uninsulated test tube was about twice that of the insulated test tube. Insulation helps retain heat.**

3. Infer whether blubber is a good insulator for mammals that swim in cold water. **Blubber may be a good insulator because it is a fat, like shortening.**

Strategy Check

_____ Can you measure and compare the rate of cooling of insulated and uninsulated test tubes?

_____ Can you relate your results to the effectiveness of blubber as a means to maintain body temperature in whales?

154

Chapter 25

LABORATORY MANUAL ● **Owl Pellets 49**

The barn owl usually feeds on small mammals such as rodents, moles, and shrews. These mammals are swallowed whole. Some parts of the mammals dissolve in the owl's stomach. The indigestible parts, such as bones, hair, and feathers, are regurgitated in an owl pellet. You can find out what an owl eats by examining the owl pellet in this laboratory.

Strategy

You will dissect an owl pellet and identify animal skulls found in the owl pellet.
You will construct a chart of the numbers and kinds of prey eaten by owls.

Materials

owl pellet
white sheet of paper
forceps
dissecting needle
plastic gloves

Procedure

1. Use the forceps to place the owl pellet on the white paper.
2. Break the owl pellet apart. Carefully separate the bones of the animals from the feathers and fur.
3. Use the forceps and dissecting needle to clean skull bones. **CAUTION:** *Use sharp objects with care.*
4. Identify the skulls of the animals that the owl has eaten, using the drawings on this page. You will also need to use a Field Guide to Small Mammals. Record the number of skulls of different animals in Table 1.
5. Make a class record of the kinds and numbers of animals found in the owl pellets.

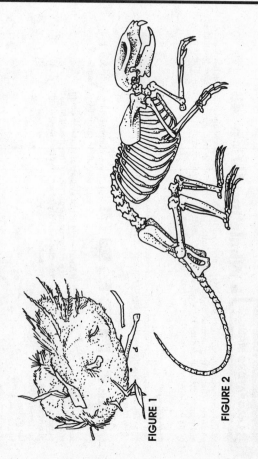

FIGURE 1

FIGURE 2

Data and Observations

Table 1

Animal	Number—individual	Number—class
Shrew	Answers may vary.	
Mole sparrow		
Vole		
Deer mouse		
Rat		
Other		
Total		

Questions and Conclusions

1. What was the outside covering of the owl pellet? **feathers and fur**

2. An owl regurgitates one pellet a day. How many animals did your owl eat in one day? **Answers will vary, usually 4–7.**

3. What animals did you find in the owl pellet? **Answers will vary.**

4. What is the owl's role in the environment? **predator**

5. Is the owl an herbivore or a carnivore? **carnivore**

6. Poisons found in the environment often accumulate in the bodies of small mammals. How would this affect the owl that preys on these animals? **The owl takes in more food than the organisms it preys on so the poison would accumulate faster in the body of the owl.**

Strategy Check

___ Did you dissect an owl pellet and identify animal skulls?

___ Did you construct a chart of the kind and numbers of prey eaten by owls?

Chapter 26

Human Impact on the Environment 50

Human beings are agents of change, and the rate at which they are changing the environment increases as population increases. Only recently have people become aware of their impact on the atmosphere, water, and the crust of Earth.

Strategy

You will make a survey of your neighborhood or town to observe people's impact on the environment.

You will use the accompanying matrix to estimate the ways in which humans have affected your local environment.

You will suggest some ways people can change their impact on the environment.

Materials

clipboard
environmental impact check sheet, Table 1
pencil

Procedure

1. Look over the check sheet on the next two pages. A, B, C, and D are general categories for the way people change the environment. Across the top are the various areas of the environment that may be affected by the processes and materials that people use.

2. Walk through your neighborhood (in the city, at least a 10-block square) taking the sheet with you.

3. Place a check after each type of environmental influence found in your neighborhood. For example, if new houses are being built, put a check after "houses" in category A.

4. In the boxes to the right, put a diagonal slash under the area(s) affected by this influence. If the effect is good, put a plus in the lower right part of the box. If you think the effect is bad, place a minus in this position.

5. In the upper left of the box, place a number from 1 to 10 to indicate how much impact you think the change has or will have. If you think the change is small, write in 1; if you think it is or will be very large, write in 10. Use your judgment and observations to assign numbers 2 through 9 on this impact scale.

6. Find your total for each influence and for each affected area. Record your totals in the chart.

7. Find the class total for each influence and for each affected area. Record those totals in the chart.

Data and Observations

Table 1—Environmental Impact Check Sheet

	Biological	Scenic	Recreation	Temperature	Air	Water	Eutrophi-cation	Other	Totals
A. Construction—									
(Example) ✔		2 / +				3 / -	1 / -		2 / -
Houses									
Roads									
Transmission lines									
Fences or other barriers									
Canals									
Dams									
Shore structures									
Cut and fill									
Tunnels									
Mines									
Industrial plants									
Landscaped lawns									
B. Traffic—									
On roads									
Pipelines									
C. Chemicals—									
Fertilization									
Weed and insect control									
Deicing highways									

	Biological	Scenic	Recreation	Temperature	Air	Water	Eutrophi-cation	Other	Totals
D. Waste disposal—									
Litter and dumps									
Sewage									
Stack and exhaust emissions									
Cooling water discharge									
Used-lubricant dumping									
Totals									
Class Totals									

Questions and Conclusions

1. List three ways in which the construction of concrete pavement (roads) changes the environment. **prevents infiltration, adds calcium carbonate to adjacent areas, reflects heat and light, adds lead poison to strip along road**

2. How does an automobile affect the atmosphere? **It adds hydrocarbon gases to the atmosphere as well as some smoke.**

3. What other ways could people use to travel that would have less adverse effects on the environment? **bicycling, walking, driving newer cars with anti-pollution devices, taking forms of public transportation such as trains**

4. If there is smog in your local area, what is its source? **Answers will vary. Possibilities include local industries, cars, and burning of dumps.**

5. What can be done to reduce or eliminate the smog? **Answers will vary. Answers may include scrubbers on smokestacks to remove some gases and electronic air cleaners to remove some particulate matter.**

6. What resources are being used in local construction? **Possibilities include granite, limestone, or sandstone blocks and clay, limestone, sandstone, and gravel for concrete or asphalt.**

---

7. What resources are lost to humans when cities move into the surrounding countryside? **farming areas, resources of sand, gravel, clay, recreation areas, wood**

8. Are there alternatives? **Alternatives include leaving green areas in cities and zoning certain areas for recreation and/or farming. Students may think of others.**

9. Discuss the drawbacks of the alternatives you have listed in the questions above. **Answers will vary; most drawbacks will involve costs.**

Strategy Check

___ Can you recognize human influence on your local environment?

___ Can you estimate the impact, good or bad, using the matrix?

___ Can you suggest and evaluate alternatives?

Chapter 26

LABORATORY MANUAL

● Reclamation of Mine Wastes 51

Mine wastes, which seem to be worthless, can be made profitable. For example, copper metal can be reclaimed from copper mine waste. When open pit copper is crushed and smelted, copper(II) sulfate is left in the waste rock. The copper(II) sulfate can be dissolved in water. Then more metallic copper can be removed by reacting the copper(II) sulfate with iron ores.

Strategy

You will investigate a process by which copper is reclaimed from open pit waste.

Materials

apron	copper(II) sulfate crystals, CuSO$_4$	litmus paper (blue)	apron
balance	goggles	nails (iron scraps)	gloves
beaker (500-mL)	graduated cylinder (50-mL)	water	

Procedure

1. Place 3 g of copper(II) sulfate in the beaker. **CAUTION:** *Copper(II) sulfate is poisonous. Avoid contact with skin.*

2. Cover the copper(II) sulfate crystals with 50 mL of water. Record the color of the solution in Table 1. Test with litmus; record your results in Table 1.

3. Place the iron scrap in the solution. Observe and record what happens in Table 1.

4. Test the solution with blue litmus paper and record your results in Table 1.

Data and Observations

Table 1

Solution	Color	Litmus	Other observations
Copper(II) sulfate	blue	no change	clear solution
Copper(II) sulfate and iron	clear	turns red	copper coating on iron

Questions and Conclusions

1. Why did you add water to the copper(II) sulfate crystals? **The copper(II) sulfate dissolves in water and makes available copper ions.**

2. What happens to the copper in the solution when iron is added? **The iron provides a means to extract the copper from the solution.**

3. Is this a chemical or physical method of reclaiming the copper? **A chemical method is being used.**

---

4. What happened to the water in which the copper(II) sulfate is dissolved? **Sulfuric acid is formed.**

5. Does this method use up all the waste material? **No; iron and sulfuric acid remain.**

6. What might happen to a stream if large amounts of the water used in this reclaiming process were flushed into it? **The stream might become too acidic for fish and water plants to exist. Most copper mines try to find a market for the sulfuric acid.**

7. What might happen to an abandoned copper mine in a humid climate? **Heavy rain would dissolve the copper(II) sulfate and carry it into streams or into underground water.**

Strategy Check

___ Can you recognize the copper deposit on the iron?

___ Could copper be reclaimed from waste using this method?

___ Would reclaiming the copper be profitable?

Chapter 27

LABORATORY MANUAL ● **Smoke Pollution 52**

In 1967, the former U.S. Bureau of Mines adopted the Ringelmann Chart as a basic scale for measuring smoke pollution. Using an adapted version of the Ringelmann Chart, you can recognize smokestacks that may be polluting your environment.

Strategy

You will observe an industry that is sending out smoke.
You will keep track of this industry for a week to see how often you observe it emitting smoke.

Materials 📖 🔬 ✂️

cardboard (thin)   Ringelmann Chart
compass   (adapted), FIGURE 1
glue or paste   scissors

Procedure

1. Cut out FIGURE 1 and glue it to the cardboard. CAUTION: *Use care when handling sharp objects.*
2. When the glue is dry, cut out the center window by cutting along the dotted lines.
3. Go outside and observe a source of industrial smoke.
4. View the smoke through the window while holding the chart at arm's length.
5. Match the color of the darkest part of the smoke plume to one of the examples on the chart.
6. Continue observing the smoke plume for about 5 min. Record the wind direction, wind speed, time of day, and the number of the matching smoke column in Table 1.
7. Repeat these observations every day for a week. Make your readings the same time each day.

Data and Observations

Table 1

Day	Wind direction (north, south, southeast)	Wind speed (light, strong, gusty)	Time of day	Darkness of smoke (from chart)
1				
2				
3				
4				
5				

Questions and Conclusions

1. If accidental air pollution occurred, what kinds of readings would you expect? **4 or 5 on a one-time basis**

2. What does Number 5 on the Ringelmann Chart indicate about the relative amount of pollution entering the atmosphere? **Maximum measurable amount of air pollution is present.**

3. What effect does wind have on air pollution in your local area? **Usually, answers will vary. Wind disperses smoke and smog but may also carry it to a new location that normally has pure air.**

4. What processes are involved in the industry that is emitting smoke? **Answers will vary.**

5. How might the smoke pollution be reduced? **Answers will vary.**

6. Some industries emit invisible gases. Might these gases also be pollutants? Explain. **Yes, some gases are colorless and can be injurious in small amounts and over short periods of time.**

Strategy Check

___ Can you determine an average Ringelmann Number for smoke emission you observed?

___ Can you see how wind influences smoke?

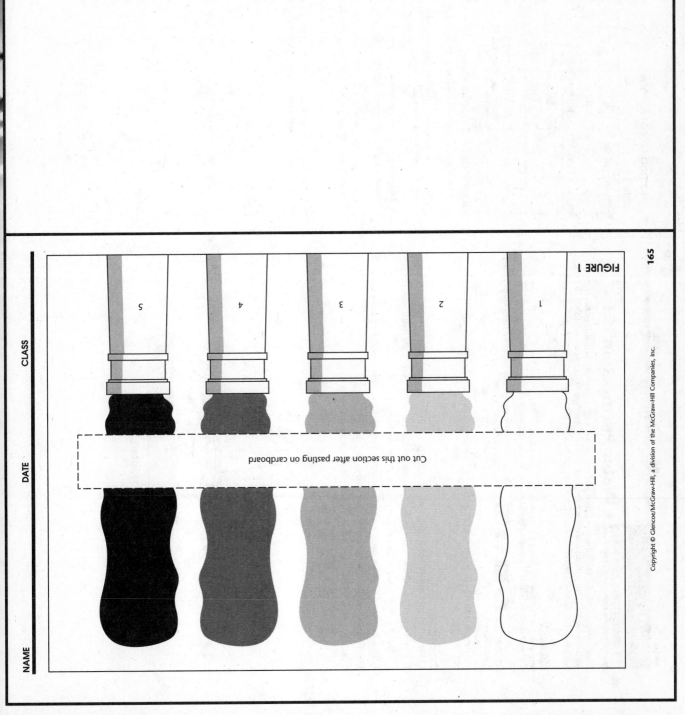

Cut out this section after pasting on cardboard

FIGURE 1

Chapter 27

LABORATORY MANUAL • Water Purification 53

Pure water is essential to all life forms. But what about a situation in which you do not have pure water available? Life rafts on boats are equipped with an apparatus that can be used to distill water from salt water. Desert safety survival rules provide another means to distill water.

Strategy

You will purify water by using a simple distillation process.
You will discuss how this process could be used in an emergency situation.

Materials

The distillation apparatus is available from some garden catalogs and plant stores.

cereal bowl
2 coat hangers, or bendable wire
pan (larger than the circumference of the bag)
pen (felt-tip)
plastic bag (clear)
sand (fine) or soil
sunlamp or bright sunshine
water

Procedure

1. Bend the coat hangers into a frame (see FIGURE 1).

2. Mix the sand or soil into water in the cereal bowl. Mark the water level on the inside with the pen.

3. Place the cereal bowl in the pan and place the wire frame over it.

4. Pull the plastic bag over the frame until it touches the pan. Record the appearance of the water.

5. Set the apparatus in direct sun or under a sunlamp.

6. Allow the apparatus to stand undisturbed. Observe and record your observations after about 10 min and again after 30 min in Table 1.

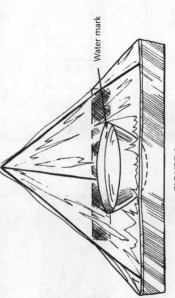

Water mark

FIGURE 1

Data and Observations

Table 1

Time (min)	Observations
0	Water color _____
	Inside of plastic bag _____
10	Water level _____
	Inside of plastic bag _____
30	Water level _____
	Inside of plastic bag _____

Questions and Conclusions

1. What happened to the water level in the cereal bowl? **decreased**

2. Why did water form on the inside of the plastic bag? **The drops of water condensed from the water vapor inside the plastic bag.**

3. What two processes are involved in this activity? **evaporation, condensation** Identify the energy source. **heat from the sun or sunlamp**

4. How could you prove that the water that forms on the inside of the plastic bag is pure? **use various tests: litmus for acids, phenolphthalein for carbonates**

5. What equipment should you carry in a vehicle in order to have pure water if you are going to cross a desert? **clean plastic, shovel, clean container**

Strategy Check

___ Can you observe the distillation of water by natural processes?

___ Can you understand how this process could be used in an emergency situation?